Word List

Here is a list of words that might make it easier to read this book. You'll find them in boldface the first time they appear in the story.

pepperoni	pe-puh-ROH-nee
squad	skwod
regional	REE-juh-nuhl
commitment	kuh-MIT-ment
disappeared	di-suh-PEEARD
demonstrate	DEM-uhn-strayt
spaghetti	spuh-GE-tee
mechanical	mi-KA-ni-kuhl
accessories	ik-SE-suh-rees
embarrassed	im-BAR-uhst
accessible	ik-SE-su-buhl
official	uh-FI-shul
coordinator	koh-OR-duh-nay-tor
loudspeaker	LOUD-spee-ker

Barbie™

Three Cheers for Becky

© 1998 Mattel, Inc. Barbie and associated trademarks are owned and used under license from Mattel, Inc. All Rights Reserved. Published by Grolier Enterprises, Inc. Story by Lynn Offerman. Photo crew: Lee Katz, Shirley Ushirogata, Lars Auvinen, Patrick Kittel, Todd Young, and Lisa Collins. Produced by Bumpy Slide Books. Printed in the United States of America.

ISBN: 0-7172-8828-5

Grolier Books

Chapter One

"Boy, am I full!" said Courtney, falling backward onto Skipper's bed.

"Yeah, me, too," said Skipper. "I think I ate too much pizza."

Skipper and her friends Courtney and Amy had just finished off a **pepperoni** pizza. They were having a Friday-night sleepover at Skipper's house. The plan was to gobble down pizza and soda, change into their pajamas, and then watch TV.

Amy plopped down on Skipper's beanbag chair and smoothed her long, black hair. "It's impossible to eat too much pizza," she said, shaking a bottle of nail polish. "Pizza is the perfect food."

Skipper was flicking through the channels using the remote control when something caught Courtney's attention.

"Hey, back up a channel!" exclaimed Courtney. "I think that's Colleen!"

Skipper pressed the button on the remote.

"Colleen Hayes? You're kidding," said Amy, looking up from painting her toenails with glitter nail polish.

"This must be the cheerleading finals," said Skipper. "Colleen is the head cheerleader for our school's **squad.**"

The girls watched as members of the squad climbed on top of one another to make a pyramid.

Courtney sighed. "Wow! I'd love to be able to do that," she said.

"So why don't you try out for cheerleading next year?" asked Skipper.

"Skipper, it's me, Courtney. I can't cross the lunchroom without knocking over somebody's tray, remember?" said Courtney. "Besides, I'm already on the volleyball team. I can't be on the cheerleading squad, too."

"I agree," said Amy. "Those cheerleading moves look pretty difficult. Especially the splits."

"I know what you mean," added Courtney. "The only splits I do usually involve bananas!"

"Don't be so hard on yourselves, guys," Skipper told them. "Do you think Colleen Hayes woke up one morning and did a back flip? It takes a lot of practice to be good enough to compete."

Amy thought about it and shook her head. "Even if I thought I could become a cheerleader, I have the same problem that Courtney has," she explained. "I'm already on the soccer team."

Suddenly Skipper's face lit up. "Wait a minute, guys. I have a brilliant idea!" she exclaimed. "We could cheer for a community team."

"*We?*" asked Courtney. "I only see you, me, and Amy. We're supposed to be a *squad,* not the Three Musketeers!"

"I know," Skipper said. "But I'll bet Melissa, Emma, and Nikki would join us."

"Slow down, Skipper," Amy said, raising her hand. "Let's say they are interested. Just how are we going to cheer for a community team?"

"Easy," Skipper replied. "My big sister, Barbie, helps out with the town's sports teams. I'm sure she'll know where we can find a coach and get started."

Amy nodded slowly. "Hmm, I could be a cheerleader *and* a soccer player. Maybe this isn't so bad. What do you think, Courtney?"

Courtney jumped to her feet. "Wouldn't I look great in one of those uniforms?" She put her hands on her hips and posed.

"Sure. But you had better lose the bunny slippers!" said Skipper.

The three girls laughed. Then they turned back to watching the cheerleading competition.

The next day, Skipper could hardly wait to tell Barbie at dinner.

"How was your slumber party, Sis?" asked Barbie.

"Amy, Courtney, and I had the greatest time last night. *And* we had the greatest idea!" Skipper said excitedly. "We want to form a cheerleading squad. I've already called up the rest of the gang, and they all said they'd love to form a squad with us. We'd like to cheer for town teams. But we're really interested in competing against other squads. Then we could—"

"Whoa, slow down," Barbie cut in, patting her sister's arm. "I haven't seen you this excited about something since you decided to take drum lessons."

"Yeah," chimed in their younger sister Stacie. "Only this time, we won't have to wear earplugs!"

Skipper pretended to smile at Stacie and said, "Very funny."

"Seriously, I think it's a great idea," Barbie told Skipper. "I was on a cheerleading squad when I was your age. You could compete in **regional** competitions just like I did. But cheerleading isn't just about winning trophies or wearing cute uniforms. It takes hard work and **commitment.**"

"I know, Sis. But we've talked it over, and we really want to do this. All we need is a coach. We thought you might know someone," said Skipper hopefully.

"Well, yes," said Barbie, "I know just the person to coach your squad. My friend Becky would be perfect. She already volunteers coaching time for some of the town teams."

Barbie took a last bite of dinner and got up from the table. "I'll call Becky right now and see if she's interested."

Skipper could hear her sister talking on the

phone in the other room. When Barbie returned, she had a big smile on her face. "Good news. Becky would love to coach your squad. In fact, she said she could come over for lunch tomorrow."

"Great!" said Skipper. "Amy is coming over tomorrow to bake brownies with me for the school bake sale. I'm sure she'd like to meet Becky, too!"

Skipper gave her big sister a hug. "Thanks, Barbie. I knew you'd come through. You always do!"

Chapter Two

The next day, when Amy was visiting, a red van pulled up in front of Skipper's house. "Hey, Skipper! I think Becky's here!" Amy shouted.

Skipper rushed over to have a look. The driver was a young woman with strawberry-blond hair.

"Wow, she's *really* pretty," Amy whispered to Skipper.

Both girls were surprised when the visitor came out of the van in a wheelchair.

"Did I hear you say that Becky was here?" Barbie asked, walking into the room.

"Well, we *think* it's Becky," said Skipper

slowly. "It's someone in a—"

But Barbie had already opened the front door. Skipper and Amy could hear Barbie saying hello to the young woman. A moment later, Barbie was inviting her friend into the living room.

"Becky," said Barbie, "I'd like you to meet my sister Skipper." Skipper reached out to shake Becky's hand. "And this is her friend Amy."

Becky smiled and held out her hand toward Amy. It took a moment for Amy to put hers out, too. Amy was still surprised that Becky was in a wheelchair.

"Skipper made her special chili for lunch," Barbie proudly told her friend.

"I hope it's extra-spicy!" said Becky.

While Barbie and Skipper went to the kitchen to get the chili and corn bread, Becky and Amy headed for the table. Becky's wheelchair got caught on the leg of a chair. Amy looked away as Becky struggled to free herself.

"Becky, do you need a hand with that chair?" asked Barbie, setting some bowls down on the table.

"Thanks," said Becky with a smile. "Furniture fighting isn't one of my favorite pastimes."

Soon everyone was enjoying lunch.

"Skipper, this chili is excellent!" exclaimed Becky. "I didn't realize how hungry I was. I've been so busy, I haven't stopped since eight o'clock this morning."

"Busy with what?" Barbie asked.

"Well, this morning I taught a photography class at the community center," Becky explained. "Then I finished developing some photos in the darkroom. Finally, I picked up tickets for a concert that Mike and I are going to Friday night."

"Still the same Becky," said Barbie, smiling. "Even back in high school, I could hardly keep up with you."

"And I get to do it all sitting down," Becky replied, her eyes sparkling with laughter.

"What a cool coach," Skipper thought happily.

Soon the chili bowls had been scraped clean and the corn bread had **disappeared.**

"Anyone in the mood for ice cream?" Barbie asked. Three eager voices chimed in at once. "Great!" said Barbie.

Barbie returned minutes later with bowls of ice cream and toppings.

"So can you and your friends meet for practice tomorrow at the gym, say, at four o'clock?" Becky asked Skipper.

"I know I can," Skipper replied, licking her spoon. "How about you, Amy?"

"Uh, okay, I can meet then," Amy said softly.

"I'll call the others later to make sure they can all be there," Skipper exclaimed. "They'll be so excited!"

"There's one more thing," Becky began, turning to Skipper. "I'll need someone to help lead the squad in cheering. Can I count on you to be my assistant?"

"You bet!" Skipper replied.

Becky reached into her backpack and pulled out a videotape. "Hope you're a fast learner," she said, handing the tape to Skipper. "This video will teach you the basic cheering moves. Watch it tonight so that you can **demonstrate** some of the moves tomorrow."

Then Becky turned to Amy. "The squad will also need a property manager. It'll be her job to keep track of equipment and uniforms. Are you up for that, Amy?"

"Sure, I'll do it," Amy answered quietly.

"Boy, I can't wait!" said Skipper. "We're really going to be a cheerleading squad!"

Chapter Three

The next day, the squad met for their first practice. Skipper was thrilled to see that the rest of the team seemed to like Becky as much as she did. The girls had a great time learning some cheerleading moves.

Becky carefully watched each girl's movements. "Courtney, don't be shy about making your arm motions bold and strong, like this." Becky gracefully lifted her arms to form an L. Then she turned to Emma and told her quietly, "You lunged left instead of right again."

Emma winced. "Sorry, Becky," she said.

"Don't worry, Emma," said Becky. "Lots of cheerleaders have this problem in the beginning. In time, you'll all be going in the same direction."

Becky soon announced that practice was over. The girls sat down on the mat for the team's closing meeting. "We need to pick a name for the squad," said Becky. "Any suggestions?"

"Hey, I have one," said Courtney. "How about 'The Glitter Bells'?"

Emma made a face. "'The Glitter Bells'? I don't know, Court. It makes us sound like a bunch of overgrown Christmas ornaments."

Everyone giggled, even Courtney.

They came up with other names, but none of those sounded any better.

"Don't worry," Becky told the team. "You'll have plenty of time to choose a name that you *all* like."

Becky told the girls that she had contacted an organization willing to sponsor the squad. They would help pay for uniforms and the cost of traveling to competitions. She was also expecting information about a contest coming up in three months. "Are you guys interested in competing?" Becky asked.

A loud "Yes!" filled the room. The team returned to the locker room to change.

"Gee, I was really surprised when our coach showed up in a wheelchair," Courtney whispered to Nikki while slipping on her boots.

"Me, too," Nikki whispered back. "But halfway through practice, the wheelchair didn't matter. She really knows a lot about cheerleading."

After a few weeks, Becky announced that the squad was ready to learn how to make a pyramid. It would be the hardest stunt in their routine. And Barbie had come to help.

"I've invited Barbie to be the spotter for the squad," Becky announced. "It'll be her job to stand close by to make sure no one gets hurt. A spotter is really important when the squad is performing a stunt that involves mounts."

Emma looked confused. "What are 'mounts'?" she asked.

Becky explained, "That's when a cheerleader is held off the ground by other members of the squad." Then Becky told the team, "Listen up, everyone. Let's start with some warm-up stretches. Then we'll work on the pyramid."

The first mount, which formed the front of the pyramid, wasn't too hard to learn. Skipper and Courtney made a bridge with their legs. Each girl bent one knee slightly and leaned toward the other. Then they helped Melissa to climb up and stand on their leg bridge.

"Hey, this is a breeze!" said Melissa, after they'd practiced the move for a while.

"Now comes the hard part, the second mount," Becky warned. "The second mount stands behind the first mount. It's usually best for the smallest

and lightest squad member to be on top of the second mount."

"That's you, Amy," said Nikki.

"Well, what do you say, Amy?" Becky asked.

Amy hesitated for a moment. "Um, okay," she said softly.

"Good," said Becky. "Let's begin with the 'shoulder sit'. Nikki and Emma, you'll stand right behind Skipper and Courtney. Then you'll lift up Amy with your arms so that her feet are level with your shoulders. She'll almost be sitting with her feet in your hands." She turned to Amy. "Remember, stay tight and balanced in this position, Amy."

Then Becky turned back to Nikki and Emma. "Now you two lift Amy as high as you can. When Amy straightens up, she'll be taller than Melissa, who'll be standing in front of her." Becky signaled to Barbie to stand behind Nikki and Emma. "As the spotter, Barbie will hold onto Amy's ankles from behind for support."

Barbie stood close behind as Emma and Nikki lifted Amy. Everything seemed fine. But before they knew it, all three girls were on the mat in a tangled heap of arms and legs. They attempted the mount again and again, but each try ended in disappointment. Finally Becky announced that practice was over. As always, everyone sat in a circle for their closing meeting.

"Don't expect to get a difficult stunt like the pyramid the first time you try it," Becky told the team. "Go home and relax. We'll try it again on Thursday."

Afterward, Skipper was brushing her hair in the locker room when she overheard Amy whispering to Melissa.

"I don't know about Becky," said Amy. "She says we'll be able to get the pyramid right with practice, but that seems impossible. How would she know, sitting in a wheelchair?"

Melissa shrugged. "Well, I like Becky," she said. Then she went on braiding her hair.

Skipper's heart sank. Should she tell Becky what she had heard Amy say? Or was it better to just ignore it? Skipper left the gym and headed home. She was confused. She felt angry at Amy. But she was also disappointed about the pyramid.

Chapter Four

Barbie noticed that Skipper didn't seem herself at dinner that evening.

"What's wrong, Sis?" Barbie asked.

"Oh, nothing," answered Skipper as she poked at her **spaghetti** with her fork. "I'm just not very hungry."

"Come on, Skipper. It's me. I can always tell when something's bothering you. It's about cheerleading practice, isn't it?" asked Barbie.

Skipper nodded.

"Sis," Barbie began, "don't be concerned about the pyramid. Becky is right. It really is a

23

very difficult stunt, but with practice—"

"That's not it, Barbie!" Skipper broke in suddenly. Then she told Barbie about what she had heard Amy say. "Do *you* think the problems with the pyramid have anything to do with Becky using a wheelchair?" Skipper asked Barbie.

"No, I don't," Barbie replied. "Do you?"

Skipper sighed. "Well, I have to admit that when I first saw Becky, I wasn't sure. But after weeks of working with her, I know she's a terrific coach. But what if Amy keeps complaining about Becky? Then the other girls might start to lose faith in her. What should I do, Barbie?"

"Why don't you give Becky a call?" Barbie suggested.

"And be a tattletale?" replied Skipper.

"You won't be a tattletale," Barbie told her. "You could be helping out the entire squad. Becky is smart and sensitive. She'll know just how to handle this sort of situation. You won't be getting

Amy into trouble."

"Okay, I'll do it," Skipper said finally. She picked up the phone and dialed Becky's number. Skipper felt her stomach tighten when she heard Becky's voice. But in a few moments, she relaxed. She was able to share what she had heard Amy say.

"I'm so glad that you were honest with me," Becky told Skipper. "I know it was hard. But you did the right thing by telling me."

Skipper breathed a sigh of relief and smiled at Barbie, who was standing nearby.

Becky went on, "I'm not surprised. You know, not everyone is comfortable with the idea of a coach who uses a wheelchair. Some people see my wheelchair first, not me or who I really am. The way I deal with this is by letting people know more about my life and the sort of person I am. Why don't you come over to my house tomorrow afternoon? Bring Barbie, and Amy, too. Tell her that we have to talk about uniforms for the team."

"We'll be there," Skipper promised.

The following day, Barbie drove Skipper and Amy over to Becky's house. Barbie parked in front of the pretty, one-story home. Becky was cutting flowers from a rosebush by the doorway. "Come on in," she said, gathering the flowers in her lap.

The three followed Becky up the low ramp to the front door. Skipper sniffed the air as they walked into the front hall. The smell of freshly baked cookies made her mouth water.

"Have a seat," said Becky. She pointed to a comfortable-looking sofa and chair in the living room. Then she put the flowers she had cut on the table. "I'll be right back."

Becky's house was bright and airy. Low shelves filled with books lined the walls.

"Get 'em while they're hot!" Becky said, carrying a tray with cookies. "Help yourselves. I'm going to put the flowers into a vase."

The girls watched as Becky went into the

kitchen. There she picked up a long pole with a **mechanical** hook at the end. She pressed a trigger in the handle to grasp a vase sitting on a shelf. Then she gently lowered the vase into her lap. She filled it with water and returned to the living room.

"What's that cool thing you were using, Becky?" Skipper asked.

"Oh, you mean my 'reacher'?" Becky said, putting the flowers in the vase. "It's a really big help when I need to reach things that are up high."

Soon the group was asking about the hair ornaments for the team. Amy liked headbands, Skipper wanted scrunchies, and Barbie and Becky both preferred barrettes.

"I have an idea," said Becky. "Why don't we go and check out the hair **accessories** at Sally's Place at the mall? It always has great stuff in the window."

Everyone agreed that a trip to the mall was just the thing to help them decide.

Chapter Five

"Sally's Place is straight ahead," called Becky as she zoomed quickly through the mall in her wheelchair.

"Whoa! Becky, slow down!" shouted Skipper as she, Barbie, and Amy hurried to catch up. "We'll have to bring our skates next time just to keep up with you!"

"Sorry about that," Becky replied. "Sometimes I go a little too fast for someone on foot."

Becky was right about Sally's Place. The store had loads of hair ornaments to choose from.

After a few minutes, the girls settled on blue

velvet scrunchies.

"There's only one problem," Skipper said. "The price tag."

"They are a bit expensive," Amy agreed. "But they're so *perfect!*"

"Especially since the uniforms will be blue," added Barbie.

Skipper continued excitedly, "Then we could call ourselves 'The Blue Bells'!"

Amy, Becky, and Barbie looked at each other and said at the same time, "Naah!"

"Come on, everyone," said Barbie, laughing. "Let's keep looking. I'm sure we'll find something just as nice in another store."

As they left the store, Becky noticed Skipper and Amy's disappointment. She took Barbie aside and whispered in her ear. Barbie nodded and smiled. Then she hurried to join Amy and Skipper.

"Hey, let's take a break from shopping," Barbie said. "How about a lemonade at the Juice Stop?"

"Where did Becky go?" Amy asked.

"She had to run a quick errand. She'll meet us there," said Barbie.

Soon Barbie, Skipper, and Amy were seated at a table, sipping lemonade.

Skipper took a long, slow sip. "Mmm! Shopping always makes me thirsty!" she said.

"Speaking of which," said Barbie, "we'd better remember to bring lots of bottled water to the cheerleading competition. You girls will be pretty thirsty after you perform your routine."

"You mean, *if* we perform our routine," Amy said, half under her breath.

"What do you mean?" Barbie asked.

Amy's face turned red. "It's just that the pyramid is a disaster, Barbie. I don't see how we'll ever be ready in time for the competition."

Barbie placed her hand on Amy's shoulder. "I know the squad has had its share of problems with the pyramid, but—"

"But the *real* problem," Amy broke in, her eyes filling with tears, "is *me!*"

Amy went on, "At first I wanted to believe it was Becky's fault. I even said something mean about her to Melissa. But now that I've gotten to know Becky better, I know she's not the one to blame. *I* am!"

"Why do you say that, Amy?" Barbie asked gently.

"Because my knees turn to jelly as soon as I'm lifted," Amy explained in a shaky voice. "I know it sounds silly, but I can't stop thinking that the girls are going to drop me. I guess I'm just not cut out to be a cheerleader."

"Why didn't you tell us how you were feeling?" Skipper asked.

"I guess I felt **embarrassed** because it seems like such a dumb thing to be afraid of," Amy explained. "I know that Nikki and Emma would never drop me *on purpose*. But somehow, it's still

hard to feel safe."

"Amy, at first, anyone would feel nervous about being on top of a cheerleading pyramid," Barbie said gently. "But that doesn't make you a bad cheerleader. You may grow more confident as you practice, or maybe you'd be more comfortable in a different spot. I'm sure you could trade places with one of the girls on the base."

"Barbie, you don't understand," Amy said. "I've already told my friends and family that I'm going to be the top person on the pyramid. I don't want to disappoint everyone."

"Then there's only one thing to do," said Barbie. "Talk to Becky about how you're feeling. She has a lot of coaching experience. I'm sure she'll know what to do."

Amy nodded. "You're right. I should have spoken to her in the beginning."

Just then, Becky came up to the table. "I'm sorry I took so long," she said. She looked at her watch. "It's already five o'clock."

"Yikes!" Amy exclaimed. She leapt to her feet. "I told my mom I'd be home by four-thirty. I'd better call her. Does anyone know where the nearest phone is?"

Skipper took a last sip of lemonade. "Upper level. I'll go with you, Amy."

The girls raced off, leaving Barbie and Becky at the table.

Barbie placed her hand on Becky's arm. "Amy just told us what her problem really is. It isn't you. It turns out that she is afraid to be on top of the pyramid. She's worried the girls will drop her. I told her to talk to you about it."

"Thanks, Barbie. I'm glad you did," Becky said. "I think I know exactly what will help Amy get over her fear."

Chapter Six

The next day, Amy arrived early for practice. She found Becky doing paperwork in the coaches' office behind the gym.

"Uh, Becky, can I speak to you in private?" asked Amy, nervously twirling her long hair.

"Sure, Amy. What's up?" said Becky. She set her paperwork aside and told Amy to take a seat.

Amy told Becky about her fear of being at the top of the pyramid.

"Every person has things she is afraid to do," Becky said. "Take me, for instance."

"You're afraid to do things?" Amy asked.

"Sure," Becky replied. "You know, not every building is **accessible**. Sometimes there are stairs and no ramps. Or there are narrow doorways my chair can't get through. In fact, I have been to the auditorium where the competition is being held. There's a very steep ramp there. It is going to be replaced soon, but it won't be done in time for our competition. I have to go up the ramp in order to be near the performance area. And the whole audience will be watching me. I'm worried that I might not be able to make it to the top like the other coaches."

"But Barbie could push you. Then you'd still be close to the team," said Amy.

Becky smiled. "And one of the girls at the base of the pyramid could trade places with you. That way, you'd still be a part of the pyramid."

Laughing, Amy raised her hand to stop Becky. "Okay, okay, I get it. It's as important for you to go up the ramp yourself as it is for me to be the top person on the pyramid. But how do you get over being frightened?"

"Talking helps," said Becky. "And so could working out a little harder. That always helped me when I was a cheerleader."

"You were a cheerleader?" asked Amy.

"I sure was," said Becky. "You know, I didn't always need this chair. But I've found that I like coaching even more than being a cheerleader."

"Thanks, Becky," Amy said. "I'm ready to go to practice now."

The rest of the squad was already doing warm-up stretches in the gym when Becky and Amy joined them. Becky called the girls together. Then Amy told the group about her fear of being dropped from the top of the pyramid.

"Gee, Amy, I can't imagine why you'd be afraid of being dropped with two *super-athletes* like Nikki and me holding you up," Emma teased.

"Even if they did drop you, what's the worst

that could happen? We'd all sign your cast!" chimed in Melissa.

"Thanks, guys!" Amy laughed. "I feel *so* much better now!"

"Seriously, Amy. The whole routine is going to be done on a mat," Melissa reminded her.

"And don't forget about Barbie," Nikki added. "She has had lots of experience as a spotter."

Barbie smiled at Amy. "Look how many times the pyramid has toppled in practice. You didn't get hurt during those falls, did you?"

"Well, only my pride did," said Amy. "I guess it's silly of me to be afraid."

"Everybody is afraid of something," said Becky. "Fear is nothing to be ashamed of."

"She's right. I'm really scared of thunder and lightning," Courtney said shyly. "Once I even hid under the bed with my dog!"

"Amy, if it would make you feel any better, we can train one of the other team members as a backup," Becky suggested. "That way, you can decide at the last minute whether or not you want to be the top person."

Amy breathed a sigh of relief. "Thanks."

After a quiet moment, Emma said, "I think I've got an idea. What about 'Cheer Spirit' for the team's name?"

Skipper thought for a moment and said, "Sounds like a laundry detergent."

"Actually, it sounds like two laundry detergents!" Becky added. "Let's keep thinking."

After practice, Becky offered to take everyone out for some ice cream. "I have a little surprise for you," she said.

When the team members arrived at the ice cream parlor, though, they froze in their tracks. There were three steps leading up to the shop. And there was no ramp!

"What do we do now?" Amy asked Becky.

"We have some choices. If you're willing, I

can tell you how to help me up these steps," Becky said.

Everyone agreed. Skipper and Amy tilted Becky's wheelchair back with the handles. Then Courtney and Melissa lifted the front wheels slightly. Soon Becky was inside!

Becky beamed. "I knew you wouldn't let me down!"

Amy smiled back. "We never would, Coach!"

After their ice cream, Becky gave everyone a blue velvet scrunchie. They were the ones that Skipper and Amy had seen at the mall! Everyone was thrilled!

With the competition just two weeks away, the squad spent a lot of time practicing the pyramid. Becky was happy to see the team improve. Amy got stronger and more confident as the top person. But just in case, Courtney trained to be on the top, while Amy practiced Courtney's part in the base.

Chapter Seven

At last the big day arrived! Becky and the
team met at Barbie's house a couple of hours
before the competition. They worked on their
uniforms, hair, nails, and makeup. Barbie was in
charge of French-braiding the girls' hair. Becky
helped with makeup. Even Stacie got involved.
It was her job to lay out each girl's uniform. And
little Kelly helped carry the pom-poms.

"So how is everybody feeling?" Becky asked.

"Fine, if I could just forget about the
butterflies fluttering around in my stomach,"
Melissa replied as she applied blush to her cheeks.

"*You've* got butterflies?" exclaimed Emma. "I feel like a whole family of kangaroos is bouncing around inside me!"

"I've got it!" cried Amy. "How about we call ourselves 'The Butterfly Bunch'?"

The girls looked blankly at Amy. Then Courtney shook her head and said, "Sorry." And they all went back to talking.

When the group was ready, Barbie looked around the room. "You all look great!" she told them. "Ready for your first **official** picture?"

The girls gathered around Becky and posed for a few pictures with their megaphones and pom-poms. Then they headed for Becky's van.

"I can only take four passengers," said Becky.

"No problem. I'll ride with Barbie," Melissa volunteered.

"Me, too," Courtney offered. "And we'll load the megaphones and pom-poms into her car."

Skipper, Amy, Nikki, and Emma piled into Becky's van. "See you there!" they shouted as they took off for the auditorium.

On the way, Becky reminded the girls, "It's the last possible moment. We really need to choose an official name for the squad."

"I've got one!" Nikki said excitedly. "How about 'The Pom-erettes'? You know—'Pom' as in 'pom-poms'?"

"I don't think so, Nik," said Amy. "That sounds like a new breed of dog."

"Can I make a suggestion?" Becky asked.

The girls were eager to hear what Becky had to say.

"How about 'True Blue'?" she suggested.

"Hmm. Sounds good," Emma said slowly.

"Yeah. I like it!" declared Nikki.

Suddenly a large building came into view. "There's the auditorium," said Becky. She parked the van and the girls got out. A minute later, they heard a car horn honk. It was Barbie.

"I think we have a name for the squad," Skipper announced as soon as Barbie, Courtney, and Melissa got out of the car. "What do you think of 'True Blue'?"

"I love it!" Melissa exclaimed. "How'd you ever come up with it?"

"I didn't," Skipper replied, smiling at Becky. "Our coach did."

Becky, Barbie, and the girls went into the lobby of the auditorium, where several other squads were already gathered. Courtney saw one team dressed in pink and black uniforms. "Boy, they look really sharp," she sighed.

"Not as good as we look," Emma pointed out, holding up her pom-poms.

"I guess it doesn't matter what *we* think," said Nikki. "It'll be up to the judges."

Becky called the girls together. "I'm going to speak with the **coordinator,**" she said. "I want to let her know we're here. I'd also like to find out where we are in the lineup. You can stay here or come into the auditorium with me."

The girls exchanged looks. "We'll come with you, Becky," said Melissa. "Seeing how great these other squads look is making us even more nervous!"

Everyone followed Becky down a long, tiled hallway.

"Listen," said Courtney. "What's that noise? It's so loud."

"It's the crowd settling down for the competition," said Becky.

The noise grew louder with every step. Suddenly they turned a corner and were inside the auditorium. Brightly colored banners and flags hung from the ceiling. There were hundreds of seats for the audience.

Emma watched Becky go over to the coordinator's desk. "I hope we're not scheduled to go first," she whispered to Melissa.

"Really?" said Melissa. "I'd rather get it over with."

Soon Becky returned. "We're scheduled to perform fourth," she told the girls. "You've got some time to relax." Then Becky turned to Amy. "So what have you decided? Are you going to the top?"

Amy paused and then smiled. "I'll go for it," she said.

Becky smiled. "I'm proud of you," she said. "No matter what happens, you're a winner!"

When the competition was about to begin, the coaches were called to the performance area. The other coaches climbed up the steps to the stage, while Becky started up the steep ramp.

"You can do it, Becky," Amy said under her breath. She could tell that it was hard work for Becky to manage by herself. But she did it! At last, Becky joined the other coaches on the stage.

"Yes!" Amy cried softly and punched the air with her fist.

"What was that, Amy?" Skipper asked.

Amy blushed. "Uh, I was just practicing our cheers."

The girls nervously watched the first three squads perform. Then they heard Becky's voice over the **loudspeaker.** "Let's have a round of applause for 'True Blue'!"

"'True Blue' took its place in the middle of the stage. They performed their cheers well, thoug they looked a little stiff. Then came the pyramid.

Becky watched as Skipper, Courtney, and Melissa completed the first mount.

"So far, so good," Becky said as she held her breath.

The audience was quiet, watching every move the cheerleaders made. Becky glanced at the judges, trying to guess what they were thinking

Nikki and Emma took their places for the

second mount. Amy walked up to her teammates and braced herself for the lift.

"Come on, Amy. Stay calm," Becky said to herself.

Nikki and Emma lifted Amy up to their shoulders. Barbie stood behind and held onto Amy's ankles while she began to straighten up. Suddenly Amy's knees bent. She reached her arms out to steady herself.

Becky flinchcd. She knew that even the smallest mistake would cost points. "Keep going," she said under her breath. "You can do it."

Amy fought to keep her balance. Slowly she straightened herself up. Emma and Nikki bent their knees and carefully lifted Amy high over their heads. Amy raised her arms and beamed at the audience. The pyramid was a success!

'True Blue' finished their routine. The audience cheered as the squad ran off the stage.

"Way to go, girls!" Becky shouted from

the sidelines.

Moments later, the team met Becky near the awards stand. "You did a great job!" Becky told the girls. "You all came through like champions!"

"What about the mistakes we made?" Emma asked. "I guess we won't be winning any trophies."

"We'll find out as soon as the final squad finishes its routine," said Becky.

A few minutes later, the audience applauded as the last squad left the stage. Then the announcer said, "Ladies and gentlemen, here is the moment you have all been waiting for—the winners of this year's cheerleading competition."

"Third prize goes to 'Spirit Sisters'!" said the announcer. Members of the squad in pink and black ran up and collected their trophy.

"I *told* you they looked good," said Emma.

"Second prize," the announcer began, "is awarded to 'True Blue'!"

Skipper and her friends couldn't believe their

ears! They had won *second prize!* They cheered and jumped up and down, hugging each other. Becky beamed proudly at them as they accepted their trophy.

"Well, team, you did it!" Becky said as the girls gathered around her. "Hope you guys aren't too excited to begin practicing the new cheers for next week's soccer championship."

Just then, Barbie came over to congratulate them. "You were all terrific!" she said.

Barbie opened up her backpack and let everyone help themselves to granola bars and bottled water. "Now how about a popcorn and video party at my place tonight to celebrate?"

"Sounds great!" said Amy. "Coach, can you come, too?"

Becky smiled. "I wouldn't miss it for the world!" she replied.

A Note to Parents

DK READERS is a compelling program for beginning readers, designed in conjunction with leading literacy experts.

Beautiful illustrations and superb full-color photographs combine with engaging, easy-to-read stories to offer a fresh approach to each subject in the series. Each DK READER is guaranteed to capture a child's interest while developing his or her reading skills, general knowledge, and love of reading.

The four levels of DK READERS are aimed at different reading abilities, enabling you to choose the books that are exactly right for your child:

Level 1 – Beginning to read
Level 2 – Beginning to read alone
Level 3 – Reading alone
Level 4 – Proficient readers

The "normal" age at which a child begins to read can be anywhere from three to eight years old, so these levels are only a general guideline.

No matter which level you select, you can be sure that you are helping your child learn to read, then read to learn!

DK

LONDON, NEW YORK, MELBOURNE,
MUNICH, AND DELHI

Editor Kate Phelps
Designer Sooz Bellerby
Series Editor Alastair Dougall
Production Jenny Jacoby
Picture Researcher Julia Harris-Voss

First American Edition, 2003
03 04 05 06 07 10 9 8 7 6 5 4 3 2 1
Published in the United States by DK Publishing, Inc.
375 Hudson Street, New York, New York 10014

Library of Congress Cataloging-in-Publication Data

Donkin, Andrew.
Transformers Armada : the awakening / by Andrew Donkin.-- 1st
American
ed.
p. cm. -- (DK Readers)
Summary: Three children find a spaceship deep inside a cave and
unwittingly revive an ancient conflict between the heroic Autobots and
the evil Decepticons, each fighting for control of the universe.
ISBN 0-7894-9803-0 (hardcover) -- ISBN 0-7894-9741-7 (pbk.)
[1. Science fiction.] I. Title. II. Series: Dorling Kindersley
readers.
PZ7.D7175Tp 2003
[Fic]--dc21
2003003902

Color reproduction by Colourscan, Singapore
Printed and bound in China by L Rex Printing Co., Ltd.

The publisher thanks the following for their kind permission
to reproduce their photographs:
c=center, t=top; b=below; l=left; r=right

AKG London: 25tr, 26tl; François Guenet 22tl. Corbis: George Hall 47tl.
Mary Evans Picture Library: 27tr. Nasa: 35tr; Robert Williams and the
Hubble Deep Field Team (STScl) and NASA 38bl; 44bl. Rex Features:
13br. Science Photo Library: Jeremy Walker 22b; Julian Baum 36cl;
Martin Bond 20tl; Maximilian Stock Ltd. 29tr; Novosti 25br, 34tl; Peter
Menzel 24bl, 28bl; W. Bacon 41tr; Martin Marietta Aerospace 44bl.
University of Portsmouth: 28tl.

All other photographs © Dorling Kindersley.
For further information see: www.dkimages.com

Discover more at
www.dk.com

Contents

DK READERS

PROFICIENT READERS **4**

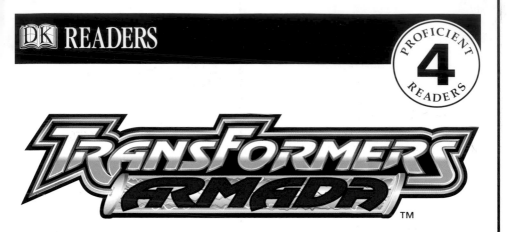

The Awakening

Written by Andrew Donkin

DK

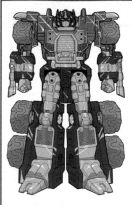

Robot beings
In robot mode, most Transformers look like 30-foot (10-meter) tall humanoid robots.

The planet of Cybertron.

Good versus evil

Millions of years ago, far across the cosmos, a race of amazing robotic beings came into existence. These creatures were known as the Transformers, and they possessed great strength, intelligence, and extraordinary mechanical powers.

Amazingly, they were capable of altering their digital structure. This meant that they could convert their robot bodies into other forms of

mechanical equipment. They could transform into land and air vehicles, such as cars, tanks, rescue vehicles, or even jet fighters.

The Decepticons turned to evil and the forces of darkness.

The planet where the Transformers lived was known as Cybertron. It was an amazing silvery world of living metal machines and cities of unimaginable beauty.

Sadly, it was not long before Cybertron was engulfed by a terrible civil war. The race of Transformers split into two equal but opposite sides. One group, the Autobots, fought for good, while the other, the Decepticons, embraced violence and evil. The future of Cybertron was in peril. If the forces of darkness conquered the planet, then the rest of the cosmos would surely be next...

Badge of honor Each race of Transformers has its own insignia, which the robots wear with pride.

The Mini-Cons

The Decepticons

The Autobots

5

Cybertronian wars

The Decepticons were rogue Transformers that were stifled by the status quo on Cybertron and realized that the planet was ripe for plunder and domination. Megatron rose through their ranks and became a powerful warlord. He led his evil robot troops to many terrible victories, taking over the planet one sector at a time.

The only thing standing in the way of Megatron was the Autobots, a force for good led by the wise Optimus Prime. The peaceful Autobots knew that the only way to end the Decepticons' reign of terror was to face them in hand-to-hand combat. The long and violent battles

Megatron
This terrifying warrior and would-be world conqueror stands over 30 feet (10 meters) tall and is strong enough to crush cars in his powerful robot hands.

Like all Transformers, Optimus Prime can change his shape and form. When danger threatens, he can operate in robot or vehicle mode.

that followed became known as the Cybertronian wars.

Now, thanks to a mysterious third race of Transformers called Mini-Cons, their galactic war is about to spread to a new battleground…a small, blue-green planet called Earth!

Super Optimus
Optimus Prime can transform himself into an extra-powerful giant version of himself called Super Optimus.

Optimus says: "Freedom is the right of all sentient beings."

The Autobots
Optimus Prime

Optimus Prime is the leader of the Autobots and their most powerful member. Optimus Prime will always work to find a peaceful solution to any problem. If that is not possible, however, he will become a fierce and brave warrior. He is immensely powerful, stands over 30 feet (10 meters) tall, and has access to many fantastic weapons.

Optimus Prime's weakness is his concern for the safety of others. He's smart, but is he really ruthless enough to defeat Megatron?

Hot Shot

Hot Shot is second
lieutenant to
Optimus Prime, and,
with his hot head, he
lives up to his name.
This young Autobot is
always itching for a
fight. He is
courageous, but
he's also very
reckless. Hot Shot is usually the first
to rush into danger, often without a
thought for his own safety.

Does he have the capability to
grow into a future Autobot leader or
will his rashness be his undoing?

Laser firepower
Among Hot
Shot's many
weapons are
his deadly wrist-
mounted
photon lasers,
which he uses
to great effect
against the
Decepticons.

*In vehicle mode, Hot Shot
becomes a supersleek sports
car with a top speed of over
120 miles per hour (190
kilometers per hour).*

Red Alert can transform to become an emergency rescue vehicle.

Red Alert

Red Alert is Optimus Prime's right-hand man and also one of his oldest friends. A long time ago, Red Alert was seriously injured during a ferocious battle. His brush with death changed him and made him realize how precious all life really is. He is still a brave fighter, but these days his energies are channeled into saving the lives of his fellow Transformers. He is the team's science officer and doctor.

Red Alert has risked his life many times to save wounded friends who have fallen on the battlefield.

Smokescreen

Smokescreen packs a punch that is second to none. Show him a battle and Smokescreen lets rip with all his considerable power. He doesn't bother with fancy fighting styles but prefers to make sure that every move hits the enemy where it hurts most.

He is a loyal friend of Optimus Prime and will stay with him until the end of any battle, whatever the odds. Will even Smokescreen's incredible strength be enough to defeat the evil Megatron and his Decepticon hordes?

Crane arm
Smokescreen's massive body acts as support to his mighty crane arm, which can be used to grab, punch, and crush the enemy. He is a formidable adversary.

In vehicle mode, Smokescreen transforms into a powerful utility crane.

11

The Decepticons
Megatron

Megatron is the leader and the mightiest of the evil Decepticons. Megatron's one ambition is to rule the entire Universe, and he'll stop at nothing to achieve it. He is hungry for power and if that means disposing of the Autobots to get it then that's a bonus.

He is an experienced warrior with a terrifying arsenal of weapons at his disposal. His main weapon is a tank cannon that can lay waste to a battlefield in just a few minutes.

Supertank
In vehicle mode, Megatron's massive super-tank comes equipped with a top-security prison cell.

Megatron is a terrifying figure on the battlefield. He likes to say to his enemies: "My power is your doom!"

Even the other Decepticons aren't safe when Starscream attacks!

Jet fighter
When in jet mode, a Transformer is known as a "seeker."

Starscream
Starscream uses his transforming power to change into a jet fighter and launch aerial attacks on the Autobots. No one can match him when it comes to his speed and skill through the sky.

Starscream is young, power-hungry, and really only interested in one thing…himself. He is Megatron's second in command, but he would love to be leader. If Megatron doesn't bring the Decepticons victory soon, Starscream just might get his chance.

Top gun
Jet fighters, like this F-16C, are fast military aircraft designed to attack enemy planes.

Cyclonus

Cyclonus is so trigger happy that sometimes even his fellow Decepticons are afraid of him. He is always looking for ways to impress Megatron—although obeying orders doesn't seem to be one of them! He has been known to desert the Decepticons in battle on a flight of fancy to attack a lone Autobot that he thinks will be easy prey. In any fight, Cyclonus finds it easier to start than to know when to stop.

Cyclonus is often heard to shout: "Out of my way! Attack!"

Army helicopter
Cyclonus transforms to become an army helicopter capable of ferocious airborne assaults!

Demolishor

Demolishor is a battle-hardened war veteran whose single goal in life is to serve the mighty Megatron. He is happy to battle on, however much the odds seem to be stacked against him.

Missile tank
Demolishor transforms into a missile tank that can launch brutal attacks on his Autobot foes.

He knows that Megatron values his loyalty, even when Megatron has abandoned him in the middle of a battle to save his own skin. However, Demolishor has never trusted the younger Decepticons. Is that a weakness that Optimus Prime could exploit?

Demolishor is a loyal soldier to Megatron. He is often heard saying to his leader: "As you command."

15

The Mini-Cons

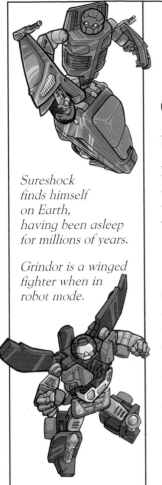

Sureshock finds himself on Earth, having been asleep for millions of years.

Grindor is a winged fighter when in robot mode.

High Wire is the first Mini-Con to awake on Earth.

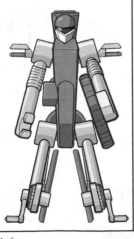

One of the strangest events in Cybertron's history occurred during the civil war. It was discovered that a race of Transformers, known as the Mini-Cons, held the balance of power between the two warring factions!

The Mini-Cons were small in size and meek in manner, but when a Mini-Con joined with a larger Transformer, it boosted the bigger Transformer's power to fantastic levels. As the Decepticons captured Mini-Cons to use in their war effort, so the Autobots were forced to do the same to avoid defeat.

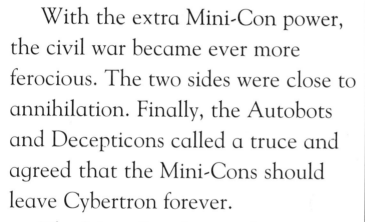

The Mini-Cons' spaceship traveled far through the Universe until it crash-landed on Earth's Moon.

With the extra Mini-Con power, the civil war became ever more ferocious. The two sides were close to annihilation. Finally, the Autobots and Decepticons called a truce and agreed that the Mini-Cons should leave Cybertron forever.

The Mini-Cons' spaceship was damaged just after they fled. It drifted through the cosmos until eventually it collided with Earth's Moon, scattering Mini-Cons all over Earth and the Moon. The Mini-Cons lay hidden, asleep for millions of years until someone accidentally awoke them…

Perceptor
In an emergency, High Wire, Sureshock, and Grindor can combine to become the powerful Perceptor.

The kids

Cosmo Scope Research Center
Scientists use the huge telescope at the research center to find out about deep space.

Also caught up in the conflict between Megatron and Optimus Prime are three humans: Rad, Carlos, and Alexis. It was their interference that resulted in the Transformers waking up on Earth!

Rad is a bright and lively 14 year old. He lives in the high desert with his parents, both of whom are scientists at the Cosmo Scope Research Center. Rad has lots of energy and is eager to protect Earth and its ecology.

Carl

Carlos is so good on his skateboard that Rad thinks he'll turn professional one day.

Rad loves riding his BMX bike more than anything else.

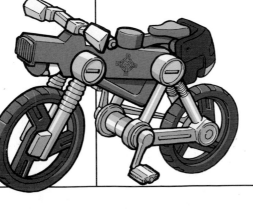

Rad

Carlos loves nothing more than skateboarding down the street at top speed. He and Rad have been best friends for years and hang out together most of the time.

Alexis is the brains of the outfit and an expert on computers. When she's not with the two boys, she'll probably be found with her head stuck in a book.

Somehow, the kids must help Optimus Prime defeat the evil Decepticons *and* protect their own planet...but can they do both?

School chums
Rad, Carlos, and Alexis go to the same school. Their motto is: "All for one, and one for all!"

Alexis's choice of transportation is a sleek scooter.

Alexis

19

First encounter

When Rad left school that afternoon, the last thing he was expecting to do was get involved in a war between a bunch of alien robots.

Rad lives in the high desert, and up in the mountain above his town is the Cosmo Space Research Center. Both his parents work in the center as astronomers.

Rad was riding his BMX bike through town in the late afternoon sunshine. As usual, his friend Carlos was speeding alongside him on his skateboard. They were planning to head up the mountain to check out a neat cave that they'd spotted on a previous visit. The mountain wasn't the kind of place that you want to get stuck in after dark.

Big dish
Astronomers search deep space using giant radio telescopes. These detect radio waves from space.

After school, Rad and Carlos head up to the mountain to check out the mysterious cave.

There were legends and stories about strange lights being seen up there at night.

The ride up the mountain was long and hot, but they made it.

"Hey! Scope it out, Rad!" said Carlos, as they spotted the entrance to the cave.

"You ready?"

"Yeah," he said, "I've got the flashlight. Let's see what's in there."

Underground
Most caves are found in limestone rock, which dissolves as rainwater seeps through it, forming stalactites and stalagmites.

Inside, the cave was even creepier than they'd expected, but that wasn't going to stop them. They followed the dark tunnels into the mountain, heading deeper and deeper underground.

As they reached the end of the main tunnel, Carlos stepped forward, and suddenly the cave floor gave way beneath them. They both fell back onto a rock slab that was shaped like a giant gravestone. The slab slipped loose and started hurtling down a steep and winding side tunnel, with them on top of it! The kids had never been so scared in all their lives. They both screamed the whole way down. The slab finally crashed to a halt in a huge chamber.

"Holy Cow! What in the world is that?" said Rad.

Inside the cavern was a weird kind of silver spaceship. And it didn't look like anything that came from Earth!

Then Rad spotted a strange green glow on the floor of the chamber.

"Look at this?"

He knelt down and touched the glowing green plate. That was his big mistake.

Space view
The world's most famous space telescope is called the Hubble Space Telescope. It was launched from the Space Shuttle in 1990.

There was a blinding white light and all around them the mountain started to shake.

"Earthquake!"

The walls of the spaceship lit up like a Christmas tree.

"Come on, dude. We have to get out!" shouted Carlos. Rad grabbed the green plate, and they ran.

Rad and Carlos got out of the cave, but before they could recover, things started to get freaky again.

"What is that?"

Above them had formed something that looked like a miniature black hole full of purple mist. The shape of a giant robot suddenly materialized inside it!

They found out later that this was the evil Megatron!

Then things started to happen really quickly. First, Alexis—Rad and Carlos's friend from school—appeared. She'd felt the earthquake and had come to the mountain to check that they were all right.

As Rad ran over to her, he dropped the green plate. The menacing robot, Megatron, moved toward it, and the plate started to glow again. Then right in front of them something amazing happened. The tiny plate started to transform.

Space travel
The Space Age started on October 4, 1957, when Russia put the first satellite, called *Sputnik 1*, into orbit around Earth.

First astronaut
The first person in space was Russian Yuri Gagarin, who flew *Vostok 1* around Earth in 1961.

Robot word
The word "robot" was invented by a Czech writer, Karel Capek, in 1921. He took the word from "robotnik," which means "slave" or "servant" in Czech.

The plate grew in size and transformed into a human-sized robot. This little guy turned out to be called High Wire.

The robot had two large eyes and, unlike Megatron, looked kind of friendly. The robot looked up at Megatron and shrugged. Then it seemed to scan the area around it, focusing on Rad's BMX bike.

Before Rad knew it, the robot had transformed itself into a super-speedy bike based on the design of Rad's own BMX. Somehow Rad

understood that the robot's electronic beeps meant that he wanted the kids to jump on board.

Pretty soon they were making their escape away from Megatron. It was going well, too, until Megatron picked up a boulder and threw it into their path. They all went tumbling into the dirt.

"You have something of mine!" boomed Megatron. He reached out a giant hand to crush them.

"Stand down, Megatron!" said another voice.

"Optimus Prime!" said Megatron.

Rad looked up and to his amazement saw there were now two giant robots squaring off for a fight. He had a strange feeling that somehow this was all his fault!

Early robots
One of the first movies to feature a robot was the classic 1926 German silent picture *Metropolis*. The robot wasn't real, though. It was played by an actor.

The kids flee from Megatron.

Spider robot
Robots don't always look "human." This one has eight legs, like a spider or a crab.

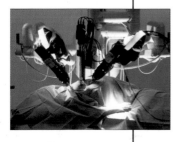

Robot surgeon
Some simple medical operations are performed by robot arms.

Metamorphosis

The giant robots smashed their fists into one another. They both groaned with the effort of the battle.

Optimus Prime took a look over at the kids and then shoved Megatron away from them. He was trying to keep the kids safe.

Then Optimus Prime smashed Megatron straight into the canyon wall, creating a great cloud of yellow dust!

"I want those Mini-Cons!" snarled the evil Megatron, looking even angrier.

The kids tried to make a run for it, but more of those weird warp holes appeared. This time two huge Decepticon robots materialized.

They were immediately followed by two mighty Autobots.

From the way the two groups of Transformers were looking at each other you could tell that

they weren't exactly friends. The kids were in danger of getting squashed in a big way.

"Back to the cave. Follow me!" yelled Alexis.

But before she could move, Megatron made a grab for her. The powerful fist of Optimus Prime stopped him just in time.

Behind them, the kids heard the two gigantic robots exchanging blows, and they ran for their lives!

Robot workers
Robots are often used to make cars on a production line.

Optimus Prime and Megatron do battle.

Reflected glory
The Moon is the brightest object in the night sky, because it reflects the light of the Sun.

Satellite
The Moon is Earth's only natural satellite. It orbits Earth about every 27 days.

Optimus Prime took a run at Megatron and sent him toppling over into the dirt!

"I'll be back!" hissed Megatron, and suddenly he and the other Decepticons disappeared into a transport warp.

Megatron and his henchmen had retreated to their base on the Moon.

"Welcome back, Sir!" groveled Cyclonus when Megatron had arrived back at their lunar headquarters. "Were you able to get the Mini-Cons?"

Cyclonus saw the look on Megatron's face and realized that he had not.

"Sir, allow me to look on Earth for the Mini-Cons' crashed ship. I just know I can find it." said Cyclonus, trying to impress his leader.

"Go ahead," said Megatron, "But don't fail me!"

Cyclonus quickly got to work, scanning the planet.

While his minion toiled away, Megatron stood at the edge of their temporary base on the Moon.

As he looked around at the barren lunar landscape something caught his eye. Glinting on the horizon was the unmistakable form of a Mini-Con!

No atmosphere
The Moon is too small to have an atmosphere. It is a dead and airless world.

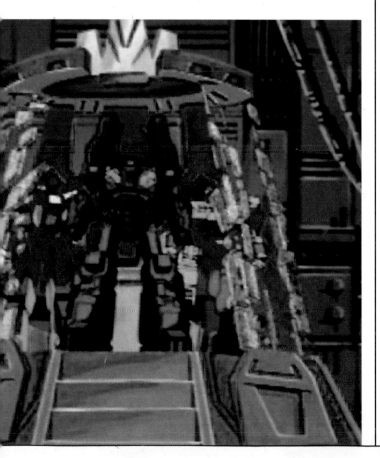

Space walk
When they are in orbit, astronauts are away from the pull of Earth's gravity so they become weightless.

Big change
Metamorphosis means a complete change of physical form. It is often applied to dramatic changes in the natural world, as when a caterpillar turns into a butterfly.

High Wire switches back into robot mode.

While the Transformers had been fighting, Carlos, Alexis, and Rad had gone back into the cave for safety. High Wire had switched back into robot mode and was with them, too.

The kids didn't know why, but it was pretty obvious that those big guys were after the little robot.

High Wire led the kids deeper into the cave system until he found what he was looking for.

"We're back at the crashed spaceship!" said Carlos, as they once again came to the spacecraft's long silver hull.

This time, however, they were actually going into the ship. Once inside, High Wire made some high-pitched noises, and a door slid open, revealing two more Mini-Cons.

They glowed with a bright green light, just like High Wire had outside in the cave.

Rad realized that these new Mini-Cons were choosing their human partners. One short scan later and Carlos had a super-powered skateboard while Alexis had a cool-looking scooter.

Now each kid had a Mini-Con partner who could transform into a vehicle for them to ride!

Leap frog
Tadpoles metamorphose into frogs by gaining legs and losing their long tails.

Moon probe
In 1966, the Russian probe *Lunar 9* became the very first spacecraft ever to land on the Moon.

Apollo 11
The first manned Moon landing was made by *Apollo 11* on July 20, 1969.

Back on the Moon, Megatron had made an interesting discovery. It was indeed a Mini-Con that he had spotted lying on the lunar surface. It wasn't just any Mini-Con either, but Leader-1, Megatron's old Mini-Con partner. They had last seen each other four million years ago on Cybertron.

Now Cyclonus was in trouble. Why hadn't he spotted this Mini-Con with his scans?

"You useless piece of junk, Cyclonus! Observe the power of this Mini-Con," said Megatron.

The Mini-Con had no choice but

to obey Megatron. It unleashed a series of deadly blasts sending the Decepticons diving for cover.

Demolishor returned with a message for Megatron.

"Sir, scans show that two more Mini-Cons have awoken down on Earth," said the robot.

"Hmm, two more. Cyclonus, you will lead our recovery team," ordered Megatron. "Once we have those Mini-Cons, we will be able to defeat the Autobots for good!"

First step
The first human to set foot on the Moon was Neil Armstrong. As he stepped onto the lunar surface, he said the famous line: "That's one small step for a man; one giant leap for mankind."

Alexis tries out her cool new scooter.

Alien life?
A mockup of a UFO (unidentified flying object). No one knows for sure if there is other life anywhere in the Universe, but many scientists think that it's possible.

Carlos, Alexis, and Rad decided to leave the cave and give their Mini-Con vehicles a try. They were fantastic. Alexis had turned into a total speed demon. They chased each other across the desert and then weaved between the forest trees. The Mini-Cons were *the best*.

Unfortunately, the kids weren't the only ones who thought so. As they reached the crest of a hill, they saw that Megatron and his minions were hiding over the other side!

"Transform! Vehicle mode!" shouted Megatron, instantly changing into a tank. The other three Decepticons changed as well. They were amazingly fast and pretty soon the kids were surrounded.

Just as they were going to grab Rad, something smashed into Megatron's tank sending him

spinning away out of control. It was Optimus Prime in truck mode!

Optimus Prime's truck opened its cab door.

"Get in!" he shouted.

One of the Decepticons tried to stop Optimus Prime's truck, but he just battered him out of the way!

Those bad guys weren't finished yet, though. They were coming after the kids again. This time it was all out war, and as usual Rad, Alexis, and Carlos were right in the middle!

Our galaxy
The spiral galaxy that includes Earth and its Sun is called the Milky Way. Our Sun is located in one of its spiral arms about 25,000 light-years from the center.

The Decepticons had all switched to vehicle mode and quickly moved in to attack the brave Autobots.

"Let the games begin!" said Megatron with relish.

The evil Starscream had transformed into a jet fighter and was speeding through a clear blue sky firing his guns wildly.

"Why don't you take your little toys back home, Megatron?" said Optimus Prime, shrugging off Starscream's attack.

"Care to surrender, my friends?" asked Megatron.

"What, and miss all this fun?" said Optimus Prime.

"I see you still have a sense of humor," said Megatron. "Well, Leader-1 will take care of that."

Carlos, Alexis, and Rad all saw that Megatron had a Mini-Con sitting on his shoulder. The smaller

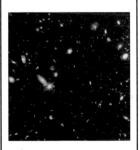

Empty space
Most of the Universe is empty with clusters of galaxies scattered throughout it.

robot was linked with the evil warlord, greatly increasing the force of Megatron's weapon.

"A little added firepower!" said Megatron, pulling the trigger.

I don't think that even Megatron knew just how powerful the Mini-Con was! The recoil threw Megatron backward, and the missile flashed through the air, heading straight at the Autobot warrior, Hot Shot.

Big Bang
Scientists think that the Universe may have started with an explosion called the Big Bang.

The recoil from Megatron's powerful weapon sends him reeling backward.

Long ago
The Universe is estimated to be around 15 billion years old.

Missile launch
A US Air Force missile on display in a museum.

Hot Shot ducked and the warp missile flashed past him. It demolished a huge rock outcrop behind him, and the whole mountain shook with the impact.

"You missed!" said Hot Shot, with relief.

"Laugh now, but that is just a taste of my new power," boomed Megatron smugly.

Megatron fires his deadly weapon straight at Hot Shot.

Rad couldn't believe how much that puny-looking Mini-Con had jacked up Megatron's power! No wonder the Transformers were fighting over them!

Megatron set his new warp cannon to automatic and let rip with blast after blast. It was so powerful, though, that even he couldn't control it. Megatron lost his footing and accidentally fired a shot at the upper slopes of the mountain.

"Avalanche!" shouted Hot Shot.

A huge wall of rock began tumbling down the mountain— right toward where the kids were hiding!

Avalanche!
Avalanches can be of snow or rock. Snow avalanches are more likely after warm weather has thawed some of the snow.

The deadly avalanche smashes into Hot Shot and Red Alert.

Hot Shot saves the kids from the avalanche by grabbing them in his enormous hand.

Solar family
Our own Solar System consists of all the bodies that orbit our Sun. It includes nine planets and their moons, as well as asteroids and comets.

Hot Shot had scooped the kids up in his giant hand and saved them.

"Check this out, chief. They're A-OK," he said opening his hand to show Optimus Prime that the three youngsters were safely inside.

The landslide had ripped a great chunk out of the mountain. Alexis saw something glinting in the newly exposed dirt.

"Look—more Mini-Cons!"

One of the Autobots, Red Alert, reached down and picked up one of the small Mini-Cons. It woke up as he held it and came alive.

"Red Alert transform!" shouted Red Alert. He knew that unless he and Hot Shot got a power boost from the Mini-Cons quickly, this was one battle the Autobots were going to lose.

Hot Shot picked up a Mini-Con from the dirt, too.

"Hot Shot transform!"

Both Autobots let loose with their new Mini-Con-improved weapons. Their blasts sent two giant Decepticons sprawling to the ground while Megatron looked on in horror.

sunspot

Hot stuff
Inside the Sun, the temperature can reach 60 million degrees Fahrenheit (15 million degrees Centigrade). Sunspots on the surface stand out as slightly cooler areas.

With the tide of the battle turning against them, Megatron only had one option left.

"Time to retreat," he declared, disappearing into an escape warp.

Demolishor and Starscream warped out and disappeared as well.

"They've retreated, Sir!" said Hot Shot.

Just then Cyclonus, the only Decepticon still around, appeared in the sky in army helicopter mode.

He flew higher up the mountain to where Carlos, Alexis, and Rad were busy trying to dig another Mini-Con out of the dirt.

The evil Cyclonus swooped down, and his giant hand grabbed the Mini-Con from right under their noses.

Robot probes
Robot space probes have been sent to many planets in our Solar System. This illustration shows the Viking lander on Mars.

"I do love surprises! Thanks!" he said, with glee.

Then he warped out and disappeared with the new Mini-Con he'd just stolen. That really burned the kids up.

They knew that back in his base on the Moon, power-hungry Megatron would soon be plotting the destruction of the Autobots and the conquest of Earth!

Weird star
A black hole is a collapsed star whose gravity is so strong that nothing, including light, can escape from it.

A gift
Now that they were working as a team, Optimus Prime gave Rad, Carlos, and Alexis an amazing gift: Laserbeak.

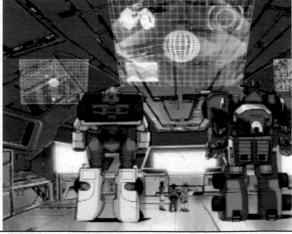

Cyber-hawk
Laserbeak is a small robot in the shape of a bird. In his spybird mode, Laserbeak can scan and record information.

A few days later, Carlos, Alexis, and Rad met at the Autobots' new base. It was packed with so many sophisticated computers that it looked like geek heaven.

"You know this whole thing happened totally by accident," Rad explained to Optimus Prime. "I never would have picked up that Mini-Con plate if I'd known it was going to start a robotic war!"

"Don't blame yourself," said Optimus Prime, gently. "We knew it was only a matter of time before someone discovered the Mini-Cons. What's important now is that we find them before Megatron does."

The Autobots' new base is full of amazing equipment, including giant scanners that can search for Mini-Cons.

46

Just then an alarm sounded in the next room. Everyone rushed there to find out what was going on.

On one wall of the room was a huge screen showing a scan of the whole Earth.

"Incredible!" everyone gasped.

Mini-Cons were coming to life all over the world. The only hope of saving Earth was helping the Autobots to get to them first!

Spy plane
Some countries have spy planes like this one that secretly gather information on their enemies' military operations.

The kids and the Autobots are united against the Decepticons.

Glossary

Ancient Egypt
A civilization that existed in Egypt around 2,000 years ago.

Astronomer
A scientist who studies the stars, planets, and other objects in space.

Atmosphere
The layer of air that surrounds Earth or another planet.

Avalanche
A large fall of rock, ice, or snow from the side of a mountain.

Big Bang
The name given to the explosion that created the Universe.

Civil war
When two rival groups fight for the right to rule their home country.

Cosmos
The entire Universe.

Digital
Information that is coded into numbers.

Earthquake
A shaking of the ground caused by movements in Earth's crust.

Ecology
The study of how plants and animals affect and are affected by the world around them.

Extraterrestrial
Anything that comes from outside Earth. It is usually used to refer to life on planets other than Earth.

Gravity
The force that pulls objects toward the ground and keeps them there.

Humanoid
Having the shape of a human being.

Light-year
A unit used to measure distances in astronomy. It is the distance light travels in one year.

Loyal
Remaining true and faithful to your friends or your ideals.

Materialize
To appear suddenly as if from nowhere.

Metamorphosis
To change from one form into a different form, such as from a tadpole into a frog.

Military
The army, navy, and air force of a country.

Orbit
The path of one body around another, such as Earth around the Sun or a satellite around Earth.

Probe
A machine sent into space to explore areas and places where humans cannot go, such as distant planets.

Reflect
To throw back an exact duplicate of light or an image.

Robot
An intelligent machine, sometimes in the form of a human.

Satellite
A smaller object that moves around a larger one, such as the Moon orbiting Earth.

Sentient
A being that has the ability to sense things and has consciousness.

Solar system
The family of planets that orbit a star.

Stalactite
A limestone formation hanging from a cave roof.

Stalagmite
A limestone formation rising from a cave floor.

Telescope
A piece of equipment that uses lenses to make faraway objects look nearer and bigger. Radio telescopes detect radio waves from space.

Obsession . . . monomania, ruling passion
fixed idea.

Roget's *Thesaurus*

Kensington . . . *owes much of its charm to its*
association with the aristocracy and the very
rich . . . but its essence is contained in the 87 acres
on which are built an extraordinary group of
museums, cultural institutions and places of
learning.

Arthur Mee: *The King's England*

Give me a place among the sheep
And separate me from the goats

Ingemisco/Lacrimosa: *Requiem*

CONTENTS

1

Fanfare

'Julian, did you hand out *all* the programmes?'

'Yes.'

'Did you make sure the *Times* man got one?'

'Yes.'

'Did you put that soldier back where I told you?'

'Yes.'

'You didn't touch him again, did you?'

'No.'

'Julian, I can't find all my music. *What have you done with my music?*'

'Andrew, there's no need to make such a *fuss* about everything.'

'Be *quiet*, Julian. The show is starting . . .'

In the other world, the outside world, things never happened properly. People were late, they did not do what they were supposed to do, they lost things, they turned up at the last minute in a rush. Occasionally, just occasionally, something happened that was halfway decent: that year, the first stereo LPs had appeared; there was a new Bobby Vee record; 20th Century Fox released the film of *South Pacific*. But for the most part life was all house rules and homework, the first of which he obeyed and the second of which he did well and hated.

The toy theatre stood on the table: its auditorium was built of bricks and at the centre was a revolving stage made out of an old gramophone turntable. The walls were lined with paper and bits of fabric cadged from sample books. On the stage lead soldiers played the parts of actors playing real people. In the darkness, his seven-year-old brother held the torch in readiness to play on them, while he himself sat at the piano. Under the table the only other living thing present, hardly stirring, was Perseus the Siamese cat.

Down went the house lights.

Up came the curtain.

Out came the first chords.

On went the torch.

Broadway 1982

At first sight, to that fabulous first night audience squinting in the theatrical moonlight, the stage looked like a giant nocturnal rubbish dump. Just as they realised that this was exactly what it was, their attention was further heightened and held, once and for all, by the mysterious notes of the synthesiser. At that moment, the overture took on more vivid visual shape. Hundreds of eyes, not human and yet somehow human, winked and blinked and stared balefully out at the audience. Slowly, too, the hitherto inert and shadowy shapes among the rubbish began to move . . . and they were the eyes of cats.

Afterwards the whole glittering company, audience and all, poured out of the theatre on to the streets and into the limousines waiting to take them to the Waldorf Astoria Hotel. Here the band played late into the night and massive plates of roast beef and Yorkshire pudding were served up to the assembled multitude. The reviews came out: the London *Times* man had done his best, the *New York Times* man his worst, and the success of the show was assured. The lights went out that night at the

2

Winter Garden and the Waldorf Astoria, and eventually in the top-floor suite of the Mayflower Hotel.

In England, in the attic of a country house, dust gathered on the remains of a toy theatre. Where were the lead soldiers? And where was the revolving stage? They were lost, and with them the high-pitched voices of the two brothers. Now their place had been taken by the voices of others – pleading, dissenting, envious, congratulatory, dismissive voices. Whose were they? And who were they all talking about?

Andrew Lloyd Webber was born in the Westminster Hospital, London on 22 March 1948. These were the immediate postwar austerity years, when clothes rationing was still in force, food-stuffs were in short supply and the Labour Government under Attlee was still in power. In Britain the railways had been nationalised, while in Argentina General Juan Perón ruled with his consort, an upwardly mobile former radio personality named Eva Duarte. In New York audiences were about to be thrilled by Rodgers and Hammerstein's ground-breaking musical *South Pacific*. In London they would have to make do with T. S. Eliot's bleak psychological drama, *The Cocktail Party*.

Andrew's father, William Southcombe Lloyd Webber, had in his own youth been an outstandingly talented pianist and organist, capable of playing Reger's massive *Phantasie und Fugue über B-A-C-H* from memory at a concert at the Royal College of Music only a week after acquiring the score. He also had a fondness for a good tune and was as capable of being moved to tears by *Tosca* as by *Some Enchanted Evening*. He was an intense, reserved man, benign but with a tendency to melancholia into which, as the years passed, he would increasingly retreat, to escape from what he saw as his failure to pursue a career as a serious composer.

Five years in the Royal Army Pay Corps during the Second

World War had given 'Billy' Lloyd Webber an intense desire to avoid doing anything he did not want to do. He had been allowed to make musical broadcasts to the forces and had managed to write one musical, a version of *Pinocchio*. Now, in 1948, at the age of thirty-four, he was about to resign from the post of organist and choirmaster of the church of All Saints, Margaret Street, to devote more time to his role as Professor and Examiner in Theory and Composition at the Royal College of Music.

It was at All Saints, Margaret Street in 1939 that Billy Lloyd Webber had first met Jean Hermione Johnstone, a student at the Royal College of Music. Jean had been deputised with other students to stand in for the absent boy trebles in the choir. Jean and Billy soon formed a mutual attraction, which led to their engagement. Billy's absence during the war had terrified Jean in an unexpected fashion: knowing how physically uncoordinated he was she was terrified lest, as an anti-aircraft gunner temporarily assigned to the batteries in Hyde Park, he unleash his shells on the Albert Hall.

Andrew's paternal grandfather, William Webber (the 'Lloyd' was passed on by Billy to Andrew and his brother Julian as a first name which somehow stuck as a surname) was a singing plumber and stalwart of such popular vocal ensembles of the early 1950s as the George Mitchell Glee Club and the Black and White Minstrels. Andrew's maternal grandmother, Laura Mary Johnstone, or Molly as she was known, was a woman undaunted by an unusual and unhappy life. Originally from a good Scottish family, her marriage to an officer in the Argyll and Sutherland Highlanders had collapsed after the birth of two daughters and a son, the last of whom died by drowning. In the 1930s she had become associated with a loose organisation known as Christian Communism. Her sister Ella, who was married to an impoverished artist, ran a café called the Wishbone in Reading. Molly was particularly fond of two books, *The Problem of Pain* by C. S. Lewis and *Why Do Men Suffer?* by Leslie Weatherhead, which seemed to make some sense of her troubled life. Her daughter Jean was to take after her in many ways, particularly during Andrew's formative, adolescent years, when her actress sister, Andrew's Aunt Viola, was to become a major influence on his life.

Molly leased and inhabited the flat where William, Jean and young Andrew and Julian lived, at 10 Harrington Court, Harrington Road, South Kensington, London SW7. The flat was in an elegant if rather run-down redbrick mansion block, sandwiched between Harrington Road and the Brompton Road. Number 10 was a large, gracious affair with high ceilings, a long hall and rooms off either side; a Chappell grand piano stood in the music room overlooking Brompton Road.

Molly was responsible for many of the day-to-day domestic chores, as Jean, having passionately championed her husband's musical talent, was now preoccupied with identifying and encouraging that same talent in children. She was an energetic and effective piano teacher who taught, among other places, at the exclusive and private Wetherby School in Rosary Gardens, a few minutes' walk from the flat. Jean's other passion was pedigree cats, which she regarded in somewhat the same light as talented people – they were to be cosseted, coached and never for one moment reminded of their origins as mere mortals.

Life at 10 Harrington Court, in the genteel Royal Borough of Kensington, meant being brought up in an otherworldly, bohemian household which none the less conformed in certain ways to the strict values of its class and time. There was little money beyond what Billy and Jean earned and what Molly made available, but Jean was as demanding in her emphasis on the pursuit of excellence as others might have been on the pursuit of material riches. This standard did not extend to the domestic level – neither Billy nor Jean cooked or cleaned – although Jean took great interest in how well the boys did their homework. Billy took no part in the running of the household. What bound them

5

together in one way or another, in spite of, or perhaps because of the general lack of house pride, was music.

The potential for disruption in the entry of a baby into these separate and well-defined worlds was only too obvious to Billy and Jean Lloyd Webber. Andrew fulfilled their worst fears. Not only did he scream and rage and lament, he became more agitated rather than less by doing so. His capacity for sleep was negligible. His sudden changes of mood equalled and surpassed even Billy's tendency to self-pity and despair. He had such tantrums that Jean felt obliged to placate him by any means. He quickly learned how to get what he wanted and she quickly learned that by giving it to him she could carry on with her own busy life. Then, when his brother Julian was born, she did what seemed the obvious thing: at the age of three and a half, she sent him to school.

The Wetherby School catered admirably for the children of genteel bohemia and discreet affluence. Andrew, who was to embody the combination of these milieux on a hitherto undreamt-of scale, became an outwardly conventional little boy. Kitted out in regulation short trousers and tie, educated both at home and at school under the eye of his mother, he quickly soaked up the curriculum. No one ever knew to what extent he was intellectually interested in life – and in those circles it was the sort of question one asked about one's child – but everyone agreed he was a very clever child.

He had a voracious appetite and seemingly limitless capacity for information. He became obsessed with architecture, preferably in ruined form, and read and wrote about it as soon as he acquired the skill to do so. His imaginary environments were invariably bereft of grown-ups. At home, his newfound ability to spend hours alone was received with relief by his parents. Besides, Molly was usually there to watch over him. At the age of four, like many children of his age and background, he began to learn the language of music.

Under Jean's tutelage he became passably proficient at the miniature violin. She also taught him to play the piano, as she had done so many other children of his age. She quickly realised two things; first, he was not particularly talented at either and second, he possessed an unusual ability to digest enough of the practice pieces to play his own, rather than other people's works. Not that they were works, in the proper academic, musical sense – they were little tunes – and a little tunefulness, to Mrs Lloyd Webber, was not an indication of serious musical talent.

Andrew's disinclination to start playing serious pieces and to stop playing tunes, soon led Jean to a rapid reassessment of how her talented if stubborn little boy might best be coached into rising above other mortals and making his mark on the world. Perhaps, she said to herself, there was a future for him as an architectural historian after all.

Life in the Lloyd Webber household thus passed into the early and mid-1950s. Elsewhere, in the outside world, great events took place of absolutely no consequence to Andrew Lloyd Webber. Here and there small things happened that would be of great consequence for the second-youngest inhabitant (not counting Perseus the cat) of 10 Harrington Court. In Argentina, Eva Duarte died and gave birth to the legend of Eva Perón. In England, a girl called Sarah Hugill was born to a rather more respectable, county family. Food rationing ended and Winifred Atwell's *Variation on A minor Caprice by Paganini* reached Number 9 in the popular music charts. The sixty-five-year-old David 'Bunny' Garnett published a novella describing the sexual and emotional antics of three generations of expatriates in France – he called it *Aspects of Love*. The eight-year-old Andrew Lloyd Webber left behind the schoolmistresses and the little girls and boys of the Wetherby School, including his five-year-old brother Julian.

Westminster Under School was the next step on the ladder Jean firmly envisaged him climbing to academic success. She was now convinced that his interest in depopulated ruins was a sign of academic talent and was terrified that his new schoolmasters would not realise this fact. To this end, she took the precaution of leaving them in no doubt as to where she thought her son's talents did and did not lie. They listened politely, told her how refreshing it was for a parent to take such a close personal interest in her son's education, and proceeded to educate him in exactly the same way as the seventy other boys in his year.

At home, the importance of homework was paramount. A place at Westminster Under School was, after all, the most likely route to a place at the ancient and great Westminster School, generally regarded as one of the top six public schools in Britain, unique in its location and thereby synonymous with the political and cultural history of London. The Palace of Westminster, Westminster Abbey and Westminster School were not only geographically but culturally in the same square mile. Westminster was also the site of the Methodist Central Hall, where Billy Lloyd Webber was to become Musical Director in 1958.

Andrew struck his Under School masters as a rather odd-looking and self-contained, but otherwise unremarkable boy of the sort of above-average intelligence they had come to expect. At home, however, he was left in no doubt of the consequences that failure to do his homework to the limits of his ability at all times would have for his precious talent. Julian, by contrast, was left relatively to his own devices and now spent much of his time practising on a miniature version of the cello.

Andrew's own ability at the violin and piano continued to leave both his schoolmasters and his parents unamazed. Julian increasingly became the performer of the two, although the brothers could still be seen performing a violin and cello duet perched on stools in their school uniforms, on the narrow balcony at the rear of the flat. But Andrew's interest continued to be in tunes. He seemed unable to absorb the most juvenile practice piece without going off at a melodic tangent. He used his parents in the same way, permitting Billy to help him with arrangement and Jean to teach him how to read and write music notation on scored paper. At the age of nine he had his first work published, a suite of six pieces – including *No. 3: Romantic Scene* in the *Music Teacher*. The work was called *The Toy Theatre Suite*.

The Toy Theatre Suite was not a work of Mozartian precocity. In fact it was not brilliant at all – as he was disappointed to discover when he replayed it years later. What made it of interest, apart from the influence of the romanticism of his father's compositions and his mother's astute publicising of her son in her trade journal, was the title.

The toy theatre in question had become the nerve centre not just of an energetic and fertile fantasy, but an entire imaginary civilisation living at 10 Harrington Court.

The dynamics of its genesis and survival were rooted in the private reality of the lives of the Lloyd Webbers. Absent for much of the time was Jean, whose missionary zeal for piano teaching took her out of the flat to schools in the mornings and private houses in the afternoons. Present for some of the time, but never prominent, was Billy, who when not performing or teaching at the Royal College was much preoccupied with his own romantic, introspective works, composed with the help of his own piano fitted out with organ pedals. Present for most of the time and thrown into each other's company were Andrew and Julian, depending on school hours. Present, too, for much of the time, was Molly. Although she did not live there, increasingly present by virtue of her influence was Molly's other daughter, the retired actress Viola Johnstone.

Viola had married a doctor called George and they lived over his practice in Weymouth Street, W1. She was the opposite of her sister in nearly every way: where Vi was bubbly, giggly, cheerful and plump, Jean was introverted, serious, nervous and thin. Vi was an exuberant, enthusiastic woman, whose retirement from the stage had not diminished her love of the theatre. Aunt Vi and

9

Uncle George had plans for his retirement, upon which they intended to decamp to the Italian Riviera. Meanwhile, they continued to brave the grey English climate of the 1950s – one of the few bright aspects of which, as far as she was concerned, was the importation of the brash new American postwar musical, in particular those written by Richard Rodgers and Oscar Hammerstein.

Rodgers and Hammerstein's *Oklahoma!*, *The King and I* and *South Pacific* all successfully crossed the Atlantic to England in the early and mid-1950s. Andrew, who would eventually cross the Atlantic the other way and sweep away the old Broadway musical tradition, was taken by Aunt Vi to see numerous West End musical shows. The young boy and his aunt formed a close and lasting attachment; so close that, when Jean suggested that his enjoyment of the real-life theatre was jeopardising his academic career, Viola suggested that he build a toy one of his own.

This was the brick auditorium and turntable-revolving stage that now stood on the table in the Lloyd Webbers' flat. Andrew's management of it was autocratic; he built and owned the theatre, wrote and played much of the music, wrote and typed the programmes and invited the audience. He also hired and fired the staff; Julian, three years younger, was a willing unpaid hand who was allowed to operate the lead soldiers that passed for actors and castigated mercilessly for any mistakes. The Andrew Lloyd Webber Toy Theatre Company, perhaps not surprisingly given its origins in the frustrated psyche of its young proprietor, was not an equal opportunity employer.

The early productions more or less directly reflected the shows he managed to see with Aunt Vi. *The Importance of Being Earnest* was an early effort: complete with backstage as well as onstage banter, it reflected Aunt Vi's ability to get herself and her stagestruck young nephew through the stage-door and into the looking-glass world of actors and impresarios. At a time when the West End stage musical was rediscovering its identity in a way it had not done since the salad days of Noel Coward,

Ivor Novello and Gilbert and Sullivan, and Rodgers and Hammerstein were giving way to Lionel Bart's cockney epics *Fings Ain't Wot They Used t' Be* and *Oliver!*, it was no coincidence that the sounds of music hall piano and a kind of patrician South Kensington cockney began to reverberate around the revolving stage of the toy theatre at 10 Harrington Court.

Outside rehearsal time and the hours of performance, beyond the toy theatre, a whole other life had to be lived. On the floor of Julian's room, before he left for the Under School, people left their houses and boarded the trains stationed on his bedroom floor. They went to work in the morning and they came back in the evening. They had rows and made it up, and in the evening they went out to the theatre. The lights went down, the curtain went up and the lead soldiers took the parts of actors playing real human beings; Billy, Vi and Jean would sometimes take the part of the audience.

Unsurprisingly, in contrast to Andrew's later shows, these audiences were very small. Aunt Vi and Billy would take the memories of these shows to their graves, while Jean would remain reticent on the subject. On the subject of Andrew's academic career, however, she was exultant. In the summer of 1960, in spite of his failure to win the Internal Scholarship — a failure which saw the Under School headmaster's wife having to comfort a distraught Julian, whom she found weeping for his brother in the corridor — the pressure on him finally appeared to pay off. At the age of twelve and a half, even younger than most of his clever little contemporaries, Andrew Lloyd Webber won a place at the 'Great School' of Westminster.

Westminster School was a mass of contradictions: a scholastic, originally monastic foundation, of medieval origin and yet dangerously contemporary in its outlook, an exclusive, expensive and at that time all-male enclave of interlinked cloisters, houses and yards located in the very centre of London. Westminster's motto

11

Dat Deus Incrementum (God Gives Increase) gave to outsiders the uncomfortable impression that Heaven was full of Old Westminsters.

But Westminster's privileged position had given it a mixed reputation: 'It will never be well with the nation,' wrote the eighteenth-century Dean of Christ Church, Oxford, 'until Westminster School is suppressed.' In order to reach the river, the Boat Club crews still had the right to pass through the Palace of Westminster. The image was one of casual ambivalence to privileges which were fiercely asserted if now largely symbolic. The truth beneath all this, as usual, was somewhat more prosaic: as the eighteenth-century playwright and another Old Westminster George Colman, observed: 'Geniuses and boobies have been brought up in it, who would have been geniuses and boobies had they been brought up anywhere else.'

Into this self-confident, self-sufficient world came the young proprietor of the toy theatre at 10 Harrington Court. He was by now a resolutely unathletic child of somewhat odd appearance. He had a Cheshire Cat's face and a tendency to forget the use of his neck. He was younger and yet at the same time seemingly more self-sufficient than the other boys. But as a new day boy 'up' Rigaud's House, in quaint Westminster parlance, he soon impressed his housemaster with a learned paper he had written on medieval architecture. His reward was to be given extra history teaching and freedom in equal measure. At Westminster this was entirely in keeping with an ethos which could equate the home of parliamentary democracy with the right of way of the Boat Club.

Andrew's housemaster at Rigaud's was Frank Kilvington, a Gilbert and Sullivan *aficionado* who had high hopes that by commissioning works in the vein of *The Mikado* and *HMS Pinafore* he could raise the flagging cultural tone of the house. To this end he recruited his head boy, Robin Barrow, to write satirical lyrics after Gilbert and based on the tunes of Sullivan. The sixteen-year-old Barrow had ambitions as a lyricist, but the result was not a great musical success and the following year he went in search of a collaborator. Barrow was not so much looking for a composer as for someone who could play the piano well enough to give substance to his own ideas. Somebody suggested the nervous, odd-looking fourteen-year-old architecture buff and composer of *The Toy Theatre Suite*, Andrew Lloyd Webber.

Barrow's first show with Andrew was a satirical pantomime entitled *Cinderella Up the Beanstalk and Most Everywhere Else*. This was considerably more successful than its predecessor. Not only had Barrow underestimated his youthful partner's extraordinary propensity for 'tunes', he also discovered in him an ally against what they both regarded as the school's excessively boring music curriculum.

Westminster's Director of Music was a distinguished teacher whose dedication to serious classical music rivalled if not exceeded that of Jean Lloyd Webber. Billy, too, was perceived as a serious classical teacher and organist in the English church tradition. But it was as if the influence of Aunt Vi, rather than Jean, was now guiding Andrew's fledgling musical career. The next Barrow–Webber collaboration was called *Socrates Swings*.

Barrow's superior age meant he left Westminster for Oxford before they had a chance for a third collaboration, but the age difference between them was making itself felt. Andrew's nervousness meant that his behaviour frequently seemed embarrassingly childish to a seventeen-year-old desperate to put childish things behind him. Barrow, by contrast, was striving to be 'shag': in Westminster parlance, a practitioner of the art of achieving a natural superiority without really trying.

In the short term it was a doomed relationship, one that would have resulted in a bruising rejection for the younger partner. In the longer term it might well have renewed itself, but for Barrow it was not to be. Sixty miles south of London, another public schoolboy left Lancing College that summer for a short-lived course of study at the Sorbonne. Timothy Miles Bindon Rice, like Robin St Clare Barrow, had been encouraged by his schoolmasters to develop a lyrical talent which was in need of a collaborator. More than three years would pass before he found that collaborator and, like Barrow, he would be more than three years older than Andrew Lloyd Webber. Tim Rice, moreover, was 'shag' in a way that Barrow was not and Andrew would never be. But while Rice practised his *insouciance* at the Sorbonne, Andrew was now propelled, minus Barrow and via a Challenge Scholarship, into a world where the importance of being 'shag' was as never before.

College House, Westminster, was the summit of 'shag'. The elite population, all boarders, all Scholars, were the beneficiaries of privileges which exceeded those of the rest of the school put together. They were expected to spend much of the day scoring points off each other and overdosing on caffeine while the rest of the school worked for its sins. Being a College House Scholar was a full-time occupation.

Andrew entered this exclusive, protected world in September 1962. His encyclopaedic knowledge of cathedral and monastic architecture and his musical ability now brought him intellectual status and emotional friendship for the first time in his life. There was something in this all-male enclave akin to a monastery fallen from grace: under the liberal eye of the housemaster and with the guidance of the charismatic history master, Charles Keeley, a loose brotherhood of like-minded souls from College and other houses took shape. With Andrew there was Ivon Asquith, who went on to be a Director of the Oxford University Press; William Cran, who became a successful film-maker; David Carpenter became a university don; William Bach a solicitor; and there was Gray Watson.

Watson was tall, dark, handsome and possessed of an outstanding intellect. Of the members of this little clique, he would be remembered as the most talented, the most entertaining and the most supremely 'shag'. Yet although he became an inspiring teacher of the history of art, few if any of his contemporaries would have suspected that, twenty-five years later, his main claim to fame would be as the first and best friend of Andrew Lloyd Webber.

Gray and Andrew together seemed to meet some need in each other that as individuals they could not quite fulfil; they combined an encyclopaedic knowledge of Roman architecture with a deeper imaginative understanding of the same; they could indulge their mutual scorn for the notions of socialism and the dictatorship of the proletariat; they could tease women like Molly and Jean about Christian Communism at Harrington Court. For Andrew, whose real and imaginary environments had for so long been bereft of close human contact, this was the beginning of a close friendship.

Andrew's weekday absence at school had occasioned a new arrival among the familiar faces at home. Billy Lloyd Webber was preoccupied with his work; Molly was still running the flat; Julian was still at Westminster Under School, which he found musically unsatisfying but which at least allowed him to concentrate on the cello — his father would divert him from a noisier career by secretly selling his younger son's trumpet to a student at the London College of Music. Jean's missionary interest in discovering and bringing on new talent was undimmed. Recently she had taken to going on long expeditions across London to Leyton in the East End. Here she had attached herself to the family of a young man who fulfilled all her criteria of promise. His name was John Lill.

Lill was a sixteen-year-old, brilliantly gifted pianist who lived with his family in straitened circumstances caused by debt. Father and son were on difficult terms, but Lill was devoted to his mother Margery who, in order to support her family, was forced into a series of exhausting and menial jobs. Her son's studies included courses of conducting and composition at the Junior Royal College

15

of Music. Jean it transpired, had heard him play and was greatly impressed by his talent. She spoke in what seemed to the East End boy a rather silly upper-class accent; but there was steel behind it. Was there, she enquired politely, anything she could do to help? One day at the Royal College he was approached by a small boy whom he had occasionally helped with timpani and percussion. The little boy's first name was unfamiliar: but his surname was well known there.

'My mother,' he told Lill, 'would like you to come to lunch.' This was Julian Lloyd Webber.

Billy Lloyd Webber opened the door. He extended a hand in his amiable way. On his shoulder was Perseus. John Lill shook Billy's hand and then reached out to stroke the family pet. Perseus gave him a six-inch scratch, and they went into the flat.

Lill's first and enduring impression was that they were an extraordinarily individualistic lot. Were these people really related to each other? Julian was so much warmer and less temperamental than his elder brother. Jean was so tense and serious: whereas Billy seemed relatively relaxed. It was only when he met Molly and saw how she acted as the buffer between them, that he understood how they all managed to live together. Molly cooked lunch and there was a vigorous conversation about music.

On many a subsequent Saturday afternoon, while Jean ministered to Mrs Lill in whatever ways she felt appropriate, John Lill, Julian and Andrew adjourned to the nearby ground of Leyton Orient Football Club. Here they could be seen behind the goal, chanting their support for the home team. It was an ironic inversion of circumstances. The two public schoolboys from Kensington took a patrician interest in the proceedings; for them this was the fabulous East End of Lionel Bart's *Oliver!*, while for the local boy it represented everything about the poor, working-class culture from which he was trying to escape. Julian and Andrew would remain Orient supporters (they even contemplated buying the club); John Lill's own success somehow never kindled in him an interest in Association Football.

Lill's face became familiar at 10 Harrington Court. Jean's pursuit of excellence, which had begun with Billy and then moved to Andrew and Julian, now alighted on him. She never taught him anything to do with the piano — she simply made herself part of his life. Lill's own career as one of Britain's foremost concert pianists was more or less under way when he met the extraordinary Lloyd Webber family, but Jean was always there to offer material and moral support to both him and his mother.

Billy and John Lill became good friends, the former teaching the latter a good deal about harmony and composition. Lill was struck by the sheer extent of Billy's theoretical knowledge and classical command, as well as his romantic creative inclinations. He was also a generous host, who specialised in mixing cocktails of innocent taste and awesome power.

Billy's career as a romantic composer was slowly being subordinated to his job as Director of the London College of Music. This was a source of deep depression. He took to making implicit comparisons between himself and Julian's godfather, Herbert Howells. Howells, an associate of Billy's at the Royal College of Music, was a composer who in Billy's view had failed to achieve greatness. The unhappiness in Billy's own mind was at times so strong as to be patently obvious to anyone in the flat. The anguish and sense of transcendence that had once characterised his best compositions, such as the beautiful *Aurora*, now spilled over in outbursts of self-pity and tears. Even Jean now found it impossible to encourage the talent of the promising young composer whom she had married. On bad days he would play recordings of Rachmaninov and Tchaikovsky, drink one cocktail too many, and weep.

Although Lill never felt as at ease with Andrew as he did with Julian, the two developed a rapport which became a useful acquaintance for the young composer. Lill gave a couple of

17

recitals at Westminster School and introduced him further to the music of Sergei Prokofiev, a recording of whose opera *The Love of Three Oranges* Billy often played at home. Prokofiev's early talent for parody had given way to a more personal, romantic orchestral style, with edgy harmonies anchored by an imaginative technique, that aroused enthusiasm among the young and mixed feelings among the classical music establishment.

Prokofiev's insistence on melody and his penchant for unusual instruments, especially the tuba, appealed to something in Andrew. He and Lill took to attending concerts featuring such instruments and within five minutes there would be tears of laughter falling from both their faces. On holiday together they would play games such as deliberately seeing how many cups of tea they could extract from one helping of afternoon tea at a café. To Lill Andrew was brilliant, mercurial, obsessive and ultimately a loner. His preferred landscapes were medieval and depopulated. He collected Ordnance Survey maps with obsessive impatience and marked out routes on them in minute detail. When Lill and the Lloyd Webbers went on day trips in Billy's elderly black Ford Consul, the two essential items of kit for Andrew were his Ordnance Survey map and Perseus the cat. He subjugated his surroundings to the impossible perfection of both.

Billy's idea of 'light' music was Addinsell's *Warsaw Concerto*, but he permitted anything to be played at home. In Julian's case this increasingly meant recordings of the cello, upon the study of which he had now embarked in a serious way. But when Andrew was home from College House, where they prided themselves on knowing about these things, the sounds of Bill Haley, Bobby Vee and the Everly Brothers would be added to those of Elgar's *Cello Concerto* and *Some Enchanted Evening*. And in the dining room, on the table, the toy theatre would still occasionally hint at the early life of its sixteen-year-old proprietor.

By the early 1960s the Edwardian drapes of *The Importance of Being Earnest* and the musical homage to Richard Rodgers and

Lionel Bart had given way under the influence of the angry young men to a rather more austere, 'kitchen sink' look. This was complete with a suitably vulgar, proletarian house decorated with blue and purple wallpaper. Then this, too, was swept away by market forces: the real-life Chelsea Palace theatre, which Aunt Vi and Andrew had regularly patronised, was closed and reopened as a television studio. This meant that the toy theatre also went 'dark', reopening as both a theatre and a television studio, to the accompaniment of indignant letters to the management.

Julian was now six feet tall and towered over his older brother. He was sufficiently free of academic and other pressures to concentrate on developing his performing talents as a cellist and was no longer available as a stagehand. Molly was growing old. Billy was distracted by work and what might have been. Aunt Vi and Uncle George were far away in retirement in sunny Ventimiglia. Jean was busy teaching. Andrew Lloyd Webber's toy theatre soon went dark for good, and the torch went off on his perfect private world. Nearly twenty years later, when it reopened among the theatres where he had once wandered as a stagestruck teenager, his own theatre would have grown to life-size and the world it contained would reveal itself to be miraculously intact.

The remainder of his career as a College House Scholar was somewhat chequered. He was probably the first Scholar to fail O level Greek but pass in music; both of which were taught in the classical manner. As the physically gauche son of ex-Pay Corps conscript Billy Lloyd Webber, he took no pleasure in the affairs of the Combined Cadet Force or the gymnasium. He helped to organise a pop concert to celebrate the first time two Old Westminsters, Peter Asher and Gordon Waller, reached Number 1 in the pop charts with *World Without Love*. The Westminster authorities lent him the seventeenth-century

Ashburnham House, where the select History Upper Seventh met under their guru, Charles Keeley, to hold a press conference for the occasion.

He was regarded by his 'shag' friends as a nervous, excitable oddball. He was possibly an original, certainly an outsider. He had more friends outside their world than in it. He seemed unwittingly to attract the attentions of older, rather raffish sorts who gravitated towards the Westminster schoolboys. His schoolmasters regarded him as gifted, if mercurial. He did not disappoint them: having achieved dismal A level results in English and History, he then proceeded to enter himself for and win an Open Exhibition in History to Magdalen College, Oxford. He was not yet seventeen years old.

On 4 January 1965, the death occurred in his seventy-seventh year of T. S. Eliot, whose poetry had perplexed many a Westminster English A level candidate. Eliot was commemorated in Poet's Corner in Westminster Abbey. Eighteen months earlier he had told the critic Herbert Read that the best of his poetry had cost him dearly in experience. His widow Valerie also later declared: 'He felt he had paid too high a price to be a poet, that he had suffered too much.' But there was a lighter side to Eliot, or 'Possum' as he was known among his friends: a devoted cat lover and owner of a succession of cats with names such as Wiscus and George, he had celebrated his love for them in a collection of fey verse published twenty-five years earlier entitled *Old Possum's Book of Practical Cats*. The book had remained in print and sold steadily over the years, returning a modest income to the publishers Faber & Faber. But through the influence of Perseus, the cat who hardly stirred except to scratch beneath the toy theatre at Harrington Court, and the efforts of the teenager now preparing for his penultimate term at Westminster, the high price Eliot paid for his poetry would be repaid in a form that would revive the fortunes of Faber & Faber and make Valerie and Andrew rich beyond the dreams of avarice.

In the avalanche of publicity that followed, Andrew would tell reporters that by the time he left Westminster he had already 'had two agents'. One of these was Desmond Elliott, a publisher who occasionally attended concerts at Westminster and formed a friendship with the seventeen-year-old Andrew. Later in life, Elliott would find fortune as literary agent to bestselling novelists such as Jilly Cooper; meanwhile his appreciation of Andrew's talents set him wondering if his own entrepreneurial skills did not also lie in that direction.

Elliott, quite by coincidence, had also taken an avuncular interest in the career of another public schoolboy, this time the son of a woman he knew. This was the tall, handsome blond from Lancing who, after a brief course of study at the Sorbonne and an even briefer career as a petrol pump attendant at a Hertfordshire filling station, had recently left his job as a trainee at a firm of Baker Street solicitors; Timothy Rice.

Mrs Rice had asked Elliott the perennial mother's question: 'Is there anything you can do for my boy?' Rice had been a languidly talented pupil at Lancing, where he had sung in a rock 'n' roll group called The Aardvarks. His contemporaries included the successful playwright Christopher Hampton; like Andrew he was lucky enough to have a brilliantly talented teacher – in his case an English master called Harry Guest – and a disparagingly capable intellect. 'English O level,' he was fond of telling people, 'is a piece of cake if you can write fast.' He was indisputably 'shag' – and he knew it.

Tim Rice's real desire, it transpired, was to become a pop singer. In the pursuit of this aim he had now taken a job as the lowliest of junior assistant trainees with the giant EMI record company, whose clients included Elvis Presley and Cliff Richard and the Shadows. He had even had one or two songs recorded and released to an indifferent public, and was harbouring a vague idea for a history of the Top Twenty. No wonder, then, that Mrs Rice threw herself on the mercies of the nearest sympathetic ear, including Desmond Elliott's.

Elliott thought the young man had talent; the least he could do, in the circumstances, was introduce him to Andrew Lloyd Webber.

Thus it was that the following letter was dispatched to 10 Harrington Court on 21 April 1965; and hot on its heels came its sender:

Dear Andrew

I have been told you are looking for a 'with-it' writer of lyrics for your songs . . . and as I have been writing pop songs for a while now and particularly enjoy writing the lyrics I wondered if you considered it worth your while meeting me . . .

When they met, Andrew took one look at Tim and said: 'I have written eight musicals.'

In case Tim did not believe him, he began to play. Extracts from *Cinderella up the Beanstalk*, *Socrates Swings* and numerous unnamed toy theatre productions flowed off the piano, but after a short time it was no longer necessary. Rice was impressed.

This guy, he thought, *is a red-hot certainty*.

He told Andrew he thought they should give it a try.

That spring five friends from Westminster went on a last holiday together. Andrew, Gray Watson, Ivon Asquith, David Carpenter and William Bach travelled the well-trodden route via Florence and Assisi to Rome. Gray and Andrew dominated the tour with their knowledge of art and their shared passion for architecture — to them, even Mussolini had his moments.

On the way back they visited Andrew's Aunt Vi in Ventimiglia. Her cool, shuttered villa stood halfway up a sunny hillside near the sea; palm trees grew near by and the veranda was filled with sweetly smelling flowers. The five stayed a while before going home to London to prepare for their university careers. Five months later, Andrew went up to Magdalen College, Oxford.

Oxford University, in the Michaelmas Term of 1965, should

ostensibly have been a good place for Andrew Lloyd Webber. He had won a place at one of the oldest and most respectable colleges of the University. As a History Exhibitioner and expert on architecture he could expect a good deal of academic and intellectual stimulation from the staff of his Faculty. As a young composer he might have expected to find like-minded persons with whom he could work. As an Old Westminster he had a ready-made peer group within his generation of undergraduates. As a seasoned adolescent points-scorer, he might have made his mark debating the burning issues of the day: should colleges be allowed to control their members' morals? Should undergraduates have parking rights? Were women a good thing? As a nervous, excitable boy from an all-male public school, he might even have found a girlfriend. But these things were not to be.

His room in Magdalen New Buildings was a little apart from the main buildings of the College, down by the river in the Deer Park. In the early gloaming of autumn, surrounded by wraith-like deer and the rooks overhead, without a piano, it was a melancholy spot even for a connoisseur of the monastic life. The academic discipline which had been barely tolerable at school, and then made so only by the presence of a charismatic history master, now seemed lifeless. The musical life of the University was multifarious – there were organ recitals, choral societies, madrigals, orchestras, jazz groups and pop groups galore – but nobody seemed to be very interested in musical theatre. His Old Westminster contemporaries at Oxford did not seem to be having quite such trouble adjusting to their new surroundings. The politics of university life were not for him. And as for the girls, he did not have a clue.

To Ivon Asquith, now up at Christ Church, he confided that he might have made a mistake. William Cran, another Old Westminster, lived beneath Andrew's room. Music always seemed to be coming from it – some light classical, such as Addinsell's *Warsaw Concerto*, but mostly early pop. Bobby Vee, the Everly Brothers and Neil Sedaka all seemed to be living in the same room. He kept playing Bernier and Brainin's *The Night Has 1000 Eyes*, over and over again.

He made no attempt to resuscitate the early musical partnership of his life. Robin Barrow was still at Oxford when Andrew arrived. Barrow would remember their discussing ideas for musicals together; Andrew, however, would have no such recollection. But then Barrow and Andrew had not worked together for three years and by the time they met again the position of lyricist and partner was no longer vacant. As far as Andrew was concerned, Barrow was no longer head boy.

For a few months after their first meeting, Andrew and Tim had not actually written anything together at all. But they had spent a lot of time having ideas and listening to records and discovering that their talents fitted together in an amazing way. On Rice, the pop expert, it had quickly dawned that this nervous, odd-looking boy could write popular music with the authority that only a classical background could bring. To Andrew, who travelled with both Prokofiev and Rodgers and Hammerstein, here was someone who could bring to musical theatre the bittersweet, street lyrics of pop.

Now that rare talent was fifty miles away and in danger of being snapped up by someone else. Andrew began slipping back to London, first at the weekends, then during the week. He began to make telephone calls, alternately angry and tearful, to his family at Harrington Court. How was everything at home? How was Perseus? Were they *really* sure that spending three years at Oxford was the right thing for him to do? These calls provoked consternation in the Lloyd Webber household. If Andrew was not to stay at Oxford, what was he to do? Look what happened to Delius — if he had only stuck to farming oranges, all would have been well; as it was, the suffering it brought on his family was proof of his mistake. The fact that all the oranges died was not the point.

At the end of the Michaelmas Term the miserable young

Oxford man was collected by John Lill in Billy's car and brought back to Harrington Court. He had persuaded the university authorities to let him take off the rest of the academic year in order to make up his mind. Privately he had already done so. After Christmas, he went to stay with Aunt Vi in Ventimiglia.

When he came back, he told them he was not going back to Oxford. He was not going to write any more essays. He was going to write music with Tim Rice.

Molly and Jean did not like this at all. Not only was his notion of a career academically doubtful, it was surely a perilous, penniless profession. One composer *manqué* in the family, they intimated, was already more than enough.

At this point, the composer *manqué* in question spoke up.

Billy Lloyd Webber had by now been Director of the London College of Music for nearly two years, during which time he had managed hardly any composition. The subject of talent wasted, as much as talent trained, was close to his heart. The figure of Herbert Howells rose briefly in corroboration.

'If he *is* going to write music,' said Billy Lloyd Webber, 'then you *have* to let him do it.'

Then he returned to the melancholy mood from which, these days, he rarely strayed. Thus began the musical career of Andrew Lloyd Webber.

2

The Likes of Us

Even if he was one of the family, the fact that the composer was back in residence soon caused problems for everyone else at 10 Harrington Court. This in part was due to the fact that in his absence the family had become somewhat extended. The balcony on which Andrew and Julian had once played duets gave access to the sitting room of flat 2a next door. This smaller, cheaper flat had fallen empty and been acquired by the Lloyd Webbers. This was ostensibly so that Molly could live within reach and away from the noise.

Flat 2a, however, had three bedrooms. Molly had the first of these and the second soon served as a Central London base for John Lill, who was now embarking on his concert career. The third bedroom was also let, first to Brian, a Scottish student, then to a friend of Lill's called David Baker and then, when he became Andrew's writing partner, to Tim Rice. All three members of this satellite household could now be seen commuting to and fro, across the balcony, at all hours of the day and night.

Julian in particular began to experience increasing problems of concentration. Now that he had decided to be a cellist, most of his waking hours not at school or at Leyton Orient were spent practising to achieve this end. But with his brother back in the flat, Julian was forced to practise in the main sitting room opening on to the balcony, through which a stream of people now passed seemingly with the sole object of preventing him from doing what he wanted to do. Likewise, Andrew usually wanted to play pop music at ear-splitting volume on the powerful record player when Julian was desperate to listen to Rostropovich or Pablo Casals.

For the first time in their lives relations between the brothers rapidly went downhill. Their arguments became heated and invariably ended with Andrew's voice rising with hysteria: 'I'm not going to *be* here much longer!' he would scream, and there would be much slamming of doors; except that Andrew had nowhere else to go. It was a reversal of the master and servant roles they had played at the toy theatre long ago. Afterwards, Julian would feel sorry for him – until the stream of people, to and fro, to and fro, resumed.

Next door, in Flat 2a, relations between the odd threesome were more stable. Molly had few ambitions left in life and her young flatmates were busy during the day. At night, Lill listened to short wave radio transmissions until the small hours (in later life he was to become a fully qualified radio 'ham'). Tim was often out late at recording sessions and had access to an apparently inexhaustible supply of pretty girls. Once, when Lill was away, Julian took the opportunity to practise in Lill's room. The relentless bowing of the cello irritated a young neighbour downstairs who later came up to complain. By this time Julian had gone and it was Rice who answered the door.

'That noise,' the neighbour started, 'that bloody oboe thing.'

'Yes, that bloody oboe thing.'

'Can't you stop it? Just for a day?'

The former lead singer of The Aardvarks and future millionaire agreed that he could. Later, Julian returned.

'How *is* the oboe?' said Rice.

'The what?'

'How's the oboe?' It became a familiar refrain; something Rice would never let Julian forget. He was older, cooler and very Lancing. Julian could take it. Andrew, on the other hand, had only to hear you incorrectly and he was at boiling point.

*

27

That summer Harold Wilson became Prime Minister and announced a six-month freeze of wages, prices and salaries. Andrew, who was all too aware that he was not earning any money and who could never see any sense in socialism, moved out of Harrington Court.

He did not move far, staying within ten minutes of the Wetherby School and fifteen minutes of Harrington Court. Flat 1, 10 Gledhow Gardens was the basement of an imposing, flat-fronted, pillared Regency terrace house. At the front there was a drawing room and at the back were two bedrooms and a long, narrow dining room virtually filled with a table and benches on either side. He shared the flat with a friend called David Harrington, a serious, bespectacled boy with an academic future. To placate his parents and show that he was at least doing something with the money Molly gave him, he signed up for a year's part-time course in orchestration with Barclay Wilson at the Guildhall School of Music.

He also signed up for a term and a half's course of conducting at the Royal College of Music with Julian's cello teacher, Harvey Phillips. But Billy Lloyd Webber, one of its most distinguished associates, had been emphatic:

'You don't want a full-time, traditional musical training,' he told him, 'it will educate the music you have out of you.'

The Eric Gilder School of Music, now long defunct, was another port of call. Here, instruction in writing out piano music was available to Andrew and other birds of passage. But Billy Lloyd Webber need not have feared that Andrew would ever see these courses as being other than brief and not particularly to the point. To Andrew the main thing, the most important thing, was to work with Tim.

The first significant joint offering from the lead singer of The Aardvarks and the composer of *The Toy Theatre Suite* was a musical loosely based on the life and works of the Victorian philanthropist, Thomas Barnardo. Doctor Barnardo had passed into popular myth in Britain as the first person to take an altruistic interest in the welfare of abandoned and destitute children. The story of Barnardo and his street urchins had everything — sex, love, theft, fortunes lost and found and the Dickensian diction of London's East End — that had already proved so successful in Lionel Bart's musicals *Fings Ain't Wot they Used 't Be* and *Oliver!*

Desmond Elliott, the publisher who took such an avuncular interest in the welfare of Tim and Andrew, offered to be their agent. Elliott had a publisher friend called Ernest Hecht who offered to produce their first musical. Eventually, they settled on a title.

They called it *The Likes of Us*:

> *'Ave you seen my bruvver Johnny?*
> *Not since yesterday*
> *Is it going to rain tonight?*
> *It's kind of 'ard to say*
> *'Oo 'as got me blinkin' rug?*
> *I need it for me bed*
> *No one knows the likes of us*
> *Are sleepin' over 'ead*

Julian, listening, thought he detected a melancholy, musical-box tune that Andrew had produced during the salad days of the toy theatre. But he had no idea that fifteen years later he would play precisely this melody on his cello on Andrew's bestselling album *Variations*.

> *I picked up a wallet*
> *From a fancy coach today*
> *I got fourpence cleaning boots*
> *Down Stepney Market way*

Ain't no one seen Johnny yet?
Perhaps they took him in
No one knows the places where the likes of us 'ave been

Pitter patter pitter patter
We can feel the rain
Little silver water drops
Are falling down again
We ain't gonna bother
It's no matter if it falls
For we know the likes of us
Are going to stay outdoors

Time to doss us down to sleep
They're putting out the light
When they make it dark and quiet
Is when we say goodnight
We don't mind the things we got
And we ain't gonna fuss
This is what we know is proper
For the likes of us.

Tim's access to recording facilities meant that his words and Andrew's music were preserved on a long-playing demonstration disc, performed on acoustic and electric instruments and sung in stage cockney accents by the off-duty choirboys from Colet Court School. Colet Court is to St Paul's School what the Under School is to Westminster. One of the music staff at the Under School in Andrew's day, a former vicar-choral at St Paul's Cathedral, was now in charge of the choirboys at Colet Court. He was to loom large in Andrew's early professional life. His name was Alan Doggett.

Doggett was a split personality: outwardly a charming, witty man, a competent keyboard player and arranger and a highly successful architect of the Colet Court choir, but inwardly a nervy, intense homosexual of unhappy inclinations which would eventually destroy him. He had taken a shine to Andrew at an early age and became his self-appointed musical minder, making sure the young composer's phenomenal aptitude for tunes was translated into music whose time signature always worked and bars added up correctly. Like Desmond Elliott and Ernest Hecht, Alan Doggett was an older man whose role in the early life of Andrew Lloyd Webber would later be little recognised.

Like them, too, Doggett was by temperament rather closer to the young composer than he was to the robustly 'shag' lyricist:

Going Going Gone

Here I have Lot 1 in this beautiful auction — a beautiful parrot in a magnificent cage.

> *Here I have a lovely parrot sound in wind and limb*
> *I can guarantee that there is nothing wrong with him*
> *Pretty feathers very clever do I hear a call?*
> *20, 30, 40, 50 goodness is that at all?*
>
> *This parrot is a sturdy fellow you can plainly see*
> *His habits are impressive he has wide vocabulary*
> *60, 80, 90, 100 going for a song*
> *Going to that well-built lady*
> *Going going gone*
>
> *Going going going going going going gone*
> *Going going going going going going gone*
> *Pretty feathers very clever going for a song*
> *Going to that well-built lady going going gone*

Now I have Lot 2, a beautiful chamber pot — very subtly decorated. Who will start with 10 shillings? . . .

Unlike Andrew, Rice liked to exhibit a relaxed attitude to his craft. He wrote lyrics off the top of his head, in the small hours of the morning, at odd moments; after a session in the recording studio, after a date with a girl, on the way home to see his parents. In a way it was just one more thing he wanted to prove he could do: like trying to be a pop singer or to pick up a girl. But if he was as unsuccessful at the former as he was successful at the latter, there was also a genuine talent beginning to fight its way out from beneath the mimetic ability.

As yet, as in the auctioneer's song, it was still the work of a public school sixth former safely impressing his peers (having first studied the lyrics of Lionel Bart's *Oliver!* and Lerner and Loewe's *My Fair Lady*). Andrew's burlesque piano accompaniment, too, sounded here like a talent idling for want of true direction. But Rice was also beginning to reveal the penchant for distinctive, bittersweet love songs that would make him famous:

Love Is Here

I ain't got no gifts to bring
This ain't Paris, it ain't Spring
No pearls for you to wear

(I wouldn't mind a bit of that)

I don't have no shinin' moon
We're bloody miles from June
But you know love is here

All them poets with their rhyme
Their pretty words in time
Are missing what's so clear

(It doesn't mean a thing to me)

Painters, they 'ave missed it too
Writers 'aven't got a clue
They can't see love is here . . .

Nine years later, the tune to this would reappear with different lyrics in a better-known, albeit unsuccessful work by Andrew Lloyd Webber.

Rice wrote several other lyrics for *The Likes of Us*, which sank under the weight of a concept he would later describe as 'square and dated'. They had titles such as *Strange and Lovely Song*, *A Man on His Own*, *Where Am I Going?* and *Will This Last Forever?* The last one, entitled *You Won't Care About Her Any More*, treated betrayal as just another move in an endless emotional game between men and women.

Andrew and Tim sold the rights to *The Likes of Us* for £100 each and waited. Nothing happened. The demonstration recording did not turn into a Number 1 hit, or even reach the record shops. Desmond Elliott and Ernest Hecht did not mount a West End smash, or any other kind of stage musical. Tim did not become a pop singer and continued working at EMI and living at Harrington Court with Molly and John Lill. Andrew continued to pursue his own haphazard course through various music schools and to live at Gledhow Gardens; he also kept in touch with Alan Doggett. Andrew and Tim spent as much time as ever writing and composing for each other. Elliott's enthusiasm, too, was undimmed; he still thought of himself as their agent. He did not know that, after the disappointment of *The Likes of Us*, Andrew and Tim were having other ideas.

By the spring of 1967, Andrew Lloyd Webber was still only nineteen years old. He had been down from Oxford for a little over a year. Since he and Tim had begun their collaboration, they had written one unstaged musical and a clutch of unrecorded and unpublished songs, the lyrics and tunes of which were subject to more or less continuous revision and change. As a tune came off the piano at Gledhow Gardens, a number of things might happen. It might replace a previous one and be fitted to an existing lyric; this lyric might then be replaced in turn by a new one; or it might wait some time for a new or old lyric to come along. The tunes themselves – for this is what they were – were produced by the same genetic process, ever changing, yet ever the same.

But as Andrew grew older, the well from which the tunes came grew deeper; at the bottom, and thus becoming less and less obvious to the ear, were the early influences of Frederick Loewe, Jerome Kern, Richard Rodgers and Lionel Bart. Closer to the surface, though still deep, lay the pure rock and roll of Del Shannon and Bobby Vee. Above them, on the surface, were their popular heirs: the Beatles. Running through them all, always, were Prokofiev and Puccini. Reaching into this well, as he had done since he first built his toy theatre, was a brilliantly talented boy with a remorselessly opportunist streak.

The first opportunity came, as it often does, in an unlikely form. This was the annual newspaper competition, announced early in the spring of 1967, to find the *Evening Standard* 'Girl of the Year'.

The *Evening Standard* set great store by this pre-feminist ploy. The year in question was not the year past but to come, during which the lucky winner's life and times would be chronicled in the newspaper. The *Standard* had a huge circulation in the London area and there was no shortage of young women wanting to submit their photographs and themselves for consideration. This meant a flood of attractive faces crossing the desks of the journalists at Shoe Lane, who took their time whittling them down to a shortlist of six from which the winner was chosen. That year's winner was called Ross Hannaman.

Ross Hannaman was an attractive blonde who differed from most of the other applicants in two respects; the photograph she submitted had been taken recently, and she could sing. The *Standard* publicity helped her obtain a two-week engagement singing at the fashionable nightclub, Quaglino's. Not long afterwards the telephone rang in the *Evening Standard* offices. Two young men, neither of whom the newspaper had ever heard of, had seen her and wanted to become her manager. Their names were Tim Rice and Andrew Lloyd Webber.

The journalist to whom they spoke was Angus McGill. McGill was one of the first journalists to specialise in strong, youth-culture and street-life features; he also wrote the *Standard*'s long-running cartoon strip featuring a schoolboy called Clive. McGill invited them to the Shoe Lane offices one evening and was immediately enchanted.

Together, to McGill's sharp eye, they were very young, very personable, very self-possessed and very fond of each other; as individuals, they could hardly have been more different. While Tim and Ross Hannaman were, to Andrew's dismay, instantly attracted to each other, McGill, whose interest in the 'Girl of the Year' was strictly professional, took a shine to Andrew. To Andrew, McGill became a friend and something of a father figure, the latest in the succession of older men to complement the role of his reclusive father. Like them, he was a useful contact.

Tim's job kept him in regular contact with the recording and publishing facilities they had tried to exploit for *The Likes of Us*. By their submission to the loose and distinctly disadvantageous terms of music publishers, and through his access to a recording process which churned out fifteen or twenty singles a week, he and Andrew managed to have their first ever single recorded. The date was 23 June 1967 and the recording was made on EMI's 'quality' Columbia label. The producers were Bob Barratt and Tim Rice and the arranger and conductor was Mike Leander. The singer was the previously unknown 'Girl of the Year', Ross Hannaman:

Down Thru' Summer

Sadness now, but my life goes on
Night and morning gone
Lost in the air
Now I watch for the afternoon

Why does it come so soon?
Life isn't fair

Yesterday, you lay beside me
Touched my hand
The world was fine
Spoke of love, your love would guide me
Down thru' summer you would stay here and be mine . . .

Ross sang in a smoky voice, with a hint of the *chanteuse à la* Françoise Hardy. She was the first woman for whom Tim had specifically written a recorded song. This was a technique he was to refine over the next few years, culminating in the biggest hit he and Andrew would ever have; a huge hit song, from a huge hit show — whose main theme was the melody from *Down Thru' Summer*.

All our words disappeared somehow
They have no meaning now
Dust in my hand
I don't care if I live or die
Days go on drifting by

They understand
Tell me why I need tomorrow
Seasons change but sadness stays
Evening comes to dull my sorrow

The 'B' Side was a ghastly, giddy gobbet of upbeat pop filler, entitled *I'll Give All My Love to Southend*.

Andrew did not like the arrangement of *Down Thru' Summer*, whose romantic orchestral sweep was calcified by a heavy-handed pop percussionist and a girl backing singer. But that melody was too good to waste; back it went, to await revision and another lyric, into the ever-deepening well.

*

That summer, the so-called Summer of Love, saw the official end of severe British economic restraint. This did not encourage the resident of Flat 1, 10 Gledhow Gardens. Andrew, who had earned approximately £200 in the last eighteen months, was still enjoying financial help from his grandmother, Molly.

While Tim enjoyed his own summer of love with Ross Hannaman and other girls, Andrew's social life was confined to giving modest dinner parties at the Gledhow Gardens flat. Half a dozen people would squeeze into the long, narrow dining-room. Sometimes there would be a couple of girls, but they were not his close friends. Both he and David Harrington were keen on good food, fine wine and jokey conversation; it was only here, on his own ground, that Andrew was able to relax.

One guest was the friendly *Standard* journalist, Angus McGill. McGill was still following Ross Hannaman's year and the shadows of Tim and Andrew occasionally flitted through these accounts. But McGill never capitalised on his admiration for the young man for journalistic purposes. There was something about Andrew that inspired a feeling of protectiveness in the older man; but to enquire further within was to encounter an ironclad reserve. McGill came to think of himself as someone who knew Andrew well; but he never learned anything about Jean, or Billy, or that Andrew had left Oxford in the way he had. What he did learn was strictly on terms dictated by Andrew. Thus, the suggestion that Andrew had been less than happy with the sporting side of his school life was encoded as an idea for a character for McGill's *Standard* comic strip about his teenage schoolboy, Clive. They dreamed up an unkind gym master and called him Sergeant Thrust.

That autumn, on 27 October, Columbia recorded a second 'A' side sung by Ross Hannaman and written by Tim and Andrew. This time the publishers were Southern Music. Angus McGill went along to the recording, which was arranged and conducted by Tony Meehan. This song was called *1969*:

1969

> *And then I heard a darker sound*
> *I turned around*
> *But it was gone*
> *They glide across the endless day*
> *As if to say*
> *The time has come*
> *The world had died*
> *And no one saw*
> *And no one tried*
> *To see what for . . .*
>
> *Hey I hate the picture 1969*
> *Lord I hate the picture 1969 . . .*

Ross intoned this apocalyptic epitaph for flower power over a harpsichord and bass drum, around which snaked an electric guitar; as she sang the chorus the brass section took off in accompaniment and the two strands ended in an echoing detonation: then it started all over again:

> *And then I heard the songs they sung*
> *A hundred tongues*
> *Began to shout*
> *And then a panic in the hall*
> *I heard them call*
> *We can't get out . . .*
>
> *Hey I hate the picture 1969 . . .*

Although the arrangement was superior to that of *Down Thru' Summer*, Andrew did not like it any better. The melody was a good one but he would not use it again, not least because it was not his to use in the first place. It was Beethoven's *Für Elise*.

The 'B' Side, however, was a pleasant surprise:

Probably on Thursday

Can you see all of me?
I am hiding nothing
Must you stay so far away?
Won't you whisper something?
You're going to leave me
Don't have to tell me, don't have to tell me
You'll be unfaithful
Probably on Thursday
Probably on Thursday

The innocent timbre of Ross's voice brought piquancy to Tim's soliloquy on infidelity. This was the territory in which he was most at home: writing for the female player in what he saw as the 'endless game' of love. He had an instinct for the inherently dramatic potential of such a situation. It had yet to find formal shape but he was learning fast by writing sensitive lyrics in what was effectively the old Tin Pan Alley tradition of the ready-made pop song:

I spend all my precious time
Wishing you would love me
You are trying hard to find
Ways to get rid of me
You used to love me
Look at you now love, look at you now love
You'll be unfaithful
Possibly on Wednesday
Probably on Thursday

Andrew, Tim, Ross, McGill and all who heard it liked the 'B' Side better, with its textures of harpsichord and clarinet built against a moderate rock beat. But EMI Columbia released *1969* as the 'A' Side, with grainy black and white cover photographs of Ross looking moody and soulful and Tim's lyric superimposed on her long dress. Ross always dressed well, whatever the occasion; this was to be her last appearance on a record cover. She married a rock musician, had a family and ended up running a dress shop in Notting Hill. *1969* was played several times on Radio 1, to great excitement in Gledhow Gardens and Harrington Court, but it was not a hit record. *Probably on Thursday* went back into what Andrew called 'the bottom drawer': the well on which he drew. Undeterred, he and Tim went on trying to write a hit single for Southern Music.

One of their other offerings around this time was based on Tim's theory that a song had a better chance of succeeding if it mentioned the name of a place in America. On the strength of the worldwide success of such songs as *Chicago, New York New York, Let's Go To San Francisco, It Happened in Monterey* and *Massachusetts*, he had a point.

Unfortunately, however, he chose to try to emulate them with the following:

Kansas Morning

I love the Kansas Morning
Kansas mist at my window
Kansas winds shift and sigh
I can see you now
We're flying high
Kansas, love of mine . . .

Afterwards, long afterwards, they had a good laugh about it. The funny thing was that, for *Kansas Morning*, Andrew had written his best tune to date. But for the time being it went straight back into the bottom drawer.

As the winter of 1967 drew closer, so the prospect of fame and fortune receded. Southern Music continued to buy the publishing rights to the odd song by Rice and Lloyd Webber. Ross Hannaman had retired and there was no commercial replacement for her among the small circle of friends and acquaintances who occasionally sang on their demonstration discs. The second opportunity, like the first, came in an unlikely form; this time, in the person of Alan Doggett.

Doggett had wasted no time in revolutionising the Colet Court choir. Was he, he asked Andrew, remotely interested in writing a piece for them? Given the circumstances, they might consider something short; a cantata, say, for the boys to sing in the presence of their parents at an end of term concert at the school premises near Hammersmith Broadway.

Hammersmith was not quite the Broadway they had in mind, but given the circumstances and a guaranteed audience, if only of bored parents, there was little else they could say. With a certain amount of prompting from Doggett, they began to chip away:

– It had to be short. This was a relief, as they had been writing three minute pop songs since *The Likes of Us*.

– If it was to be short it had to be sharp. Therefore, it had to have a strong story line.

– It had to be suitable for an end of term concert at Colet Court. Since Colet Court was the junior school to St Paul's, which in turn had close links with St Paul's Cathedral, of which both Alan Doggett and his assistant Ian Hunter were ex-vicars-choral, might they not consider a religious theme?

– It had to be sung by boys under the age of thirteen. Therefore it might conceivably concern the same.

– Brothers? They turned to the Old Testament and the Book of Genesis. Or more precisely, to Tim's copy of *The Wonder Book of Bible Stories*.

– Cain and Abel?

– Esau and Jacob?

41

– Shem, Ham and Japheth?

– Joseph?

– Joseph.

> Joseph, a young man of seventeen, was tending the flocks with his brothers. . . . Now Israel loved Joseph more than any of his other sons, because he had been born to him in his old age; and he made a richly ornamental robe for him. When his brothers saw that their father loved him more than any of them, they hated him and could not speak a kind word to him. . . .

If they had started reading the full text of *Genesis 37*, they probably would have run out of patience. As it was, *The Wonder Book of Bible Stories* gave them the encouragement they needed.

That Christmas, they started writing.

In the early weeks of 1968 Andrew and Alan Doggett were frequently to be spotted in the music room on the top floor of the old listed redbrick building of Colet Court. Downstairs, through the iron gates, across the Hammersmith Road, were the main buildings of St Paul's School.

They made an odd and yet somehow well-matched couple: the prematurely balding Doggett with his thick black spectacles and his vulnerability to mockery; and the mop-haired, feminine looking youth whose facial hair seemed to be concentrated in a pair of thick, black eyebrows which rose and fell incessantly. His eyes darted everywhere at once and rested on nothing and no one long enough for you to hold his gaze. He wore a long frock coat, which he was reputed to have designed himself, invariably with the collar turned up. The intention was deliberately eccentric, and it succeeded.

Doggett's assistant and fellow ex-vicar-choral of St Paul's Cathedral was a bluff northerner, Ian Hunter. Hunter had a great appreciation for Doggett's abilities to motivate the Colet Court choir and secure time and money for them in the face of competition from the athletics lobby; and few illusions about the more volatile aspects of his personality. Nor, on their first meeting in the Colet Court music room, was he particularly well-disposed towards Doggett's self-absorbed young protégé. Then Andrew invited him to dinner, not at Gledhow Gardens but at Harrington Court.

Billy and Jean were out and Julian and John Lill were secreted away, practising for all they were worth. Andrew cooked dinner and he and Hunter, who by nature was not one to overstay his welcome, talked about music late into the night. Hunter, like Andrew's housemaster Frank Kilvington, was an *aficionado* of Gilbert and Sullivan. He would remain so after he left the Lloyd Webbers' flat that night; but the conversation gave him a rare insight into the imagination and clarity of mind of his young host.

Like John Lill, Hunter was struck by the uninhibitedly acquisitive nature of Andrew's talent. He not only seemed unable to talk about Richard Rodgers without mentioning Prokofiev in the same breath; he could not help tossing out his own ideas for melodic and thematic syntheses of these and half a dozen others. Where Andrew lost him, as he did most others apart from Tim and occasionally Billy, was in his unstinting devotion to pop. The enduring impression Andrew gave, even if he did not intend to and did not know how to go about achieving it, was that he desperately wanted a Top Ten single.

On 1 March 1968, the parents of Doggett's choirboys assembled for the end of term concert. It was a rainy Friday afternoon at Colet Court. The choir sang, Doggett conducted, Hunter played the piano, Julian played the cello and the parents took their sons home for the school holidays. Not all the parents shared their sons' musical interests; but some of them did remark on how the concert had bored them less than usual.

What they had just heard was a fifteen-minute cantata, sung by the boys, based on the well-known Old Testament story of Joseph and his coat of many colours. The story was more or less faithfully retold: Joseph, the favoured son of Israel, is given the coat of many colours, arouses the envy of his brothers and is sold into slavery through their agencies to the Egyptian, Potiphar. Potiphar's wife tries to seduce him, fails and causes him to be imprisoned; Potiphar's dreams trouble him, Joseph interprets them and is released. Joseph returns home in triumph, reveals himself to his treacherous brothers and all are saved.

What remained in the minds of certain parents, however, was not so much the tale, as the manner of its telling.

For a start, there was its title:

Joseph and the Amazing Technicolor Dreamcoat

> *When Joseph tried it on*
> *He knew his sheepskin days were gone . . .*
> *Such a dazzling coat of many colours*
> *How he loved his coat of many colours*
> *In a class above the rest*
> *It even went well with his vest*

There was something fascinating about a multi-colour coated dreamer having ideas above his station and enduring the consequences. The boys loved singing it:

> *Potiphar had very few cares*
> *He was one of Egypt's millionaires*
> *Having made a fortune buying shares in Pyramids*
>
> *Potiphar had made a huge pile*
> *Owned a large percentage of the Nile*
> *Meant that he could live in style — and he did*

Although the voices were those of boys trained after the manner of the Vienna Boys Choir, the words they sang were taken at a brisk clip in the style of swing and pop. Who could resist the naïveté of the following?:

> *'Joseph's dead' they told their ageing Dad*
> *Jacob wept — he really loved the lad*

The Director of the London College of Music, now fifty-five years old, had not lost his iconoclastic instincts. If they could extend *Joseph* to, say, twenty minutes, said Billy Lloyd Webber, they could put it on at the Central Hall, Westminster. As Musical Director he would be happy to supply other artists to fill out the bill.

Thus it was that the programme for Sunday 12 May 1968, ran as follows:

John Lill: solo piano
Julian Lloyd Webber: solo cello
William Lloyd Webber: Bach *Toccata and Fugue in D Minor*
The choir and orchestra of Colet Court School and The Mixed Bag: Rice and Lloyd Webber, *Joseph and the Amazing Technicolor Dreamcoat*

Admission: 2/6d on door

Half the boys of Colet Court were bussed over to sit at the sides of the grand Victorian hall and make up the choruses. Alan Doggett conducted with his usual gusto, Ian Hunter played the harpsichord and Billy Lloyd Webber the organ. The hastily assembled pop group known as The Mixed Bag included Tim Rice. This was not least because, in the song where the Pharoah revealed his bad dreams in a parody of Elvis Presley's *I'm All Shook Up*, Tim at last had the opportunity to let his rock and roll fantasies rip:

> *Hey, hey, hey, Joseph*
> *Won't you tell your old Pharoah*
> *What does it mean?*
> *Whoa, yeah . . .*

To which Joseph blithely replies:

45

All these things you saw in your pyjamas
Are a long-range forecast for your farmers

Tim's lyrics, like Tim, worked brilliantly for all the wrong reasons.

The combined performers, orchestra and choir nearly outnumbered the audience at the Central Hall performance of *Joseph and the Amazing Technicolor Dreamcoat*. But there were two journalists in the audience — Peter Cole of the *Evening News* and Derek Jewell of the *Sunday Times*.

Cole may have been there for professional purposes, but he wrote nothing about the evening. Jewell, on the other hand, was there merely because his son Nicholas was a pupil at Colet Court School and not because he was Britain's foremost middlebrow pop and jazz critic. In the event, however, it was Jewell who wrote the first major review of a work by Tim Rice and Andrew Lloyd Webber:

A SPRINGBOARD CALLED *Joseph*

'Give us food' the brothers said,
'Dieting is for the birds.'
Joseph gave them all they wanted,
Second helpings, even thirds . . .

Even on paper the happy bounce of lyrics like these comes through. They are exactly right for singing by several hundred boys' voices. With two organs, guitars, drums and a large orchestra, the effect is irresistible.

The quicksilver vitality of *Joseph and His Amazing Technicolor Dreamcoat*, the new pop oratorio heard at Central Hall, Westminster, last Sunday, is attractive indeed. On this evidence, the pop idiom — beat rhythms and Bacharachian melodies — is most enjoyably capable of being used in extended form.

Musically, *Joseph* is not all gold. It needs more light and shade. A very beautiful melody, *Close Every Door To Me*, is one of the few points when the hectic pace slows down. The snap and crackle of the rest of the work tends to be too insistent, masking the impact of the words which, unlike many in pop, are important.

But such reservations seem pedantic when matched against *Joseph*'s infectious overall character. Throughout its twenty-minute duration it bristles with wonderfully singable tunes. It entertains. It communicates instantly, as all good pop should communicate. And it is a considerable piece of barrier-breaking by its creators, two men in their early twenties – Tim Rice, the lyricist, and Andrew Lloyd Webber . . .

Jewell's unexpected review appeared the following weekend in the *Sunday Times* of 19 May 1968. Scenes of jubilation broke out at Gledhow Gardens and Harrington Court. Copies were distributed to all and sundry with rapid effect. Eight weeks later, when Andrew Lloyd Webber might otherwise have been graduating as a BA(Hons) Oxon in the presence of his proud parents and wondering what job vacancies existed for an authority on monasteries, he was at the EMI studios at Abbey Road, where the likes of the Beatles recorded, attending the first recording of *Joseph and the Amazing Technicolor Dreamcoat*.

This was an expanded version for an augmented ensemble with solo voices and rock musicians, for which the dozen Colet Court choirboys became a backing group. Doggett conducted and Billy Lloyd Webber helped out on the keyboards. Andrew and Tim listened through headphones and supplied vocal backing. Also present, as he had been a year earlier at the recording of *1969* and *Probably on Thursday*, was Angus McGill.

But none of them was under any illusions that the Decca recording of *Joseph* was made because anyone knew what to do with a thirty-minute pop cantata. In record business terms it was simply just another commodity bought for stock: recorded at low cost over a short period and scheduled to be released at an unspecified future date. That year, the popular releases were dominated by the Beatles's *Sergeant Pepper's Lonely Hearts Club*

Band and *Beggar's Banquet* by the Rolling Stones. The ethos of *Joseph* seemed as yet out of kilter with the times.

If this was an era of innovation, it was also one of corrosive nihilism, of received opinions passed round like a soggy joint of marijuana, interspersed with violence at home in schools and colleges and savage rearguard actions overseas in the gloaming of the British Empire. It was an era superficially hinted at in Tim's lyric for *1969*. Ironically, when he and Andrew did try to write something longer which reflected their public school indignation at the state of the nation, they failed miserably. By the time they abandoned it and reverted to what they thought was a less topical, if infinitely more controversial theme, the fashions of the time would have changed – as if to suggest that they had been right all along.

That summer, while *Joseph* languished on the shelf at Decca, the big musical and theatrical event was the London opening of Galt McDermott's hippie rock musical *Hair*. *Hair* had a number of good tunes, such as *The Age of Aquarius*, and a number of awful lyrics:

> *She asks me why I'm a hairy guy, I'm hairy noon and night, hair that's a fright . . . It's not for lack of bread, like the Grateful Dead . . .*

Among the lowly paid backstage toilers on *Hair* was a personable twenty-two-year-old called Cameron Mackintosh. Mackintosh had something of a showbusiness background, had briefly been a drama student and desperately wanted to be a producer. He would shortly come to know Andrew by reputation and in the longer term each would be instrumental in making the other enormously rich. But meanwhile he took on extra cleaning work to finance his expensive rented flat in Half Moon Street, Mayfair. Like Andrew, Mackintosh was something of a gourmet who believed in keeping up appearances; like Mackintosh, Andrew was having trouble paying his way.

For the privilege of having *Joseph* immortalised on vinyl by the self-styled 'Greatest Recording Organisation in the World', he and Tim had received around £100 each. Molly's money paid the rent at Gledhow Gardens and Tim's day job with EMI paid for most of the cheap restaurant meals over which they wondered what to do next.

Tim was keen to write something on the theme of another Bible story; it was not that he was particularly religious, but the Dean of St Paul's had indicated that he might be prepared to countenance a performance in the Cathedral; and *Joseph* might eventually even translate successfully to the stage. Besides, Tim was obsessed with people who lived short, fast lives, during which they somehow changed society. In a way, it was the rock and roll ethos of Buddy Holly, Jimi Hendrix and Janis Joplin; but underscored neither by a religious nor a political interest, but by an apparent determination to reduce life, just as he had reduced love, to the boldest of dramatic ingredients.

He had written as much in *Joseph*, for girls to sing in correct, standard English pronunciation to Andrew's blithely satirical, 1920s sound:

> *The greatest man since Noah*
> *Only goes to show . . . Ah,*
> *Anyone from anywhere can make it*
> *If they get a lucky break*

Among the recipients of copies of the Derek Jewell review was a property developer named Sefton Myers. Myers was fascinated by show business and had been Chief Barker, or leading light, of the Variety Club of Great Britain, the showbusiness organisation dedicated to raising funds for charity. (His daughter would grow up to be a successful pop singer under the name of Judi Tzuke.) Myers was not known personally to Andrew, but through the good offices of David Ballantyne, who had sung on numerous Rice–Lloyd Webber demonstration recordings.

Andrew, who was by now in desperate financial straits, wrote to Myers with a bizarre suggestion: how did Myers feel about the idea of a pop music museum? Exhibits might include P. J. Proby's trousers (which he was regularly in the habit of splitting), the lavatory door of the Cavern Club in Liverpool, the tail section of Buddy Holly's plane, etc . . . Curator, A. Lloyd Webber Esquire. As an afterthought, along with the Jewell review, he enclosed an advance copy of the Decca recording of *Joseph*.

Myers, though only forty-one, was a sick man and now left many of his showbusiness interests to his partner, David Land. Land and Myers had a company, one of many, called New Talent Ventures Ltd., based at Land's offices in Charles Street, Mayfair – not far, but as yet a whole world away, from the struggling young Cameron Mackintosh.

It was at an informal board meeting of this company that Myers first raised the names of Tim Rice and Andrew Lloyd Webber.

'Here, David,' said Myers, 'you're always saying you're interested in new talent. How about investing in these two?'

Land was a successful managing agent whose main claim to fame was that he represented a female bagpipe group from the Ford motor company's British base called the Dagenham Girl Pipers. He had respect for Myers's intuitive powers. Besides, the pop museum was not a totally ridiculous idea. Land and Myers listened again to the recording of *Joseph* and resolved, in their capacities as directors of New Talent Ventures Ltd., to invite its young authors to pay them a call.

A few miles east of Mayfair and away from the land of Mammon, the Colet Court connection was continuing to prove useful. The Very Reverend Martin Sullivan, Dean of St Paul's and spiritual descendant of Jonathan Swift, was that rare creation, an eminent cleric who had not lost touch with the fundamentals of Christianity. He had taken a particular interest in the two young creators of *Joseph and the Amazing Technicolor Dreamcoat* and now formally invited them to mount a production in the Cathedral.

The St Paul's Cathedral production of *Joseph* took place on the night of Saturday 9 November 1968. The Cathedral's famous echo proved something of a problem for the combination of boys' voices and electric instruments; but Doggett conducted gamely in the place where as a vicar-choral he had so often sung and Billy played the Cathedral's main organ. Ian Hunter, Angus McGill and Ray Connolly, another *Evening Standard* reporter, were also there.

Connolly went away impressed, as his *Standard* article the following Monday revealed:

> Despite what many prefer to believe, pop is already a serious and experimental art form with its own history – however brief – and its own standards, with truly exciting prospects for its immediate future. Too often, however, in its attempt to be taken seriously it can be pretentious and gimmicky. No one could accuse Andrew Lloyd Webber and Tim Rice of any such conceit.
>
> I don't know how long it will be before someone composes a good pop symphony, but I do know that Saturday night's performance of *Joseph and the Amazing Technicolor Dreamcoat* brought the likelihood of such a production considerably closer.

The Dean, too, pronounced the evening a success and told people so. He also formed a firm friendship with the two personable young men whose company he found so stimulating. What, he asked, were Tim and Andrew planning to do next?

That month, they had their meeting with Sefton Myers and David Land.

Myers and Land, both of whom drove Rolls-Royces, humoured the two unknown composers over their idea for a pop music museum; then, in their capacities as directors of New Talent Ventures Ltd., they came down to business. They knew a little about *The Likes of Us*, hardly anything about *Down Thru' Summer*

51

and even less about *1969*; but they had listened with interest to the advance recording of *Joseph and the Amazing Technicolor Dreamcoat*. They were interested in Tim and Andrew's plans for the future.

One of the things they planned to do was sever their business connection with Desmond Elliott.

Elliott, who did not then own a Rolls–Royce but still thought of himself as their agent, had represented them to the best of his abilities. His friend Ernest Hecht had failed to raise the money to stage the first Rice–Lloyd Webber musical – not least because it was unstageable. Andrew meanwhile had formed a friendship with the proprietor of Southern Music, who had given him some friendly advice about publishing deals. He and Tim consequently had a loose arrangement with Southern Music, under which they were irregularly paid for their pop songs. They were ambitious, talented, in need of backing and broke – and it showed.

Myers and Land tentatively proposed a deal. The first thing they offered was a living wage: £1,500 a year each, for a minimum of three years, with New Talent Ventures taking twenty-five per cent of the proceeds of anything they wrote during that time. After three years the retainer would rise to £2,500 a year each, with the profit percentage remaining the same and options built in to extend the arrangement for a total of ten years.

Given the proposed duration of the deal, they said, there was no hurry. Three years was a long time. Why not go away and think about it?

Three days later, Tim and Andrew had thought about it. They agreed.

Desmond Elliott was not pleased.

That January, the first month of a year whose apocalyptic nature Tim had had fun forecasting in *1969*, began on key for adherents to the idea of the decline of the West. A previously unknown Czech student called Jan Palach burned himself to death in Prague's Wenceslas Square. The London School of Economics closed down, belatedly in some people's opinion, after students smashed the gates installed during the Christmas vacation; there was no indication that they were attempting to reach the library, or any other seat of learning. The British government rejected the Wootton Report recommending the legalisation of marijuana; and the magazine *Black Dwarf* declared 1969 the year of the militant woman.

Decca (UK) released the LP of *Joseph and the Amazing Technicolor Dreamcoat*. The record sold quickly at the new south of the river premises of Colet Court. Novellos took up the publishing rights to sell to other schools. Elsewhere, the record did not immediately sell quite as well. *Joseph* was a *succès d'estime*, a calling card on the strength of which someone else had at last taken over from Molly as supplier of funds to pay the rent.

But under the new arrangement, there was very much a quid pro quo. Tim already had one job and Andrew was probably unemployable; but now they both had to work for a living.

Tim's enthusiasm was undiminished for the short, fast lives of people who had passed into history. He even had a list of their names, which was subject to continuous revision and change like the Top Twenty of the record charts. *Joseph* in record industry parlance was a sleeper; John F. Kennedy had promised much but then slid off the bottom of the list; Robin Hood had done likewise. But currently in with a bullet at Number 1 was Richard the Lionheart.

Richard I, *Coeur de Lyon*, 'the Lionheart', was King of England from 1189–99. Born in 1157, he fought on the Third Crusade, a disastrous joint venture with Frederick Barbarossa and Philip Augustus of France, against the legendary Moslem empire-builder, warrior and conqueror of Jerusalem, Salah-ad-din. The

Crusaders managed to capture Acre but failed to retake Jerusalem, and on his return journey Richard was captured and ransomed by the Austrians. Richard was an Englishman who lived fast, loved popular music, especially that of his troubadour Blondel and died young fighting the French. He made it all look so easy: he was 'shag'. As far as Tim was concerned, he fitted the bill.

The title they thought up was: *Come Back Richard: Your Country Needs You*. Britain was struggling through a period of bad industrial relations, high inflation and a shrinking Empire; even the standard of cricket had declined. England needed a hero and Richard the Lionheart might be just the saviour to extricate his beloved country from this sorry state of affairs.

Land and Myers, meanwhile, were pleased to see their protégés getting down to work.

Having agreed upon the idea, they set about it in their established way: Andrew fed the idea of Richard and his arch-enemy Saladin into his mind and reached down into that ever deepening well of melodies. When he brought one up, he played it to Tim who would attempt to supply a lyric. Then they would fit it into the growing jigsaw.

In the spirit of *Joseph*, Tim's approach and his lyrics were robustly unstuffy:

> *Those were the days, good old Saladin days . . .*

Andrew gave Saladin, like Potiphar before him, a pop tune of his own. (Saladin, Tim was in the habit of telling people, was 'a rather violent cove, who hung around in the Middle East when Richard the Lionheart was on his Crusades'.)

They recorded a single of *Come Back Richard: Your Country Needs You* for RCA Victor; the 'B' side was called *Roll On Over the Atlantic*. Then the pressure on them to follow *Joseph* with a bigger success seemed to backfire. What was the purpose of the single? to promote an album? a stage show? and if so, in what order? When were they going to release it? RCA Victor did not seem to know, and neither did they.

Besides, he and Tim had no actual experience of writing for the stage: *The Likes of Us* had never been produced and *Joseph* was written and performed as a pop cantata. *Come Back Richard* was given one *ad hoc* trial performance, and went the way of the Third Crusade.

Depressed but undaunted, they pillaged it for workable tunes and left the rest to rot. The noble lord Saladin suffered a particularly ignominious fate. *Saladin Days* became *Try It and See*, which they submitted as a possible British competitor in the Eurovision Song Contest. It flopped here too and was cast deeply back into the well from whence it came.

Then they turned their minds back to the names currently on Tim's Top Twenty. John F. Kennedy and Robin Hood had not returned. *Come Back Hitler: All Is Forgiven* was perhaps too controversial and certainly not Eurovision material. The Bible stories had proved successful once, but could they do it again? Who else could follow Joseph? And how about, for a change, a young, misunderstood anti-hero?

Tim had for some time been toying with the idea of a story in which Judas was the central character and Jesus merely a walk on part. Just as he had been inspired by the theme of betrayal in the love songs he wrote for Ross Hannaman, so the twenty pieces of silver for which Joseph's brothers had sold him into slavery appealed to his imagination. Perhaps, in Tim's mind, there was even something about the way the story of Jesus was usually told that was just too good to be true. Now Judas, too, could be a star — just like James Dean in *Rebel Without a Cause*:

> *Jesus Christ, Jesus Christ*
> *Who are you, what have you sacrificed?*

Judas's traditional role was as a traducer condemned by his own guilt; now he was resurrected as a profane but vital gospel in his own right. So far, so good. But although the lyric rhymed and scanned, something was still not quite right:

> *Jesus Christ, Superstar*
> *Do you think you're what they say you are?*

The next stage was to find someone to record it. Tim, in his capacity as apprentice record producer at EMI, had made the acquaintance of a personable young singer of some dramatic ability, called Murray Head. Head, in spite of his talents, had yet to make a record that was bought by more than a dozen people. As long as Tim was not superstitious about this, he was happy to spare the time.

Tim managed to put Head together with the Grease Band, a highly talented group of rock session musicians whose wider claim to fame was that they had backed Joe Cocker on his neanderthal version of the Beatles hit *With a Little Help from My Friends*. Together, they recorded a demonstration single called *Superstar*, which Tim and Andrew then played to Sefton Myers and David Land.

With Myers stricken by ill-health, Land was increasingly occupying the front seat at New Talent Ventures. He was not best pleased to discover that their two talented protégés had abandoned *Come Back Richard* and were now working on a musical about Judas Iscariot. What, he asked politely, were they going to do next?

Tim, who was by far the more articulate and urbane of the two, replied that they were going to do a musical about Judas Iscariot. He repeated that he had long been fascinated by the idea of a story in which Judas was the central character and Jesus merely a walk-on part.

Besides, he said, they needed a story with a strong central character. At this, Land's restrained London Jewish intonation reached new heights. '*Judas*?' he said, 'a strong central character?'

Eventually, they calmed him down.

Tim was also thinking of Bob Dylan, folk singer and CBS recording star. One of Dylan's many hit songs was entitled *With God On Our Side.*

The lyric went as follows:

> *I can't think for you*
> *You'll have to decide*
> *Did Judas Iscariot*
> *Have God on his side?*

Land had to admit he had a point. But Tim was not going to leave the matter there. While Andrew sat there and twitched, his eyes darting here there and everywhere, Tim continued in the same vein. Think of the Beatles, he said: the greatest EMI recording artists in the world. Think of Abbey Road, where we recorded *Joseph.* John Lennon, their most talented and turbulent member, had started a similar debate years ago.

Back in 1966, Lennon had claimed that the Beatles were more popular than Jesus Christ. The backlash had been considerable: while the Beatles's manager Brian Epstein had gained extensive publicity by explaining how Lennon's remarks had been mis-interpreted, thirty-five broadcasting stations in fifteen states, and one in Manitoba, Canada, announced they would no longer play Beatles records.

In Fort Knox, Kentucky, a radio station which had never before played a Beatles record played one every thirty minutes, preceding each airplay with an announcement condemning what it saw as the hypocrisy of banning the group's music. Numerous other American radio stations followed suit. In Pamplona, Spain, home of the Spanish Inquisition and wary of the influence of General Franco, Radio Requete declared that until Lennon recanted it would play no more records by Los Beatles. In Johannesburg, South Africa, a local businessman called Pieter

Boshof announced that he was going to burn all his Beatle records: 'I believe it is every Christian's duty to rebel against the Beatles,' he said. Hong Kong's two radio stations, meanwhile, said they would stand by the Fab Four.

As a result of all this, the Beatles's album *Yesterday and Today* was the Number 1 bestseller wherever people could buy it. Jesus, said Tim, was big box-office.

David Land said he would give it a try.

That summer, the single of *Superstar* was offered to the record companies.

RCA Victor, who had recorded and still not released *Come Back Richard: Your Country Needs You*, turned it down. Land was approaching the outer limits of his contacts in show business. He sent *Superstar* to his friend Cyril Symons of MCA (UK), the British subsidiary of the Music Corporation of America. By chance it transpired that Tim, too, had a friend at MCA: his name was Alan Crowder. Crowder, in turn, had a friend: his boss, the head of MCA (UK). Crowder offered to introduce him to Andrew, Tim and Land. For the four of them, and above all for Andrew, it was a fruitful meeting. His name was Brian Brolly.

Brolly was a soft-spoken Ulsterman of a determined disposition. Once he decided to put his weight behind a project it usually went ahead. Brolly was impressed by the two young men and by the fact that they had already persuaded Myers and Land to invest in their talents. The recording of *Joseph*, too, showed that they were capable of exploiting a snappy new musical form to treat a potentially difficult theme.

Brolly felt they could achieve the same artistic success on a bigger commercial scale with their Judas idea. He decided to take a calculated risk and invest some of MCA's vast profits in recording *Superstar* as a single for commercial release. Murray Head again sang the part of Judas, this time at Olympic Studios in Barnes with rock musicians and orchestra. The 'B' side was

Andrew's wordless orchestral interpretation of *John 19:41*; his writing here recalling the best of Billy Lloyd Webber:

> *At the place where Jesus was crucified, there was a garden,*
> *and in the garden a new tomb, in which no one had*
> *ever been laid . . .*

Superstar was one of the most expensive singles ever recorded. It was released in November of that year to critical acclaim, but failed to reach the Top Twenty in either Britain or America. Elsewhere, it acquired a cult reputation: on all-night radio stations in America's midwest; in a gay bar in Amsterdam. At MCA, this was not generally regarded as sufficient return on a substantial investment.

Brolly found himself in a minority, a potentially embarrassing situation for the head of MCA (UK) which aroused the steelier side of his temperament. Land and Myers were sceptical about the idea of their protégés committing themselves to writing another work which would most likely never see the light of day. Brolly pointed out that the single had not actually stopped selling, but Andrew and Tim, too, were depressed by the lack of sales. As a possible anti-hero for a story, Judas began to slide back down Tim's Top Twenty. Brolly tried to reassure them that they should continue to think about an album on the theme.

Other voices, however, were making themselves heard from outside the commercial sector. Whether or not some divinity moved their hands was not recorded. The Dean of St Paul's, Martin Sullivan who had been so enthusiastic about *Joseph*, told Andrew he and Tim were right. 'Please,' he said, 'try to take Jesus down from a stained glass window.'

Father Kenneth Hewitt was Chaplain to the Royal College of Music, where Andrew was still occasionally to be seen in the library. He had heard about *Joseph* and was taken by the idea of *Superstar*. He was priest at the church of St Augustine in Queen's

Gate, not far from Harrington Court and Gledhow Gardens and a striking example by Butterfield of the Victorian gothic architecture for which Andrew had a longstanding passion. Medieval mystery plays and T. S. Eliot's *Murder in the Cathedral* had been performed in the church. Over coffee in the vicarage kitchen, the Chestertonian priest and the young composer struck up a lively conversation on the subject of using biblical stories as entertainment.

Father Hewitt felt that the New Testament stories were unnecessarily sanitised: '*This,*' he told Andrew, 'is what offends my Christianity.' He talked about Jesus and Judas as real people who should be depicted as such, not just as remote, static figures on stained glass windows. One of the things he liked about the medieval mystery plays, was that they were realistic and earthy and consequently got the message across to an illiterate and otherwise uncomprehending peasantry.

Andrew particularly liked that, but despite these vicars' enthusiasm, remained sceptical about the idea of writing a full-length work featuring Jesus Christ. That, in fact, was precisely the point: surely nothing that made a clergyman excited could ever make any money?

Early that November, RCA Victor finally released *Come Back Richard: Your Country Needs You*. The sentiment proved to be an erroneous one: the record sank even faster than the show.

Superstar, however, sold steadily for MCA. The giant company had recently held an executive meeting in New York. Among the items on the agenda was that expensive new single from the unknown Tim Rice and Andrew Lloyd Webber.

Richard Broderick, MCA's International Vice-President, was uninhibited about articulating what hitherto had been only a thought in the deepest recesses of the mind of Brian Brolly. Broderick's pitch was worthy of *Citizen Kane*. 'This,' he told the assembled executives, 'is something quite unusual, gentleman. I feel it can be something . . . *monstrous.*'

Broderick paused for his words to sink in. After a moment or two, the grey suits in the audience turned to each other and nodded. *Monstrous.*

The order went down the corporate command chain, precise as a piano sonata. Broderick called Brolly, who called David Land, who called Tim, who called Andrew. The question was the same in each case: how were they doing with that full-length work featuring Jesus Christ?

Andrew and Tim had rather a long and anxious discussion before giving their reply. The fact was, they were not writing it at all; the failures of first *Richard* and then apparently of *Superstar* had left them depressed. They were unaware of quite how steadily the record was selling – or that the marketing potential of the religious controversy already stirred up by the single had been spotted by the men in New York. Perhaps it was time to resurrect Robin Hood.

They called Land back and told him they were doing fine.

Land was pleased to hear this was so. He said he had some good news for them. It was a moment worthy of the quip made by the Broadway legend Sammy Cahn. When asked by an earnest critic which came first, the words or the music, he replied: 'the phone call.'

Afterwards, there was a stunned silence. MCA Records had decided to commission them to write the story of *Superstar* as a full-length, four-sided, double album pop opera.

The silence soon turned to panic. The combined forces of God (via St Paul and St Augustine and their vicars) and Mammon (address c/o MCA Records Inc. New York) had succeeded where they had failed. Together they had faith, where in the minds of Tim and Andrew there had been only doubt. This was the big time. Now all they had to do was deliver.

That winter, the winter of 1969, was not one of the coldest in memory, but on the border of England and Wales it was always cold at this time of year. Hay bales were helicoptered to sheep on snowy hillsides, flickery images of which appeared on urban television screens. In the city stores, people were still buying records: *Abbey Road* by the Beatles, *Let It Bleed* by the Rolling Stones and Bob Dylan's latest slender offering *Nashville Skyline*. One or two of them even bought *Joseph and the Amazing Technicolor Dreamcoat*.

But the composers of this and *Superstar* were far away from their usual stamping grounds: in desperation, they had ventured as far as the little Herefordshire village of Stoke Edith. Here, at the Stoke Edith Hotel, they had locked themselves in a room with a piano. Bits of paper were strewn about with lyrics written down, crossed out and rewritten. The tunes came off the piano as hybrids of the latest pop and soul music, with interludes of classical purity. Then there would be a pause, a clink of glasses, and the voices would be heard, before they started all over again. They were writing *Jesus Christ Superstar*.

In London, John Lennon, formerly of the Beatles, played a concert at the Lyceum Ballroom in aid of UNICEF. Supporting him were his new group, the Plastic Ono Band and his new groupie, the Japanese performance artist Yoko Ono. Lennon had already found himself in trouble over his remarks implying that the Beatles were more popular than Jesus Christ. Now he let it be known that he was more than willing to be considered for the role of Jesus, in a musical version of the Messiah's life which he had heard was entering production.

Shortly afterwards a reporter telephoned David Land's office. Was this offer really true?

'But of course,' he was told, 'he'd be perfect for the part. After all, the pictures of Jesus make him look like a well turned-out John Lennon.'

This was just a bit of fun: a piece of publicity at no one's expense. Then Lennon threw what he termed 'a Spaniard' in the works: he wanted Yoko to play Mary Magdalene.

To a nation of British Beatle lovers brought up on the memory of Japanese war crimes, this could hardly have been a less enticing prospect. Enthusiasm for the idea suddenly waned at the offices of New Talent Ventures. The Dean of St Paul's, who had offered to stage the projected musical in the Cathedral, also found himself issuing a stream of 'no comments.'

Pressed, he finally told reporters: 'Well, yes, I mean, yes. I did tell them that I thought they should take Jesus down from a stained-glass window. No, I have not met Mr Lennon. But you must understand, I don't have anything to do with the actual casting.'

Back in the Stoke Edith Hotel, the two of them began to thrash out the *dramatis personae* of what had seemed like just another good idea at the time. Judas, the anti-hero, the hitherto unacknowleged commentator on the Messiah's road to fame and martyrdom. Mary Magdalene, the fallen woman of Tim's fantasies. Jesus, the Son of God made all too human, destined as fodder for the starmaking machinery of rebellion in the Roman world. Herod, a sardonic yet vulnerable potentate, like Potiphar in *Joseph.* Swiftly, although it seemed slow at the time, a story began to emerge which had been there all along.

The John Lennon rumours disappeared with their author back to New York. In London, David Land concentrated on grappling with the idea of a stage musical about Jesus Christ – the implications of his never having produced one before were beginning to dawn on the manager of the Dagenham Girl Pipers. The Dean of St Paul's prepared for Christmas in the Cathedral. Andrew, having just written the basic tunes for a musical based on the last six days of the life of Christ, spent Christmas with Aunt Vi in Ventimiglia. Then he came back to London, and Tim, and an interview with Peter Cole of the *Evening News.*

Cole had attended the Central Hall, Westminster performance

of *Joseph* but not written about it. Now he seemed determined to outdo his rivals on the *Standard* with the latest news on youth culture. Andrew told him *Jesus Christ Superstar* was an opera — he stressed the word — that attempted to turn 'don't cares into don't knows.' Beyond that, he said, it had no message.

Tim promptly supplied one: 'There's nothing in it which we say, which the Bible doesn't,' he told Cole, 'What is likely to be controversial is the way we treat Judas. Judas was the most intelligent of the disciples. Jesus was a super prophet, a man close to God,' Tim went on. 'Judas saw that some people wanted to use Jesus for their own political ends and he came to the conclusion that Jesus would have to die.'

Tim had plenty more where that came from.

The Men Who Put *Jesus* In The Charts

Tim Rice and Andrew Lloyd Webber spent the week before Christmas writing and reclusing.

They escaped to peaceful Wales with a piano to set about turning a series of thoughts and ideas into a coherent musical work called Jesus Christ. Now it is almost finished . . .

Rosy

So 1970 looks rosy for the two young writers: Tim, 25, who writes the lyrics and Andrew, 21, who composes the music.

Andrew's vast basement flat in Kensington is dominated by a huge grand piano . . .

He is one of the modern breed of trained musicians who doesn't turn his nose up at pop. He believes some kind of synthesis between pop and classical is possible, but he doesn't think anybody has achieved it yet.

Tim is more the pop man . . .

The musical is a serious attempt to translate an ancient story which is accepted by fewer and fewer young people into something which might be meaningful or helpful today. I look forward to hearing the finished work.

So did Brian Brolly, Sefton Myers and David Land. Tim and

Andrew were still a long way from finishing *Jesus Christ Superstar* and as yet had no idea of the implications of those few frenzied days in Herefordshire. Tim had other priorities apart from the taking down of Christ from a stained glass window. Julian, now a rangy eighteen-year-old still living with his parents, also had a steady girlfriend: Celia, the daughter of Sefton Myers's doctor and sister of David Ballantyne, who had sung on the early Rice–Lloyd Webber demonstration recordings. Ballantyne, too, had a girlfriend; in fact everyone, it seemed, had one except Andrew. It was at this point that Andrew met and fell for a young woman for the first time in his life. Her name was Sarah Hugill.

They came from different worlds. Sarah Jane Tudor Hugill's father was a wealthy director of the great white sugar monopoly, Tate & Lyle. She was a commonsensical county girl, close to her mother and light years away from the ethos of the toy theatre. But when Andrew took her to meet Jean and Billy, Jean's tacit approval set the seal on a transfer of feminine influence from her to this mere girl. For Sarah was young, so young that Andrew spent much of his time waiting for her a short distance from Harrington Court and Gledhow Gardens, outside the doors of Queens Gate School where she was still a pupil.

But it was the future of the relationship which had already lasted nearly five years with which he was most preoccupied. When asked what he was doing now, he replied that he and Tim were thinking about what to do next.

'We want to stay together,' he told people, 'and be a recognised team. Just like Rodgers and Hart.'

He was right in more ways than one.

3

Just Like Rodgers and Hart

In the beginning, they had got along famously. Five years later, this was still the case. Not only that, but the parallels between themselves and Rodgers and Hart were undeniable.

Richard Rodgers, whose most famous song *Some Enchanted Evening* made Billy Lloyd Webber weep and whom his son so desperately wanted to emulate was, like Andrew, born into a comfortable middle-class family. His mother, like Jean, was a talented pianist. The young Rodgers had music lessons from an early age, composed his first song when he was eleven and saw his first musical, Jerome Kern's *Very Good Eddie*, when he was only fourteen. By the age of seventeen he had had three songs published. He started writing musical shows as a Columbia University student and never contemplated anything other than a career in musical theatre.

The parallels did not stop there. At the age of sixteen, Rodgers met Lorenz Hart, a man seven years his senior. Hart had a talent for writing verse, wrote love songs with wit and outrageous lines such as *I've got a mania for Pennsylvania* and *I'd go to hell for ya, or Philadelphia* and loved to party. Where Rodgers was hardworking and single-minded, Hart was mercurial and inspired. Where Rodgers was punctual, Hart was late. Where Rodgers was well turned-out, Hart was probably not even out of bed unless there was a party to go to. They had little or nothing in common with each other on first meeting but swiftly saw that each had something the other needed and could not supply. It took them five years, and countless songs, before they found success. By that time it was still not yet evident that, like all such relationships, the circumstances of their meeting contained both the seeds of their brilliant creative partnership and of its demise.

Andrew and Tim had left that Herefordshire hotel with a rare commodity indeed – the rough version of a musical account of the last six days of the life of Christ that would satisfy the criteria of both the Dean of St Paul's and the proprietors of New Talent Ventures. But whether or not Andrew realised it, *Jesus Christ Superstar* was to be their last truly happy collaboration.

They could not have written their version of the story – the 'greatest story ever told' – without having written *Joseph and the Amazing Technicolor Dreamcoat. Jesus Christ Superstar* was the realisation of the potential promised in *Joseph*; but in its un-ashamed application of the profane, four-square rhythms of pop to the sacred Passion of Christ, it went far beyond the short piece written for the choirboys of Colet Court.

In *Jesus Christ Superstar* pop became hard rock, the only language immediately comprehensible to affluent but spiritually impoverished young Westerners ignorant of history and of the Bible stories, and with a voracious need for heroes. Popular music was full of idols like Buddy Holly, Jimi Hendrix, Janis Joplin, Jim Morrison, Elvis Presley and John Lennon. Rock music, as Lennon himself had noted, had in a sense become bigger than Jesus – now it would be used to show that Jesus was still the biggest star of all – and this was where the controversy began.

Just as he had found inspiration in *The Wonder Book of Bible Stories*, so Tim had here made use of Fulton J. Sheen's *Life of Christ*, which compared and explained the Gospel stories. Leaving out the dramatically tricky subject of the resurrection, he concentrated on Christ's attracting the attention of the Roman authorities, the Last Supper, the betrayal and the Crucifixion. Tim had already established Judas as a key character with the release of the single of *Superstar*: now he had Judas voice doubts about Jesus which echoed contemporary suspicions of the bogus messianicism of the whole hippy era:

> *Jesus! You've started to believe*
> *The things they say of you*
> *You really do believe*
> *This talk of God is true*
> *And all the good you've done*
> *Will soon be swept away*
> *You've begun to matter more*
> *Than the things you say . . .*

> *They think they've found the new Messiah*
> *And they'll hurt you when they find they're wrong . . .*

Judas even broadcast his commentary from beyond the grave, back and forth across the 2000-year gap in history; and in words that were vintage Rice:

> *Why d'you choose such a backward time*
> *and such a strange land?*
> *If you'd come today you would have*
> *reached a whole nation.*
> *Israel in 4 B.C. had no*
> *mass communication . . .*

But when he tried to depict Jesus cursing the fig tree, even Tim had to admit defeat.

Mary Magdalene, too, was given as much prominence here as in the Gospels, but freed from their stereotypical image of her as fallen woman. Tim, who had written so many bittersweet love songs to be sung by women of the world, returned to her some of her Old Testament qualities. He and Andrew also decided she needed a big ballad to sing — but as yet, she did not have one.

What they did have, after their chilly week in Herefordshire, was a catchy blend of modern, godless, Town Hall politics and the inexorable undertow of popular movements for change. Thus Caiaphas, Annas and the priests sang against the background of the mob:

> *Listen to that howling mob of blockheads in the street*
> *A trick or two with lepers and the whole town's on its feet!*
> *He is dangerous*
> *(Jesus Christ Superstar)*
> *He is dangerous . . .*

The motif of the title song, in its orchestral form, with its soaring address to the heavens worked brilliantly in counterpoint to the earthbound crackle and pop of the unbelievers.

But that spring, as the date of the MCA album recording loomed closer, there were still plenty of problems to be ironed out by Andrew and Alan Doggett. Chief among them was the need for two songs for Mary Magdalene and Herod. Herod's predicament was essentially that of Potiphar before him: he needed an almost cynically poppy tune with which to taunt Christ and inadvertently expose his own lack of spirituality:

> *Prove to me that you're no fool*
> *Walk across my swimming-pool*

Saladin Days from the ill-fated *Come Back Richard* had then become *Try It and See*, in which capacity it had also failed miserably. Now it became *King Herod's Song*. Perhaps it would be a case of third time lucky.

Mary Magdalene continued to trouble them. Then they had it: *Kansas Morning*.

It had never really worked, but Andrew had written that beautiful melody that had never stayed far from the top of the well. David Land quietly bought back *Kansas Morning* from Southern Music. Then it was Tim's turn, to remind them just how good he could be:

I Don't Know How to Love Him

I don't know how to love him
What to do, how to move him
I've been changed — yes, really changed
In these past few days, when I've seen myself
I seem like someone else

I don't know how to take this
I don't see why he moves me
He's a man, he's just a man
And I've had so many men before
In very many ways
He's just one more . . .

The better things went, the more *insouciant* Rice would be. Andrew developed a different technique. Once he was sufficiently confident that people around him expected him to behave in a certain way, he pre-empted them and expanded on the theme. He grew adept, for example, at telling people that *Jesus Christ Superstar* was, if not a piece of juvenilia, at the very most a youthful extravagance.

'It isn't a major thought from me,' he would tell them, 'I just supplied . . . I mean, if one has to be pompous and use the word *achievement* . . . I just supplied the *architecture* of the piece.'

MCA recorded the album of *Jesus Christ Superstar*, like the single, at considerable expense. Murray Head, who had sung the single when no one else wanted to record him, again played the part of Judas. Pontius Pilate was sung by Barry Dennen, an established and accomplished performer. The Grease Band supplied their expert services. Mary Magdalene was sung by a newcomer, found by Andrew in a Fulham nightclub — an innocent-looking, porcelain-skinned Hawaiian with a sensuous vocal edge, called Yvonne Elliman.

Andrew worked on last-minute rearrangements and orchestrations: especially the 'Gethsemane' section which, as the *Superstar* single title song motif and its wordless 'B' side *John Nineteen Forty One* had done, embodied the burgeoning orchestral talents of the son of Billy Lloyd Webber.

David Land, meanwhile, was puzzling over how to interest theatre producers in a musical about the last six days in the life of Jesus Christ. So far, he was not having much luck. The subject matter alone put off producers, most of whose idea of a risk was a revival of *Oklahoma!* Furthermore, *Jesus Christ Superstar* was not originally written for the stage; the single had not done well; the album had not yet been released; and to date only a few schools and colleges had applied for permission to perform *Joseph*. The odds were further lengthened by the fact that Land had little experience of theatre or musical production, and Sefton Myers, his partner in New Talent Ventures, was dying of cancer.

Land grappled manfully with these and other problems and reassured himself that it was only eighteen months since Andrew and Tim had signed the contract. They had come a long way since then. Sooner or later, on the strength of past progress if nothing else, something was bound to happen.

That autumn of 1970, MCA (UK) released the expensively recorded double album of *Jesus Christ Superstar*. Andrew, Tim, Land and Brian Brolly watched and waited with bated breath.

Nothing happened. The reviewers praised it and moved on to the next release. The album failed to enter the Top Twenty or even the Top Fifty. The few radio stations in existence at the time largely ignored it. Gloom descended even more heavily on the offices of New Talent Ventures. Andrew began to think he was right after all: nothing that made a vicar excited could ever make any money.

Soon afterwards, the gloom began to lift. That November, MCA had decided to release the record in America. Furthermore, they had decided to invite the composers over for the occasion.

Ellis Nassour, an MCA PR man, was seconded to look after the two young Englishmen in New York. Neither of them had any money, apart from their strictly controlled retainers from David Land. The PR man, too, had strict instructions: keep them happy at minimum cost. Nassour obliged, even accommodating the lanky Rice in his compact Greenwich Village apartment. Tim charmed him, as he did everyone else; but the New Yorker found Andrew standoffish and difficult to know.

Andrew and Tim then moved to the Drake Hotel. MCA threw a party to launch the album of *Jesus Christ Superstar* in St Peter's Church on Lexington Avenue. The music press and radio stations were well represented. William Bender of *Time* magazine was particularly attentive; as were the two young Englishmen in return.

Bender asked Andrew about his main musical influences:

'Bill Haley,' Andrew told him, 'and Stravinsky. Listen to the *Symphony in Three Movements* — it's an object lesson to any rock band that wants to play with precision and tight sound.'

Billy Lloyd Webber would have been proud. Bender, for his part, had never met anyone quite like this twitchy, hyper-articulate little Englishman.

Tim, too, was ready with the quotable remark: 'It happens,' he told Bender, 'that we don't see Christ as God, but simply as the right man in the right place at the right time. Great story, though.'

Back at the Drake Hotel, Andrew ordered wine with dinner and the record company, which owned four other labels, Universal Studios and numerous other enterprises, demurred at his extravagance. The next day the first reports came in: the album was selling heavily. Afterwards, they would sit back at leisure and try to work out exactly why a record which had flopped in Britain should now be reordering at every record shop in New York City. As usual, apart from the enormous attraction of the words and music, the answer lay in part at least in the ability of the right person to be in the right place at the right time:

Time 9 NOVEMBER 1970

ROCK PASSION

A quasi-religious revival is stirring in pop music. Three of the biggest hit singles of 1970 bow deeply to religion – Simon & Garfunkel's *Bridge Over Troubled Water*, the Beatles' *Let It Be*, and Norman Greenbaum's *Spirit in the Sky*. Bob Dylan's latest album, *New Morning*, contains a new song, *Three Angels*, that chides everyday people for their indifference to God. Far and away the most ambitious pop venture into the Scriptures is a new English rock opera, *Jesus Christ Superstar*, released last week in the U.S. on an 87-minute, two-LP album by Decca. As a musical retelling of the seven last days in Christ's life, it rivals the St John and St Matthew Passions of Bach – in ambition and scope if not in piety or musical exaltation.

With an appealing variegated score by Andrew Lloyd Webber and words by Tim Rice, *Superstar* builds to considerable impact and evocativeness, in part because it manages to wear its underlying seriousness lightly. What Rice and Lloyd Webber have created is a modern-day passion play that may enrage the devout but ought to intrigue and perhaps inspire the agnostic young . . .

Almost exactly a year earlier to the day, Richard Broderick had paused for his words to sink in. The grey suits in his audience had turned to each other and nodded. *Monstrous* . . .

Superstar occupies the same assimilative position in the pop world that Ginastera's *Don Rodrigo* does in serious opera. Webber and Rice do not outdo the Beatles or the Rolling Stones or the Edwin Hawkins Singers, Prokofiev, Orff, Stravinsky or any other musical influence found in their work. But they have welded these borrowings into a considerable work that is their own. *Tommy* (by The Who) was the first, flawed suggestion that rock could deal with a major subject on a broad symphonic or operatic scale. *Superstar* offers the first real proof.

Less than a year ago, they had emerged from the Welsh mists with the murky outline of a rock opera. Not even they could have foreseen that it would be plastered across the pages of *Time* magazine, in a fashion beyond a publicist's wildest dreams:

> Whatever the reaction to *Superstar* may be, Webber and Rice have fused words and music into such a convincing narrative style that rock may never be quite the same again.

That night, Andrew again ordered wine with dinner. The record company did not demur; from now on, they reasoned, the funny little guy could have anything he wanted. Besides, people in his position usually realised they could afford to lighten up a little after they had sold a few hundred thousand records. Look at his partner, they said; now there was a guy who knew how to relax and enjoy life. The fact that all Andrew apparently wanted to do was work came as something of a surprise.

He was also interested in deals, and managements were beginning to queue up outside the MCA offices. Most of these were sharks; some were reputable. None was more astute than Robert Stigwood.

Stigwood was a brilliant Australian impresario who had represented such hard rock artists as the Bee Gees, the Moody Blues and Jimi Hendrix, and who had first come to prominence as joint managing director of NEMS Enterprises — and thereby co-manager of the Beatles — during the tragic, twilight stewardship of Brian Epstein. A tall, outwardly affable bachelor of intensely private disposition and an inconvenient personal weakness — he was terrified of flying — he had gone on to become a showbusiness tycoon whose properties included musicals such as *Hair* and more profane productions such as *The Dirtiest Show in Town*.

The week *Jesus Christ Superstar* began to sell heavily in New York record stores, Stigwood put a call through to the MCA offices. He wanted to know if it was possible for him to meet Tim Rice and Andrew Lloyd Webber. The two agreed. A couple of nights later a limousine arrived at the Drake Hotel. No other producer had thought to send one. Stigwood, meanwhile, was at his large rented house on New York's Upper East Side with the British theatre producer, Bob Swash. Swash and Stigwood had already collaborated on a couple of shows in London. Now Stigwood had a couple of Londoners whom he wanted Swash to meet.

'Come downstairs,' he said, 'and meet Andrew Lloyd Webber and Tim Rice, who have written *Jesus Christ Superstar*. I want to do it on stage. But they're leaving New York tonight. I've got to get them out of the country before the sharks get at them!'

To Tim, this was just another agreeable manifestation of the rather droll interest taken in himself and Andrew by gentlemen with limousines. Andrew, on the other hand, was hyper-alert, his eyes everywhere, tense and nervous. Over a good dinner, Stigwood gave them both one of the all-time great lessons in the art of the deal.

Later, much later, Andrew would resent the terms of the deal done by Stigwood that night in New York. But the fact was that it was a turning point in his career. Land had more or less inherited them from Myers and supported them for a year, during which time they had more than rewarded his efforts. But Land had no experience of mounting successful stage musicals or capitalising on successful musical albums. Nor had Tim, whose entrepreneurial abilities, apart from recruiting Brian Brolly, had hitherto extended only to securing the services of out-of-work rock musicians. The net result was that they were all now out of their depth – except Stigwood.

Stigwood proposed a deal based on his superior experience that was designed to capitalise on all these factors. David Land would remain their personal manager. Stigwood, in return for substantial inducements in the form of shares and cash, would buy a fifty-one per cent stake in New Talent Ventures and take over the rights to twenty-five per cent of Andrew and Tim's earnings over the next five years, plus all rights to film and stage productions of their works in the English-speaking world. He

75

also persuaded MCA to give Andrew and Tim a better deal in return for a share in their future compositions. There would be further dimensions to the Stigwood deal, but for the time being this was as far as it went. There were nine years left of the Myers/Land deal to run.

Andrew and Tim thought about it. So did David Land. They agreed.

That winter Stigwood and Land put the finishing touches to the deal, and Sefton Myers died of cancer at the age of forty-three. Thus passed the man who might justifiably have claimed to have launched the career of Tim Rice and Andrew Lloyd Webber.

Andrew had returned from New York to South Kensington. The contrast could hardly have been greater: Billy was as absorbed as ever in administrative duties and his melancholy private world; Jean still taught piano; and Julian still lived at home, where he practised like a man possessed in preparation for his concert debut. Tim had a place of his own, on the borders of Notting Hill and Bayswater. Like their old flatmate John Lill, who had recently won first prize in the Tchaikovsky Competition in Moscow, his and Andrew's horizons had been forced far beyond Gledhow Gardens and Harrington Court.

But while Tim was a law unto himself, Andrew was hopelessly impractical and still needed to be mothered and nannied. This responsibility had now passed from Molly and Jean, to the schoolgirl Sarah Hugill. The two appeared absorbed with each other, and while Mrs Hugill watched with some trepidation from the sidelines, her daughter and Andrew were spending more and more time together. He was still only twenty-two and she was seventeen; in such circumstances, and such circles, the question of marriage could not be avoided for long.

That Christmas, Andrew did not invite Sarah to Harrington Court; nor was he present at the Hugill family home. Instead he took her to stay with the person to whom he had always gone for approval and support: his Aunt Vi, in Ventimiglia. And Vi, true to character, did not disapprove.

By February 1971, *Jesus Christ Superstar* had sold over two million copies in America, having toppled Janis Joplin and ascended to Number 1 in the American pop charts. As Peter Cole and Derek Jewell had done in a much smaller way in England, William Bender's *Time* magazine review thrust their work in front of a young, middle-brow, vinyl-hungry public. *Time* was also planning to run a cover story on what it called 'The Jesus Revolution', in which it endeavoured with some success to identify a current resurgence of Christian spirituality among the young. *Jesus Christ Superstar* was cast firmly as a symptom of this phenomenon and the idea pushed for all it was worth. Other American magazines, with other, massive audiences, followed suit, for example the conservative Protestant weekly *Christianity Today*:

> Many Christians have ignored this generation's questions about Jesus. For those who will listen, *Superstar* tells what young people are saying.

It was all a rather long way from Tim's Top Twenty, in which, together with John F. Kennedy, Robin Hood and Richard the Lionheart, Judas and Jesus were just another couple of characters vying for the title role in a new star vehicle. But for every practising Christian who went out and bought the record, there were half a dozen pagan hard rock fans who bought it for Deep Purple's Ian Gillan and Joe Cocker's Grease Band, the British artists who supplied its distinctly American hard rock sound. Yvonne Elliman's beautiful rendition of Mary Magdalene's torch song *I Don't Know How To Love Him* also became a massive hit.

In New York, MCA fanned the publicity and Stigwood concluded the deal begun that night over dinner. He now acquired, for a further substantial consideration, the remaining forty-nine per cent of New Talent Ventures, purchased a £100 'shelf' company and renamed it Superstar Ventures. Superstar Ventures purchased the Land management contract with Tim and Andrew for £10,000 and then sold fifty-one per cent of itself to the Robert Stigwood Organisation. Stigwood now had twenty-five per cent of all their income from the stage show, controlled the company which assigned the stage rights and had an equal share partnership with MCA to finance the stage productions. This was not a bad deal for a man whose 1970 share issue had been described in one British newspaper as 'one of the most dramatic new issue flops of all time.'

In London, both Tim and Andrew made themselves into limited liability companies through which they hoped to exploit their earnings. Tim named his company Heartaches Ltd. after Elvis Presley's 1957 hit *That's When Your Heartaches Begin* — he also gave the name to his cricket team. Andrew's was called Escaway Ltd., an elision of escape and getaway and a Sergeant Thrust-like hint of his attitude towards Britain's punitive tax system. Despite the unconducive climate — Britain in 1971 was still riven by political unrest and inflation — he and Tim still had the entrepreneurial ambitions that dated back to the days when they wanted to manage Ross Hannaman and open a pop museum. With David Land, they formed a third company called Roseway Ltd., in which Land held fifty shares and Andrew and Tim seventy-three shares each: now they, too, would become mini-tycoons on the trail of Robert Stigwood. Then, on an un-Stigwood-like whim, they changed the name from Roseway to the unpronounceable Qwertyuiop — the joke was that, being the top row of letters on a typewriter keyboard, it was easier to type.

Qwertyuiop did not flourish as a business enterprise, but the name endured; as did Andrew's penchant for childish names for grown-up limited liability companies. Furthermore, the next one he dreamed up would achieve success on a rather different scale.

That spring, the album continued to sell in vast quantities across

America. In New York, Stigwood pursued his plans for a Broadway première. There were also other concert productions in hand of what Tim now referred to as *JC*; some were more welcome than others. In London, Andrew celebrated his twenty-third birthday and continued to fret about what he and Tim were going to do next. This was a question with which Tim was conspicuously unconcerned, but Andrew brooded on it and spent hours at the piano at Gledhow Gardens.

There were also non-professional matters in need of attention. In May, he attended the Royal College of Music's eightieth birthday tribute to its President and Master of the Queen's Musick, Sir Arthur Bliss. The programme included performances of Bliss's *Morning Heroes* and Prokofiev's *Cello Concerto* (soloist Julian Lloyd Webber).

Julian had slogged up and down Britain's provincial recital circuit and now it was his turn to enjoy the limelight. Bliss took a shine to him and sent him a copy of his new cello concerto as a souvenir of the evening. Since the only person to have played this to date was the fabulous Russian Mstislav Rostropovich, this was something of a compliment. Later, Julian also played for Bliss at the latter's home.

But the life of a budding concert cellist was hard and Julian, who was among very few people who knew how long Andrew had worked to achieve what was now inevitably being described as overnight success, now began to appreciate the part played by publicity in bringing that success within reach. Once, Rostropovich had been someone to whose recordings he had listened in awe at Harrington Court. Now they had something in common. If only he too, like Andrew, could tap the awesome power of the press.

On 24 July, Andrew and Sarah were married in the country church of Holy Cross at the village of Ashton Keynes in Gloucestershire; thirty miles south-east of the hotel where, eighteen months earlier, he and Tim had created the bare bones of

Jesus Christ Superstar. Now *Superstar* dominated everything; the American pop charts; the mind of Stigwood who was fending off pirate performances while setting up the Broadway production; the minds of Andrew and Tim who were faced with the problem of having to compose and write extra material for the show; the accountants of Heartaches Ltd. and Escaway Ltd.; even the wedding ceremony, at which a musical setting of the Lord's Prayer was played which Andrew had written for the stage production.

As the newly linked Lloyd Webber and Hugill families mingled in the churchyard before departing for the reception, the bride and groom posed for photographs like any bridal couple. In truth, they were an odd pair: the small, thin, long-haired young man with the darting eyes and slightly raffish, Victorian look; and the even more youthful and wholesome Kensington schoolgirl, whose A level results were still not known and who had never lived away from home. She had long brown hair and an even-toothed smile that gave rise to her nickname 'the vole'.

Her father helped them buy their first home, Summerlease Farm near Shaftesbury in Dorset. Summerlease was a fine, Victorian, six-acre affair, set in fertile farmland eighty miles south-west of London. But the distance was also a problem; and their real home remained the flat at Gledhow Gardens. From here Andrew could keep in closer touch with Tim and with his family in South Kensington. For in spite of her appreciation of his talent, Jean's tastes did not extend to the good food and drink, the convivial young company and the swimming-pool on offer at her son and daughter-in-law's house.

That summer, the new Mr and Mrs Lloyd Webber relocated again, albeit temporarily, to the less genteel surroundings of New York City. But this was a far cry, though only a short taxi ride, from Nassour's flat and the Drake Hotel. Now they and Mr Rice occupied adjoining suites at the Waldorf Astoria Hotel on

Park Avenue, at the south end of Central Park. From here, Andrew and Sarah launched themselves on occasional forays around the country by train, to see concert performances and later the pre-Broadway touring production of *JC*.

The success of the album in record shops and on radio stations had also proved too great a temptation for dozens of churches and religious groups who had praised and now appropriated it for their own purposes. Because *Jesus Christ Superstar* was a continuous, through-sung piece of music and not a conventional dramatic work, more or less anyone could perform it; all that was required was a cast of singers who did not necessarily need to know how to act. The evangelistically minded churches and religious groups, who usually had choirs, now succumbed in droves.

Pirate performances of the piece sprang up across America. At first Stigwood and MCA ignored them. But bogus 'original' productions and 'official' touring companies soon began to capitalise on this at his expense, to the point where the record's tremendous success was jeopardising the profitability of his show. The wrath of Stigwood now descended on all and sundry. Sensing his percentages – and his out-of-town audiences – slip away, he instituted a series of swingeing court actions against the pirate producers. Regardless of motive, Mammon or missionary, his agents descended on them armed with court orders and stopped the show. In Sydney, Australia, Stigwood's home territory, they even thwarted an unlicensed performance produced by an order of nuns in aid of charity.

Stigwood's official licensee and representative on earth, Sydney impresario Harry M. Miller, elected to speak on his behalf.

'Like all Christians, these nuns believe Jesus Christ is theirs,' he explained, 'What they are forgetting is that there is such a thing as copyright.'

Elsewhere, Mammon triumphed in far from mysterious ways. Along with the officially licensed badges, buttons and T-shirts on sale, there were now Jesus Christ jockey shorts and Jesus Christ bikinis.

The frenetic pace of the merchandising and expensive legal activity made it imperative that the Broadway show opened as soon as possible. The composer and writer now spent much of their time in their adjoining hotel suites, writing additional material.

Tim escaped periodically from the mounting pressure by going out to parties and rock concerts, from which he would cheerfully return in the small hours to pick up work where he had left off. Andrew simply did not know how to relax or work in this way; instead, he stayed in his hotel room, ringing room service, brooding over the changes, communicating his anxiety to Sarah, missing Tim when he was absent and driving him to distraction when he was there. The paranoia was infectious, it ran to and fro; from Stigwood, to the director Frank Corsaro, to the cast which was as yet incomplete, to the backers, and back again.

This build-up of pressure was essential to the success of any Broadway production, where the demand for sure-fire success was such that the critics could kill a show on its opening night. There was a standard method of releasing just enough pressure to enable the production to go ahead at full steam without blowing itself up. This was to fire someone whose departure could be interpreted as a propitiatory sacrifice to the pagan gods of Broadway. Unfortunately for him, the director Frank Corsaro was injured in a car accident at about this time. His recovery was not helped by a message to the effect that on leaving hospital, and in return for a percentage of the show's anticipated takings, his services would no longer be required.

Stigwood's choice of a replacement conformed to the standard showbusiness theory that nothing succeeds like success. The new director was the short, pony-tailed bachelor Tom O'Horgan, who had successfully directed *Hair*. He took over in early August and immediately set about casting the key roles by auditioning singers and actors from the concert tour and his previous show. The Mark Hellinger Theatre now began to smell strongly of marijuana, as hundreds of hopefuls came and went in search of a part on Broadway. Yvonne Elliman and Barry Dennen again took the parts of Mary Magdalene and Pilate, while Judas and Jesus were played by Ben Vereen and Jeff Fenholt.

The allotted cast now had to become accustomed to O'Horgan's somewhat individualistic way of working: he arranged Vereen and Fenholt in a cruciform shape on the floor and made the cast close their eyes and touch them, in order to 'think about what the Crucifixion really was'.

He also had Fenholt lie on the floor with honey on his chest, which a blindfolded cast was then encouraged to lick off.

As he put it: 'The theatre has gone through the cerebral trip, and now the swing is back to the supernatural consciousness, where things have to be felt.'

O'Horgan's attitude to work also applied to relaxation. A keen collector of musical instruments, his relationship with them was somewhat different to Andrew's.

The collection included a three-hundred-and-fifty-year-old Japanese gong. 'I can't tell you,' he told people, 'what going home and flailing away at that gong does for me.'

To others, he confided that he was thinking of having a 'vinyl-clad, hip Christ' crucified on the handlebars of a Harley-Davidson motorcycle. Eventually, however, he settled for a surrealistic golden triangle, which was slowly moved towards the audience by a concealed fork-lift truck of the kind normally used for cherry-picking.

Jesus Christ Superstar opened at the Mark Hellinger Theatre on Broadway on Wednesday, 12 October 1971. The spectacular set had already led to myriad technical problems, poor sound levels, demands for danger money from the young cast and the cancellation of several previews that were supposed to have taken place two weeks earlier.

But the delay had only fanned the flames of advance publicity.

The show, which had cost $700,000 to stage, had already taken more than $1,000,000 in advance bookings. The 1700-seat theatre was sold out and hundreds of people queued down Broadway in the hope of buying tickets from touts at $30 apiece. Religious groups and church parties dominated the audience inside and outside, where police patrolled the pickets of protesters clutching banners that read *You've Got Your Story Twisted! Jesus Is The Lord.* The American-Jewish Committee had already issued its review, in the form of a seven-page document claiming that *Jesus Christ Superstar* was bad for the Jews (they said the show rivalled the Oberammergau Passion Play in threatening 'Christian–Jewish relations'). The newspaper critics were yet to reveal their views; Stigwood, in a gesture unprecedented even by Broadway standards, had flown over a contingent of the British press and installed them in the Plaza Hotel on Fifth Avenue.

The previous night Andrew, Tim and Sarah had stood in the theatre which had launched *My Fair Lady* and watched the preview in a state of shock. Under O'Horgan's direction, the relatively chaste rock oratorio they had written for Sefton Myers and David Land had been transformed into an extravaganza worthy of something designed by Salvador Dali for Cecil B. de Mille. O'Horgan seemed to be obsessed with Sam Goldwyn's dictum, that a successful production should 'start with an earthquake and work up to a climax'. The opening sequence, for which Andrew had so carefully laboured over the overture, consisted of the back wall leaning over while cast members clung to it until it flattened into the floor of the stage. Jesus rose from the stage floor on a hidden elevator in a $20,000 robe like a designer alien; Judas thrashed about in silver jockey shorts and an overdose of guilt quite alien to the bold original conception; and Pilate appeared in lipstick and full drag.

But the Roman comparisons did not stop there: Stigwood's first-night party at the Tavern on the Green was attended by a thousand guests drawn from just about every corner of New

York. Transvestites nibbled at hams decorated to look like Indonesian masks and topless models danced to live rock music into the small hours. The press tiptoed away to file their reviews, which were no longer crucial to the fate of a show whose success, for the time being at least, was assured.

The only one who mattered, in any case, was the 'butcher of Broadway', another Englishman, Clive Barnes of the *New York Times*. That night he wrote:

> Nobody could convince me that any show that has sold two and one half million copies of its album before the opening night is anything like all bad. But I must also confess to experiencing some disappointment with *Jesus Christ Superstar*. It all rather resembled one's first sight of the Empire State Building. Not at all uninteresting, but somewhat unsurprising and of minimal artistic value . . .
>
> For me the real disappointment came not in the music — which is better than run-of-the-mill Broadway and the best score for an English musical in years — but in the conception. There is a coyness in its contemporaneity, a sneaky pleasure in the boldness of its anachronisms, a special undefined air of smugness in its daring . . . *Superstar* seemed to me less than super — but the novelty of its aspirations should win it many adherents.

Tim was rather annoyed by this. For a day or so he insisted on answering the telephone at the Waldorf Astoria with the words: 'This is the Clive Barnes fan club.' He soon came to see the funny side; after all the audiences — and the dollars — were rolling in. Besides, *JC* was not the sort of show to be torpedoed by what was in truth a fair review in the *New York Times*. The same feelings that made people picket the David Frost TV show when he and Andrew appeared made sure that *JC* was booked far into the coming year.

Tim decided it was time for a holiday: from Andrew, from the show, from Stigwood, from everyone. He booked a flight to Japan, where he had lived as a child and where they had not yet heard of *Jesus Christ Superstar* or Tim Rice and Andrew Lloyd Webber.

Andrew was not amused. He told Tim that, as far as he was concerned, they had work to do. For a start, there was the little matter of what they were going to do next. Stigwood had already suggested a musical based on the story of Peter Pan, the boy who never grew up. They were a team, were they not, like Rodgers and Hart? Tim confirmed that they were, and that he was going on holiday. Then, just like Rodgers and Hart, they had a violent argument and flew off in opposite directions.

That autumn, Stigwood continued to tour *Jesus Christ Superstar* in America at venues where he was guaranteed a minimum $50,000 box-office take. He had now fought fifteen court actions over pirate shows and was preparing stage productions in Paris and London. Universal Pictures, who were owned by MCA, had bought the film rights. Norman Jewison announced he would direct the movie in Israel.

Andrew was looking forward to working on the soundtrack; he had already contributed music for *Gumshoe*, a spoof *film noir* starring Albert Finney and directed by Stephen Frears. In London, he and Tim were presented with gold and platinum records by Anthony Grant, Secretary to the British Board of Trade, in recognition of 3.5 million records sold and their services to hard-pressed British exports.

In South Kensington, Andrew's grandmother Molly died; and his brother wrote a letter:

Dear Sirs

I am the twenty-year-old younger brother of Andrew Lloyd Webber, composer of *Jesus Christ Superstar*. Fortunately, I have also had some success recently in the very different musical sphere of classical cellist . . .

86

The recipient was the London *Observer* newspaper. The *Observer* had its fun at Julian's expense; but did also mention that he had been contracted to perform during the coming year at London's prestigious Queen Elizabeth Hall, the piece in question being none other than Sir Arthur Bliss's *Cello Concerto.* They also had to hand it to Julian for cheek:

> ... and plans are under way for my first recital at New York's Carnegie Hall

Julian had learned a fundamental lesson about the media; however much you may hate to admit that you need them, remember they need you even more. It was a lesson he had learnt from Andrew; but Andrew would never quite learn to practise it the way he did.

That winter, the film of *Jesus Christ Superstar* began shooting in Israel. The director, Norman Jewison, even managed to extract a promise of $1 million of the $4 million budget from the Israeli government. Andrew and Tim made their first eager visit to the Promised Land which had brought them such fame and wealth.

But, in truth, neither Israel nor the movie lived up to their legend of a land in 4 BC with no mass communication. The locations were in a fly-blown piece of desert taken from the descendants of Salah-ud-din, the 'rather violent cove who hung around the Middle East'. Jewison had little interest in Andrew and Tim's notions of how it should be filmed. He hired a rewrite man, a jobbing arts journalist called Melvyn Bragg, and shot the rump of the original cast as modern-day tourists in the Holy Land. Once Andrew realised that his control over the film was a token one, his interest in the project waned. He and Tim returned to London where Sarah was waiting, where the food was better, *Peter Pan* beckoned and the British stage production of *JC* was in preparation. Then the prospect of *Peter Pan* palled and, in the manner of young people who have fallen out and made it up, they flew to Paris.

Paris, where Tim had briefly studied 'La Civilisation Française', was to be the setting for the first European performance of *Jesus Christ Superstar*. Stigwood had licensed the French producers and the show was, naturally, to be in French. The musical director was a bilingual Englishman and friend of Alan Doggett, Anthony Bowles.

Bowles had neither heard the piece nor met the composer. He obtained the album and what there was of a score from David Land. His first impression was that the piece proceeded 'from orgasm to orgasm' — an impression which would have been confirmed had he seen O'Horgan's Broadway production. He identified improvisations which had been grafted on during the studio recording and were not organic parts of the show. But what struck him most about *JC*, more than its minor defects and its sheer vitality and drive, was the deceptive nature of the composer's talent.

On paper, a tune like *Heaven on Their Minds* appeared ugly and vulgar to Bowles's trained eye. But when he played the song, and saw it performed, he saw how it worked. Andrew's best tunes had a kind of inimitability which was utterly logical. They did not do what you expected them to do; but when they were over they had an air of inevitability which made you disbelieve they could have ended any other way. To Bowles, who had met and worked with many musicians, this was a rare talent.

The Paris production of the work whose composer had tried to pass it off as a piece of juvenilia, took place at the Palais de Chaillot. Singers converged from all over France for auditions and the giant concert hall rang with their *chansons*. During rehearsals, the management were keen to secure the blessing of the Cardinal Archbishop of Paris; his veto would have ruled out the sizeable clerical audience and alienated many churchgoers. But although there were many who did object, and ensured welcome media coverage as they had on Broadway, the prelate did not.

Besides, the Paris production was chaste by comparison with O'Horgan's. The entire cast and orchestra were on stage in the proscenium theatre and the orchestra wore tailcoats. Stained-glass windows of the sort from which the Dean of St Paul's had suggested Christ should be taken down, were a central part of the set. Stigwood was there, representing Mammon, and the first night was a sell-out. When Mary Magdalene, an unknown seventeen-year-old from Arles sang *Je Ne Sais Pas Lui Aimer*, the show came to a halt amidst tumultuous applause at the arrival of a new *chanteuse*.

Stigwood pronounced himself pleased and asked Bowles if he would care to be musical director of the show in London. Bowles had enjoyed working on it in Paris so much that he had doubts about repeating the experience elsewhere. He told Stigwood he would think about it. Then he finished his month as musical director in Paris, handed over to his French successor and returned to London.

For Andrew, the Paris show had taken away some of the bad taste left by the Broadway production. The income from the latter had enabled him to buy his first house in London. Tim was ensconced in fashionable Bayswater with a Tibetan terrier and a growing collection of paintings of Christ; he was also looking for a place in the country. Now Andrew, too, could become a man about town. 37 Brompton Square SW3 was a mile or so north-east of Harrington Court; a splendid six-storey, flat-fronted affair, early Victorian of course, opposite private gardens and just down the road from Harrods.

Andrew filled it with Victoriana in general and Pre-Raphaelite paintings in particular; apart from the fact that they were a good investment, there was something about their androgynous, perfectly sanitised world that appealed to him. His own appearance, a hybrid of the fey and the eccentric, now included shirts from the more fashionable and expensive Knightsbridge shops. Sarah, who in less than twelve months had changed from schoolgirl to wife of the composer of the biggest smash on Broadway, now assumed the part of proud housewife as well as chatelaine of the house in the country.

Life was pleasant at 37 Brompton Square. There was plenty of work to do: the score still had to be reworked for the film of *JC*; preparations for the London opening of the stage show had to be made; and now that *Peter Pan* had fallen through they had to decide on the next step.

Andrew had visions of a musical based on the Jeeves stories by P. G. Wodehouse. Wodehouse, he started telling people, was 'the greatest writer of the 20th century'. Sarah approved of the idea. Stigwood and Land were trying to tie up the rights with Wodehouse and his associate Guy Bolton. Tim was interested too, in spite of the fact that Bertie Wooster and his butler hardly qualified for the list of short, fast lives which changed the world. But in his capacity as the young would-be Richard Rodgers, Andrew was shortly to experience further evidence of just how trying life could be without a Hammerstein.

Although Andrew liked to tell people that he and Tim were supervising the soundtrack of *JC* the movie, this was not strictly the case. They were beginning to make substantial amounts of money and were thus enhancing their reputations as a bankable commodity, but neither had the power or the expertise to supervise the soundtrack recording of a big-budget Hollywood movie. Nor, in Tim's case, did he have the remotest desire to do so. Tim's attitude to success continued to be robustly unpretentious. He told Anthony Bowles his ambition was to become the King of Television Trivia – and Bowles, a shrewd judge of character, believed him.

It was the sort of remark that infuriated Andrew, for reasons which even Sarah did not understand. What neither she nor Tim fully realised was that they were both in their different capacities parts of the Andrew Lloyd Webber Toy Theatre Company; vital parts, but only parts, of a whole of which Andrew, since childhood, had felt compelled to be in total and utter control.

The *JC* movie soundtrack, like the movie, soon revealed to him the limited extent of his control over the project. He worked hard at the orchestrations, but there were problems with it of a somewhat embarrassing nature. They concerned Alan Doggett.

Doggett had by now left his job at Colet Court and was running his own choir, the London Boy Singers. In his capacity as longterm friend and musical adviser to Andrew, he had undertaken to provide his singers and conduct the film soundtrack, but he proved unequal to the task. His role was eventually taken over by his former assistant and successor at Colet Court, Ian Hunter, and the Colet Court choir.

MCA were so unhappy with the soundtrack, that they also hired the services of another conductor, André Previn. Previn, who had won four Academy Awards as a composer of film scores and was at this time Principal Conductor with the London Symphony Orchestra, was happy to oblige. Although MCA were happy with the result, for Previn *Jesus Christ Superstar* was not a recording credit he was particularly happy to have publicised, either in his biographies or in his extensive *Who's Who* entry.

Meanwhile, preparations went ahead for the first London stage production of *Jesus Christ Superstar*. Andrew's control over this was also limited, but so was his first-hand experience of the grown-up theatre. He was pleased when he heard from Stigwood that Anthony Bowles had agreed to come to the West End. This had not been achieved, however, without some negotiation on Bowles's part.

Within a few hours of his return from Paris to London, he had received a telephone call from Stigwood's London office. Stigwood had not wasted any time in setting up the London production: he had already acquired the services of Bob Swash – the independent British producer who had been at his house in New York the night he first met Tim and Andrew – by buying him out lock, stock and barrel. Swash wanted to know if Bowles was still interested in the job.

Bowles took himself off to the Stigwood offices in Brook Street, Mayfair. They were all there: Stigwood, Swash, Brian Marshall, the designer, and the Australian director, Jim Sharman. Marshall's design was on the table. Bowles took one look and saw that the set covered the orchestra pit.

'Where,' he asked, 'is the orchestra?'

'There's bags of room at the back of the stage,' they told him.

'Where is the conductor going to be?'

'At the back of the stage . . . there's bags of room.'

'How does the conductor do his job?'

'Well, there'll be closed circuit TV . . . you won't have the slightest difficulty seeing what the cast are doing on stage.'

'I am not concerned about seeing the cast,' Bowles told them, 'I want to know how the cast will be able to see me. Because this show needs a musical director, not an accompanist. And I have absolutely no interest in doing this show if I can't direct the performances and tell the cast how I think it is going as it is going. Good day to you.'

The next day Swash telephoned Bowles at his home on the other side of the North London Victorian Gothic square, where they both lived.

'Anthony?' he said, 'we've redesigned the set.'

Jesus Christ Superstar opened at the Palace Theatre, London, on 9 August 1972. Julian, Jean, Billy and various of Billy's friends from the London College of Music and the Royal College of Music were in the audience. So of course were Andrew, Sarah and Tim, the last of whom was off the following morning to see the show in Los Angeles.

Tim rather enjoyed jetting around the world to different productions of his work; so far he had seen nine, all except Los Angeles and Brazil. Before the London opening, he had told Jim Sharman he did not want it to be a religious show; he wanted the supernatural side played down. But although the London staging mercifully lacked the excesses of O'Horgan's Broadway production, it inevitably attracted the same kind of protests from religious groups.

Outside the Palace Theatre, while the traffic roared past Cambridge Circus, groups of churchwomen sang hymns and clutched banners that read; *J.C. Superstar — not our Jesus*. Nobody took much notice of them apart from the press. The Bishop of Southwark had, like the Cardinal Archbishop of Paris, issued an edict approving the show, but still the theological furore rumbled on, albeit in less spectacular a fashion than it had done in America. Thus it was that Anthony Bowles found himself defending it at a party to which he was invited by the Chaplain of the University Church of Christ the King: why, asked the prelate, was it such a *vulgar* production? Why had the director obscured Tim's text — which as anyone could see bore a close resemblance to the Gospel of St John?

Bowles, who was himself a warden at the church of St James, West Hampstead, tried to make the man see sense. 'You are absolutely in error. There is not the slightest comparison with the Gospel of St John and Jim's production, whether you like it or not, adheres faithfully to Tim's text.'

To which the Chaplain replied: 'I don't believe it.'

The Church of England, it seemed, would go to any means to enable them to endorse the show to their congregations: even to the point of reading into it things that simply were not there.

The critics, meanwhile, could only file their reviews in the knowledge that they would be as chaff in the wind of such colossal advance bookings:

. . . little here for card-carrying Christians . . .

The Second Coming itself could not have aroused more tumult than broke out last night among the stalls patrons . . .

. . . noisy, mawkish . . . electronic gospel is not for me!

Mr Webber's score is mainly built from three- and four-note phrases repeated over elaborately instrumented but rhythmically obsessive accompaniments. The effect is like switched-on Carl Orff and it is mind-stunning . . .

Not to mince matters at the start, I might as well declare now that I have seen it, that the whole concept of *Jesus Christ Superstar* stinks in my nostrils . . .

. . . from my expensive seat I could not hear what they were singing above the din . . .

. . . if you like the record, I should stay home and listen to it . . .

. . . this remarkable opera . . .

The composer and librettist in turn found themselves making their inner thoughts known to the public. Unsurprisingly, they tended not to stray far from the subject of money.

'I would be happy having all my money in pound notes under the bed,' Tim told one reporter, and he meant it. 'But that's too simple. You have to think of the future,' he added, 'and inflation.'

Andrew had always been preoccupied with the lack of money; now, confronted with piles of it, his immediate reaction was to ask for an estimate of his tax bill. The Escaway accountants kept launching into long and complicated monologues about the British Finance Act but, unlike Tim, he was prepared to obtain a copy of the Act; and read it, if necessary.

'We were unprepared for financial success,' he told another reporter, 'now a lot of our old friends don't like to ring us up, because they think we're so grand. That's sad.'

Andrew was himself having trouble getting through to one old friend on the telephone. Tim was forever arriving back at Heathrow from one far-flung *JC* production, only to depart almost immediately for another. This jetting about the world was taking it out of him, so he was also indulging in an increasing number of foreign holidays as a result. Andrew, whose idea of a holiday, apart from his trips to Aunt Vi in Ventimiglia, had never extended much beyond a day out in Billy's old car with Perseus and an Ordnance Survey map, now began to lose patience. When, he repeatedly demanded of his partner, were they going to start work on something new?

Meanwhile, other eyes had been cast at an older and less frequently performed work. Frank Dunlop, Artistic Director of the Young Vic theatre company, had had the idea of staging *Joseph* and parts of the York mystery plays as a double bill at that summer's Edinburgh Festival. Stigwood had happily licensed the production; as far as he was concerned, nobody else was going to stage Rice and Lloyd Webber.

He decided to attend the first night in person, with a substantial retinue. Having boarded an aircraft at London's Heathrow Airport, he could be seen struggling to disembark before it took off, having discovered to his horror that it was powered by propeller engines: 'Hire a jet!' he told his assistants, 'I'm not going on a propeller plane!' But there was none available; eventually he had to be drugged with liquor and arrived in time for only the last five minutes of the performance.

Doggett had conducted and the production was a great success. Dunlop now wanted to bring it to the Roundhouse, a converted engine shed at Chalk Farm in north-west London. But in order for the production to travel south again, this time to a proper theatre rather than a school or church hall, additional material was required.

Andrew saw his chance. Surely the need to supply polish for a work that was so dear to his heart would concentrate the mind of his wayward partner. He was correct; but the effect did not last long.

The augmented and polished version of *Joseph* duly appeared at the Roundhouse to great acclaim. Dunlop's sparkling production played to an audience sitting on three sides of the floor space (the Roundhouse, as its name suggested, had no stage) and the work's further success was assured. So much so, in fact, that it was decided to mount a fully blown West End production. Andrew called Anthony Bowles to the Roundhouse and they chatted excitedly about the idea.

The only minor problem was that in order for the production to travel to a proper West End venue a little more additional material was required.

While Tim went his own way and Andrew fretted, the Albery Theatre production drew nearer and nearer. The idea was that, as in Edinburgh, *Joseph* should form the second half of a double bill. But this time, instead of the York mystery plays, the first half would consist of an entirely new work by Tim Rice and Andrew Lloyd Webber. This was to be entitled *Jacob*.

As Tim had already written:

> *'Joseph's dead' they told their ageing Dad*
> *Jacob wept — he really loved the lad*

Tim's idea of work still seemed to correspond to the fallow period between visits to overseas productions of *Jesus Christ Superstar*, foreign holidays and test matches. He was not actually working with anyone else; but neither was he working with Andrew. As the Albery Theatre production of *Joseph* grew nearer, Andrew brooded on the imaginary infidelity of his partner.

Joseph eventually went to rehearsal without *Jacob* having been cast or even written. It became clear that Tim was not sufficiently inspired by the project. Stigwood and Swash brought in two television comedy writers, Ray Galton and Alan Simpson, who produced a forty-five minute *Jacob* with dialogue, which *Joseph*

96

neither had nor needed and lyrics which Andrew did his best to set to music. For some reason best known to themselves, they transferred the setting for the tale of discord between Jacob and Esau to the Highlands of Scotland.

Jacob eventually went on as the first half of the bill at the Albery after Swash had been compelled to call up the overcall: the extra twenty-five per cent a backer may be asked to supply. There were disagreements with the theatre union Equity over an American actor Dunlop wanted for the role. Equity insisted on a British actor; they had their way, and he produced an under-powered performance. *Jacob* was an uninspired piece of filler, against which *Joseph* only shone more brightly – one reviewer described it as 'the golden wheat after the corn'.

The public agreed. Swash decided to act before the damage became permanent: *Jacob* was dropped and *Joseph* was augmented further into a show which could hold its own for an evening. This time Tim came to the rescue, contributing three new numbers including a hilarious country and western parody.

It was a lesson that Andrew might have learned: hired hands were no substitute for a proven organic relationship, however flawed he thought that relationship might be. Stigwood, Swash and Andrew had all been hypnotised by the clink of the cash register, the glint of the mint; but this time the audiences and the money had not flowed in.

That June, Tim went back to Lancing and in Argentina the former dictator Juan Perón returned to power. Tim's visit was for the purposes of attending a performance of *JC* in the school chapel. Perón's stay was almost as brief, but caused renewed interest in his earlier, heady period of power and particularly in his consort, Eva Duarte.

Evita, as she was known, had hustled, haggled and whored her way to the top before dying and giving birth to a legend at the age of thirty-three. Hers was the epitome of the short, fast life that changed society, which had so appealed to Tim. She was ruthless, sexy, outspoken, a compulsive player of the love game about which he had written so often. Her story had all these things and more: with its radio sequences, cinemas and tangos, it had the dramatic elements of a musical. John F. Kennedy, Robin Hood, Richard the Lionheart, Judas, Jesus . . . and now Evita. She was the first woman to have entered Tim's Top Twenty; she went in with a bullet straight to Number 1 and stayed there.

Andrew was not amused. Eventually they came to a reluctant agreement: Tim would continue to work on lyrics for Andrew's idea for a musical based on P. G. Wodehouse's Jeeves stories. Andrew, for his part, would endeavour to give musical form to any lyrics Tim might write for *Evita*.

Tim privately decided that this deal would keep Andrew happy and enable them both to work on *Evita*. Andrew privately believed that Tim would soon forget all about this Perón woman; after all, they had already written three musicals about such dynamic characters. Furthermore, Tim had long expressed his admiration for P. G. Wodehouse. Wodehouse stood for everything that was quintessentially English; for tennis and tea and the music of the 1920s; for country houses slumbering in the golden glow of an afternoon sun that set slowly on the cricket pitch. Tim was crazy about cricket. *Jeeves*, Andrew felt sure, would be their next massive hit.

That summer *Jesus Christ Superstar* closed on Broadway after seven hundred and eleven performances. At an initial cost of $700,000 it had not represented a particularly good investment but Stigwood's 'angels' who had put up $350,000, mainly from the City of London, would still receive a return of around twenty per cent. Elsewhere the show was going from strength to strength. The London production had cost £120,000 and came into profit in its twenty-second week; it was still playing to capacity houses. The show had closed in Paris and Berlin, but was a success both on tour and on stage in Australia. It had just opened in Tokyo; now Japan, too, had heard of Tim Rice and

Andrew Lloyd Webber. The record had sold over four million copies worldwide. The composer now did something he normally loathed doing; he went shopping.

Andrew and Sarah were looking for another house in the country, this time bigger and closer to London. Hale Park, a Georgian estate near Fordingbridge in Hampshire, was one candidate. For £400,000, the buyer would have seven reception rooms, a dozen bedrooms, two wings in the style of Palladio, two hundred and seventy acres of land and fishing rights on the River Avon. But the price was a little beyond their reach.

Another, more likely, candidate was a splendid early Victorian house just off the M4 in the Cotswolds. This too had highly developed formal gardens and several acres of land. It was the right size, the right period and in the right location. While Andrew went upstairs, Sarah drifted about in her jeans and *Jesus Christ Superstar* T-shirt – the kitchen would need redoing, of course, and that lighting was all wrong – then he came back down again and shook his head. They left as suddenly as they had come.

The reason was simple: having craned out of a bedroom window upstairs, Andrew had caught sight of another, meaner dwelling some considerable distance away. That was enough. He did not want to be overlooked. He wanted to own all the land he could see.

At the end of August, Universal released the film of *Jesus Christ Superstar* in Britain. The two charity premières took place at the Universal Theatre in London's Lower Regent Street. Tim bought half the seats for the first one and had them resold in aid of Guy's Hospital and the Stars' Organisation for Spastics. Andrew did the same for the second night and donated the proceeds to the Kenneth Allsop Memorial Fund, an ecological charity of which he was a member.

Allsop's favourite part of England was in Dorset, near where Andrew and Sarah had bought their first home together. But now they were on the move again. They sold Summerlease Farm and bought, as an investment, a second house in London which they planned to renovate together. This was another inscrutable, flat-fronted, six-storey early Victorian house, in Belgravia this time, at 11 West Eaton Place, only a few minutes' walk from Harrington Court. He and Sarah still lived in the house in Brompton Square; but now they had found the country house for which he had been searching.

Sydmonton Court was a country house of Tudor origin, heavily modified during Victorian times, on the borders of Hampshire and Berkshire near the tiny villages of Sydmonton and Ecchinswell. The vendor was Charles Clifford Kingsmill; he also owned 1200 acres of land nearby. Sydmonton stood among pale lawns and was approached through leafy lanes of hawthorn and rich cow pastures; it had a hint of Wodehouse's Blandings Castle, or Waugh's Brideshead. Across the lawn was a tiny church and pheasants clucked and fluttered from the hedgerows. Rabbits hopped in the lanes and the sun set on the picket fencing; it was almost too good to be true.

Andrew was nervous about money: although it was rolling in, you could have one hit and be ruined. He worried interminably about the asking price before completing the deal. In an era when pop stars routinely removed to large houses in the country and filled them with Tiffany lampshades and twenty-nine identical three-piece suites before driving their pink Rolls-Royces into the swimming-pool, he paid £150,000 and proceeded to fill the house with Victorian furniture and Pre-Raphaelite paintings. He sought quotations from builders about the cost of removing the unsightly Victorian rendering; he investigated the tax concessions available to owners of historic houses

As a concession to the mores of the *nouveaux riches*, he also installed a row of pinball machines — a hint of rebellion against the unworldliness of Harrington Court. For now he was not just one of the newly rich; he was richer than Rodgers had ever been; and about to lose his Hart.

*

Tim had done his best to work on *Jeeves*. According to the terms of their deal, he had already produced a number of lyrics which were far superior to the efforts of any of the others who would attempt to work on the project. The problem was fundamental: as had been the case with *Jacob*, the idea simply did not appeal to him. Wodehouse was notoriously difficult to adapt for the musical theatre, in spite of the fact that he was a pioneer of the genre. He had even warned Tim and Andrew that this was so. Tim had shown as much willingness, if not more, to work on *Jeeves* as Andrew had to work on *Evita*. Now, he had had enough. He told Andrew he was pulling out of the show.

At first Andrew did not believe him. Then, when the shock of rejection had worn off, he tried to pull himself together. *Jeeves* was his idea, after all. He had already written half a dozen tunes especially for the show, and there were others floating to the top of the well. Stigwood and Land had tied up the rights with Wodehouse and his longterm associate, Guy Bolton. If Tim did not want to continue with the project, that was his loss; Andrew would secure the services of another partner to complete the show.

He had already had talks to this end with the co-producer, Bob Swash. Swash told him that Wodehouse had too many jokes for a sung-through show; what they needed was a playwright.

'Who?' asked Andrew.

'Andrew,' said Swash, 'give me time.'

Andrew thought about this. He did not know any playwrights but he could see the advantage of hiring one to write amusing dialogue for Jeeves, his master Bertie Wooster and the other Wodehouse characters. He asked Swash to go ahead and find someone. Besides, this way, Tim might just be tempted back into the fold.

4

The Composer in Residence

In the spring of 1974, a number of persons settled into new jobs while Andrew and Sarah settled into Sydmonton Court.

The Wilson Labour Government took office, to the dismay of Andrew and other high-earning country-house owners. Andrew acquired the services of a personal assistant, twenty-year-old Bridget 'Biddy' Hayward. Biddy was a down-to-earth, practical person, able to stand up to his moods, who soon became an indispensable part of his life. Tim, too, had returned to temporarily regular employment after an interval of several years. At the age of twenty-nine he had taken up the offer of a job as stand-in disc jockey on London's Capital Radio.

Juan Perón, who had recently returned to power in Argentina, did not settle in the position and died in July of that year. Tim was becoming increasingly preoccupied with the story of Perón's late wife, Evita. While at Capital he had met an attractive Scottish secretary, Jane McIntosh. Jane and Tim quickly began an affair and shortly afterwards her colleagues noticed she was absent from her desk. Left in the typewriter was a note: 'Gone abroad with Tim Rice.'

They went to Argentina, in search of the legend of Eva Perón. The country was in the grip of one of its frequent bouts of industrial unrest. Perón was still alive but was losing control and his second wife Maria was no substitute for Evita. Right-wingers had blown up a theatre and a cinema where *Jesus Christ Superstar* was playing – Tim told people this was probably an artistic, rather than a political reaction. To Andrew's disappointment, he came back to Britain more than ever convinced that *Evita* was the subject for a musical.

Like Andrew, Tim was settling into a country house. This was Romeyns Court in the Oxfordshire village of Great Milton, surrounded by nine acres of fields. The house carried in its gift the right, once a year, to preach in Lincoln Cathedral. Tim was in no hurry to claim this right, but he did have plans to create a cricket pitch for his own team, the Heartaches C.C. He converted the adjoining outbuildings into his office, from which he managed the Heartaches's affairs and planned the annual Heartaches Cricketers Almanack, and which housed his enormous record collection.

To Andrew's relief, however, he and Tim were at least working together again, this time on the soundtrack for the film *The Odessa File*, based on the bestselling novel by Frederick Forsyth and directed by Ronald Neame. Neame was a near neighbour of Andrew's Aunt Vi in Ventimiglia and had first met Andrew as a teenager. Andrew and Tim wrote the music and lyrics for the songs, which were sung by Perry Como; Andrew also wrote a piece for Julian to play as soloist on the MCA recording, which was supervised by Anthony Bowles.

This last piece was unusual: a fugue written for rock group, cello and orchestra. The film was not particularly successful, but the music contained a number of new ideas and this particular one went straight back into the bottom drawer.

That summer, Sarah celebrated her twenty-first birthday and Julian married Celia, his girlfriend of longstanding whom he had met five years earlier at Andrew's own twenty-first birthday party. Andrew arranged the honeymoon in Venice; but there was to be no last-minute stag party: the night before his wedding, Julian was booked as the soloist in Richard Strauss's *Don Quixote* at the Royal Festival Hall.

Tim married Jane McIntosh that summer. Andrew, meanwhile, had still not given up all hope of tempting him back to *Jeeves*. He was delighted when Bob Swash called to tell him that he had found a playwright.

Swash had devoted a considerable amount of time to the question of who was going to write the next smash hit by Andrew Lloyd Webber. Given that *Jeeves* had to be a funny show, he asked himself who was the most successful comedy writer at that moment in Britain. In box office terms, the answer was Alan Ayckbourn, author of *The Norman Conquests*.

Ayckbourn's agent was Peggy Ramsay, who had represented the late Joe Orton and was generally regarded in showbusiness parlance as 'a legend in her own lunchtime'. Swash called her and received a rapid response:

'Oh, darling,' she told him, 'don't be so silly! He's got three plays on in Scarborough . . . two coming to the West End . . . and anyway he's on a cruise on the high seas. Why don't you have John Mortimer?'

Swash persisted, and a few days later she called back to say that Ayckbourn was interested in the idea. A meeting was arranged at which it became clear that Andrew and Ayckbourn shared a passionate interest not only in the theatre but in money and pinball machines. Ayckbourn agreed to write the book of the show, but they would still need a lyricist for the songs. Tim made it clear that he was no more favourably disposed towards working with Ayckbourn than he had been towards working with Andrew on the project. Andrew was desperate. He even telephoned his old *Evening Standard* friend, Angus McGill. McGill, a Wodehouse fan and occasional dinner guest at 37 Brompton Square, gamely offered some lyrics of his own. Eventually, however, Ayckbourn himself agreed to write the words of the songs and Andrew, who by now had learned a good deal about where lyrics should sit and so on, accepted. Now that he had a playwright and a scriptwriter he no longer needed Tim; any more, it seemed, than Tim needed him.

Through the summer and autumn Andrew and Ayckbourn, both obsessive workers, immersed themselves in Wodehouse's magical, mythical, make-believe world. They went to visit Wodehouse at his Long Island home, where Andrew played him the tunes and they discussed their ideas. Andrew fed the sounds of the ages of swing and jazz into his imagination and laboured at the keyboard. Ayckbourn, whose sense of humour as displayed through his plays was black to say the least, grappled with the character of the long-suffering Jeeves and the blithe spirits of Bertie Wooster, Madeleine Bassett, Stiffy Byng, Gussie Fink-Nottle and the Gentlemen of the Drones Club.

But what *was* the plot? There were so *many* plots in Wodehouse, all of which stoutly resisted elevation or interpretation. They were trying to reduce the irreducible; they were dealing with the supremely 'shag' writer of English. Wodehouse made it all look so easy; it was only when you tried to understand how he did it that you realised how difficult writing like this could be.

One day, the telephone rang in Swash's office. It was Ayckbourn.

'Bob,' he said, 'how long do you think *Jeeves* should be?'

'Two hours,' said Swash.

'What?'

'That includes the interval.' Ayckbourn was suddenly quiet, so Swash went on. 'Two hours, including the interval,' he said, 'and Act Two should be shorter than Act One.'

Ayckbourn began to express disagreement.

'Alan,' Swash said, 'I'm not going to impede your artistic integrity. But you did ask.'

Ayckbourn thanked him and rang off. A while later a bulky envelope landed on each of the doormats at the Stigwood offices in Brook Street, Lonsdale Square, where Bowles lived, and 37 Brompton Square. It contained Ayckbourn's script for *Jeeves*. With Andrew's music, it ran for over four hours.

Bowles's first reaction was that this was some sort of mistake. Peggy Ramsay, in his opinion, would have weighed it in her hand and thrown it back to the author: 'Too *long*, darling,' she would have cried. Perhaps they were going to stage it like *The Norman Conquests* – over three successive nights.

Swash, too, was alarmed. He called the director, Eric Thompson, who had been recommended by Ayckbourn after their success with *Norman*.

'Don't worry, Bob,' Thompson told him, 'we'll reduce it. It'll be the right length by the time we get to rehearsals. It'll be all right on the night.'

Swash then turned his mind back to other, more pressing matters, such as raising the £110,000 needed for the show. To this end he had recruited another London impresario, Michael White, as co-producer. Under Stigwood's banner, they went back to the band of City of London 'angels' who had successfully invested in *Jesus Christ Superstar*. David Land, too, had seen his money grow in *JC* and speedily came up with £3000 for *Jeeves*.

Andrew, like Ayckbourn, had been too busy writing *Jeeves* to give much attention to the length of the script. The songs had simply rolled off the piano; and Ayckbourn, having originally undertaken to write only the book, had revealed an unexpected talent as a lyricist. *Female of the Species* was a sharp little essay on the steely side of giddy Wodehouse women; and the same melodic motif was explored in *Half A Moment* in a way worthy of Richard Rodgers.

For *Travel Hopefully*, Bertie's mock exposition of his philosophy of life, in which his lines were punctuated (and punctured) by Jeeves's mordant replies, Andrew had been rather stuck for a melody. He solved this problem by the simple expedient of giving it the tune of *Love Is Here*, from the old Barnardo musical, *The Likes of Us*. Like the tune of *Down Thru' Summer* and the fugue for cello and rock band which he had written for the soundtrack of *The Odessa File*, it had never been far from the top of the well.

He was desperate to write for the theatre. The very thought of *Jeeves* on stage at Her Majesty's Theatre in less than six months' time filled him with an almost uncontrollable excitement. He could see it now: the first night party, the applause, the adulatory reviews: '*Jeeves* fulfils all the promise so heavily hinted at in *Jesus Christ Superstar* . . . With *Jeeves* Lloyd Webber has broken the mould of the English musical . . . Lloyd Webber has come of age . . .'

And of course he could see Tim reading them. He already had plans for their next collaboration: a musical about trains, based on the bestselling children's books by the Reverend E. W. Awdry: *Thomas the Tank Engine, Henry the Green Engine, James the Really Useful Engine* . . . Andrew kept the remains of his childhood train set, with the remains of his toy theatre, in the attic of Sydmonton Court. After the success of *Jeeves*, Tim would no longer be in a position to indulge his tedious obsession with fast-living heroes.

In the meantime, if, temporarily, he could not have Tim, he was not going to turn up his nose at the combination of Wodehouse and Alan Ayckbourn. Wodehouse was after all among the most successful authors in the history of English literature, and Ayckbourn was the most successful living English playwright. Ayckbourn's script was long, but it was good. Andrew, without wishing to be too pompous, knew he was the most successful new theatre composer. The fact that neither he nor Ayckbourn had ever written a musical for the stage before was immaterial; you had to start somewhere.

Eric Thompson, the director, was Ayckbourn's choice. Andrew approved of him; although he had never directed a musical before, he had more shows running in London than any other director. And Christopher Bruce was indisputably the most talented choreographer of his time. True, all his previous work was in classical ballet, but *Jeeves* had not a single dancer in the cast.

The cast too was impressive. David Hemmings was to play Bertie, Michael Aldridge was Jeeves, Gabrielle Drake was Madeleine

Bassett. Hemmings had little experience of the musical theatre, but he was a film star, he was charismatic and he could sing. They were all under the wing of Anthony Bowles and Don Walker was brought over from America to help with the orchestrations. Andrew thought they were all wonderful and told them so; and they told him he was, too.

This then, was the cast of characters who assembled in London in preparation for the launch of *Jeeves*. Elsewhere in the West End, a thirteen-year-old Hertfordshire schoolgirl made her stage debut as one of Queen Victoria's daughters in *I and Albert*. The show was not a great success, but the girl was quite unperturbed. Her own mother, Paula, had ignored George Bernard Shaw's admonition and put her on the stage at a tender age. By now her daughter was tough enough to get what she wanted. Her name was Sarah Brightman.

In January 1975, the cast of *Jesus Christ Superstar* celebrated its thousandth performance at the Palace Theatre. The chorus included a petite estate agent's daughter from Bognor Regis called Elaine Bickerstaff, who had changed her name to Elaine Paige after failing her first audition. The show had now taken over £2,250,000, which made Bob Swash and Michael White's job of raising money for *Jeeves* somewhat easier.

Meanwhile, Andrew was still trying to interest his former partner in the idea of a musical based on the Reverend E. W. Awdry's railway books, and in order to placate him, agreed at least to appear as though he believed in *Evita* as a viable proposition.

Even after all the years he had known him, Andrew was still horrified when Tim insisted on telling the newspapers that *JC* had earned him and Andrew 'around a million quid each'. Andrew's family background, though he was loath to admit it, had bred in him both the desire to make a million pounds and the guilt that went with having done so. Andrew had no desire to advertise his growing wealth to all and sundry.

Nor did he appreciate it when Tim announced that they had been working on *Evita* for a year, that so far they had reached Act One, Scene One, and that 'If we work really hard we could have it finished by the summer.'

Andrew was convinced this was not the way to break the mould of the English musical, but he kept plugging away at *Evita* and telling himself that the situation could not last for long. *Jeeves*, like its eponymous central character, would soon take charge.

Eric Thompson had assured Swash that Ayckbourn would reduce the size of script by the time of the rehearsals. By the time it had been rewritten, Ayckbourn's elaborate and involved Wodehouse pastiche had lost its motivations for character and intrigue on the cutting-room floor — and the script was still four and three-quarter hours long. Now *Jeeves* was not only long, it was incomprehensible.

The cast laboured bravely on. The director was drinking heavily, which further unnerved the actors, in particular David Hemmings who had never either sung in a musical or appeared on a British stage before. The characters of Bertie Wooster, Jeeves and Madeleine Bassett seemed to slip away; in their place were Hemmings, Michael Aldridge and Gabrielle Drake, desperately turning to the one person with experience of the musical theatre present, Anthony Bowles.

'Ant,' they wailed in unison, 'what are we going to do?'

Jeeves opened its pre-West End run in Bristol in April 1975 to one of the least enthusiastic audiences ever accorded a British theatre musical. Among them was the young Cameron Mackintosh, who by this time had risen above cleaning to supplement the rent on his Mayfair flat and become a successful musical theatre producer. He and the rest of the Bristol audience saw a demoralised cast perform a wildly overlong show, in which the first four numbers were all sung by Bertie Wooster without so much as a hint of why this should be so.

Eventually, Bowles went to Bob Swash on behalf of the cast.

'Bob,' he said, 'you have to find another director.'

'Anthony,' Swash retorted, 'we don't do that sort of thing in England.'

They fired Thompson between Bristol and London. Ayckbourn, who took over as director, had even less of an idea of how to direct a successful musical. The more the cast re-rehearsed, the less certain they were of what they were meant to be doing.

There were also problems at Sydmonton: Sarah was ill, and nobody seemed to know the cause.

Jeeves opened in London at Her Majesty's Theatre, the Haymarket on 22 April and closed five weeks later. Like *Jacob*, it sank beneath the weight of a flawed production. In spite of the post-mortems and excuses later aired by various of the participants, *Jeeves* failed for the same basic reasons as *Come Back Richard* and *The Likes of Us*: it was not good enough to succeed, and the subject was not right.

Jesus Christ Superstar had succeeded on Broadway because the album had sold two million copies and made audiences perceive there could be more to musicals than whether or not Lauren Bacall would find a boyfriend. Britain in 1975 was a country troubled by political violence and industrial unrest. Even the Third Test Match was abandoned that summer after demonstrators had wrecked the pitch. Audiences in the West End wanted something more substantial in the way of a story than whether or not Bertie Wooster would lose his butler.

To add insult to injury, the album of *Jeeves* was released after the show closed. It failed to interest the record-buying public in a show which they could no longer go and see. Andrew retreated to Sydmonton and cast the tunes back into the well; some immediately sank without trace, others remained within reach for future use.

Sarah's problems, which had brought her to the point of

110

collapse, had also been diagnosed. Ironically for the daughter of a director of the sugar giant Tate & Lyle, she was suffering from diabetes. Fortified by daily insulin injections she was recovering rapidly; more rapidly, it seemed, than her husband was recovering from the collapse of his cherished musical.

Outwardly he seemed philosophical, but inwardly he was deeply hurt. Why had they allowed such a flawed show to go into rehearsal? Had he written too many ballads and not enough pop songs? Perhaps they should have changed directors earlier. He refrained from openly criticising Ayckbourn, but they never worked together again.

Hal Prince, who had produced *Cabaret, Fiddler on the Roof* and *West Side Story* on Broadway, had written to him after the failure of *Jeeves* telling him to 'bank the score'. Prince, who could never have been accused of such a thing, warned him that the English could be 'over-nice' to each other when they put on musicals. Andrew liked the sound of Hal Prince. But, as usual, the problems boiled down to one thing and one thing alone: would he have failed, could he have failed, if he had written *Jeeves* with Tim?

Tim had taken no delight in the fate of *Jeeves*; nor had he been surprised by the failure of the production. He remained indifferent to Andrew's idea for a musical based on the E. W. Awdry railway stories. Tim was more in love than ever with the idea of *Evita*.

Andrew suddenly found himself warming to the idea; of a hit recording, if not a successful stage show – a successful stage show currently seemed a rather distant prospect. But just in case Tim did not realise he was interested in the idea, he took the step of transmitting loud and clear to him through the offices of one of Angus McGill's colleagues at the *Evening Standard*.

'The old Lloyd Webber–Rice partnership must get together again and get down to basics,' he told the reporter, as they sipped drinks on the terrace at Sydmonton, 'even if what we write never sees the light of day. We must really concentrate on what we do best. Tim is the most marvellous lyricist.

'I suppose you could say I'm an averagely successful film composer and Tim is an averagely successful disc-jockey, but they are not the things we do best.

'Tim and I have got to get down to writing. Both of us find good excuses for not getting down to it. We had this intense period of working together and then it all happened and we allowed people to come between us. It's ridiculous. Tim and I are very close, actually . . .'

In the hiatus that followed the death of *Jeeves* and Sarah's illness, the young Mr and Mrs Lloyd Webber did something out of character: they went on holiday. This took them to a Greek island at the invitation of Gary Bond, who had played the lead in Frank Dunlop's production of *Joseph*. They made an awkward couple as they splashed ashore from the ferry, white-skinned and fully dressed, on to a beach full of nude sunbathers; after a few days they returned to England.

Andrew turned his attention to a new project about which, together with his desire to work with Tim, he had fretted on holiday and which now occupied his waking hours. This was the occasion of the first Sydmonton Festival.

On Midsummer's Night an unusually large congregation gathered at the little church of St Mary's which stood just across the lawn from Sydmonton Court. The church was usually visited by only eight or nine locals, even on Easter Sundays; tonight eighty people, friends from London and people from the village, filled the church. The performers were Julian and his accompanist, a young Singaporean who had recently won the BBC Piano Competition, Yitkin Seow.

Seow played a Chopin *Ballade* and the two gave a rendition of the rock-style fugue for cello which Andrew had first written for Julian to play on the soundtrack of *The Odessa File*. On the terrace in front of the great house, Sarah's young friends wandered between the tables of good food and fine wines. The lawns were floodlit, Hollywood-style. Angus McGill admired the Pre-Raphaelites and Gary Bond played in the room full of pinball machines. The actress Lynn Farleigh dived fully clothed into the swimming-pool, as actresses were prone to do. Biddy Hayward was in charge of proceedings. She was tough, capable and she knew how to delegate. As Andrew's personal assistant she was playing an increasingly important part in his and Sarah's life, and would shortly become a director of Escaway, their private company.

Andrew and Sarah seemed dwarfed by the great house on this idyllic summer evening: two young people, looking even younger, the one shy and the other nervous and ill at ease. Andrew struck more than one guest that Midsummer's Night as a man who did not know how to relax in his own home. But the festival was a great social and musical success and dispersed much of the cloud which had gathered during the year. Now the way was clear for him and Tim to work on the musical they called *Evita*.

Through the summer the two men commuted between each other's country houses as they picked up the pieces of their partnership. Tim had produced an historical synopsis of Evita's career which they plundered for dramatic opportunities: her early life and her rags-to-riches ascent to power as consort to the most powerful man in a land of poor *descamisados* (shirtless ones), fascism and Latin music, and her early death. Andrew, who as a baby had often been lulled into a semblance of sleep by the Latin rhythms of Billy's Edmundo Ros records, translated these dramatic opportunities into music, to which Tim then wrote the lyrics.

Tim also added an extraneous and entirely fictional device to the true story of Eva Perón. This took the form of a sardonic and far from impartial commentator and bit-part player in the main action, the Argentine-born revolutionary Ernesto 'Che' Guevara. But instead of spouting revolutionary rhetoric, Che's attitude towards Eva in the new story was the line Tim had given to the chorus of *Joseph*:

> *Anyone from anywhere can make it if they get a lucky break*

Evita, like *Jesus Christ Superstar* and unlike *Jeeves*, was to be a through-sung show. This time, too, the record was to be released before the stage show and after the composer and lyricist had assured themselves and each other that they were satisfied. The painful memory of *Jeeves* gradually receded.

That autumn, Mr and Mrs Lloyd Webber exchanged their first London home in Knightsbridge for a smaller early Victorian pied-à-terre in Belgravia. This was 51 Eaton Place, SW1, a two-storey basement and ground-floor flat a mile or so to the east and still only a couple of miles from Harrington Court.

They also formed another private limited company. Escaway managed the private Lloyd Webber finances and Qwertyuiop, the joint Rice–Lloyd Webber production company, was more or less inactive. The Stigwood contract still had three years to run; but Andrew was looking to the future. As far as he was concerned, Stigwood and Land were not going to own him for ever.

The new company was incorporated in the usual manner, with an authorised share capital of £100 divided into a hundred ordinary shares of £1 each. Ninety-eight shares, forty-nine each, went to the two directors, Andrew and Sarah.

A name was required: he decided on the name of one of the trains from the railway stories of the Reverend E. W. Awdry. Thus, for £100, was the business born with which he hoped one day to regain control over his affairs and outdo Robert Stigwood. He called it the Really Useful Company.

Evita rolled off the keyboard with a strength and homogeneity which startled even the composer. It was as if all the promise of the other pieces had come together in one work. The score, as it had done in *JC*, ranged brilliantly from Puccini to hard rock and back again. As in *JC*, too, where *Saladin Days* had become *Herod's Song* and *Kansas Morning* had become *I Don't Know How To Love Him*, *Evita* contained one melody which had been used unsuccessfully before and whose time had now indubitably come.

This was the romantic orchestral sweep of the single they had written for Ross Hannaman, *Down Thru' Summer*:

> *And as for fortune and as for fame*
> *I never invited them in*
> *Though it seemed to the world they were all I desired*
> *They are illusions*
> *They're not the solutions they promised to be*
> *The answer was here all the time*
> *I love you and hope you love me*

Tim's words were for Evita to sing to her adoring *descamisados*, whom she was in the process of betraying. Later he came up with the next line, that made the song and the show into a huge hit, the biggest he and Andrew would ever have:

> *Don't Cry For Me Argentina*

Neither of them knew quite *why* it worked, but it did, on all who heard it:

> *Don't cry for me Argentina*
> *The truth is I never left you*
> *All through my wild days*
> *My mad existence*
> *I kept my promise*
> *Don't keep your distance*

The *Evita* recordings began that April at Olympic Studios, in West London. Julie Covington, a little-known and rising stage actress sang the part of Eva Perón. Paul Jones, once lead singer with Manfred Mann, sang Juan Perón. Che was sung by Colm Wilkinson, who had taken over as Judas in *Jesus Christ Superstar*, which was still sold out nightly at the Palace. Anthony Bowles conducted the augmented London Philharmonic Orchestra and the eighteen-strong Superstar Choir; Alan Doggett, more successfully than he had done for the soundtrack of *JC* the movie, supplied the services of the London Boy Singers and rejoiced in the title of Musical Co-ordinator.

The line-up of rock musicians was extensive and impressive: apart from members of the Grease Band, they included the legendary Shadows guitarist Hank B. Marvin. Seven years earlier Tim had been a lowly assistant producer for Cliff Richard and the Shadows; now he was employing the likes of them in his own right.

The *Evita* recordings cost MCA £90,000, a considerable sum by current standards, which they hoped to recoup through album sales before and particularly after *Evita* became a successful stage musical. Money in general was much on the mind of the composer of *And the Money Kept Rolling In (and Out)*. Not long after the *Evita* recordings began, he wrote a letter to the *Sunday Telegraph* supporting government plans to introduce tax concessions for owners of country houses.

The richer he became, the more frightened he was of losing his money. While Tim gave his accountant the simple brief that he would 'really rather not lose' what he already had, Andrew surrounded himself with bank managers, tax lawyers and financial advisers. He was terrified of how much it would cost to stage *Evita* successfully and so avoid the disaster which had befallen *Jeeves*. He had taken care to agree a fixed price with the local builders who were still busy removing the rendering from Sydmonton Court's original Tudor brickwork. This year the Sydmonton Festival was to be a full-blown affair, like Glyndebourne and Aldeburgh in every respect; and this included paying its way.

This year, guests at the festival were promised activities and recitals which effectively constituted a reunion of the inhabitants of

Harrington Court. Tim organised a cricket match. The performers in St Mary's church included John Lill, now an internationally established concert pianist and Julian, with his accompanist Yitkin Seow. The choir of Marlborough College sang a tractarian evensong to celebrate the ninetieth anniversary of the nearby church of St Lawrence. Dinner was a grand affair, followed by entertaining speeches from Arianna Stassinopoulos, Frank Muir and the rising Conservative politician John Selwyn Gummer. Guests could also listen to tapes of the new Lloyd Webber–Rice *opus* in progress, *Evita*.

Julian and Yitkin Seow were advertised as including in their recital a piece by Billy Lloyd Webber. At the last minute, however, Seow was offered a scholarship to the rather more prestigious festival at Tanglewood, in the United States. He accepted and withdrew from Sydmonton, only to incur Andrew's wrath.

That year's festival also yielded a useful television contact. Frank Muir was a well-known television personality whose son Jamie worked on *The South Bank Show* at London Weekend Television. *The South Bank Show* was an influential weekly arts programme, whose presenter had come a long way since, as a jobbing journalist, he had helped rewrite the script of *JC* the movie; his name was Melvyn Bragg.

Andrew asked Jamie Muir to the Savile Club. Over lunch they discovered a mutual interest in architectural history and Muir joined Andrew's small circle of friends. Andrew invited the Muirs *en famille* to lunch at Sydmonton – where Jamie Muir was surprised to see his old friend Gray Watson. David Crewe-Read was another regular visitor; he and his wife Lisa had lived upstairs from Andrew at Gledhow Gardens. Architecture buff, dealer in antique furniture and flamboyant socialiser, Crewe-Read appointed himself full-time jester at the court of Andrew Lloyd Webber.

Tim came and went as ever. Crewe-Read, Watson, Biddy,

Doggett and Muir were a coterie; they revolved around Andrew, and they were useful to him. When Andrew wanted furniture and paintings, Crewe-Read made sure he had them. Watson was the handsome, brilliant idol of Andrew's Westminster youth. Biddy was synonymous with Really Useful and Escaway. Doggett too remained loyal, although he was living on past glories and was fast approaching his nemesis.

Muir became unpaid road manager and stage hand, making video recordings of Sydmonton Festival workshop performances and supplying technical services. When Andrew wanted certain sound effects for the recording of *Evita*, Muir made sure he had them: he supplied the sound of applause in a nightclub, for example, from the London Weekend sound effects department. Thus it was that in *Evita* the applause in Magaldi's nightclub was that of a cricket match.

That summer, once the *Evita* recordings were under way, Andrew flew to Majorca where the American producer and director Hal Prince had a summer house. Andrew played Prince the score of *Evita*. He remembered what else Prince had said after the failure of *Jeeves*: the English could be 'over-nice' to each other when they put on musicals. This was not why *Jeeves* had failed, of course, but Andrew was not going to have another musical fail on those grounds.

Prince liked the score and wrote to him with suggestions about the production. Andrew decided he wanted Prince to direct the stage show.

As the *Evita* recordings came to an end the advance publicity began, and so once again did the differences between composer and lyricist. But this time it was Andrew who appeared to be holding back. The prospect of staging *Evita* still alarmed him, not least because of the remarks Tim was making at this time.

'*Evita* will probably cost around £200,000 to stage,' Tim told people, 'after all, there's a chorus of thirty and there will be a big weekly wage bill. If it flops? I'm not worried financially about 1977 or 1978. 1982 or 1983 could be a problem . . .

'I think,' Tim went on blithely, 'the record of *Evita* will do quite well in England, although it's rather expensive and it's not going to appeal to the people who normally buy most records. I think it'll sell steadily and consistently – like *JC*. All our records in England are catalogue items. They just potter along.'

This sort of talk filled Andrew with dread. *Jesus Christ Superstar* was still playing profitably to packed houses at the Palace and he himself had neither invested nor lost money in *Jeeves*. Nor was he planning to invest in *Evita*. But as far as he was concerned, *Evita* had to sell as a record – preferably by the million – before there was a show.

'We became victims of the success of *Superstar*,' Andrew told people. 'The image stuck and somehow we've been regarded as precocious phenomena rather than working pros. With *Evita* we're aiming at a universal audience. I hope it won't be taken up just by opera critics or by rock critics – at present I feel that rock music is going round in ever-decreasing circles. It's intended for everyone.'

He promoted the image of himself and Tim as he would have liked them to be. He told people that the failure of *Jeeves* was partly caused by his failure to do the orchestrations. This was in spite of the fact that Andrew's name was among those credited with them on the record cover. Tim, if asked, merely told people that he thought Andrew's tunes had not worked in that context.

Likewise, Andrew conspicuously omitted to mention that after *Jeeves* he had no option but to compose *Evita* if he still wanted to work with Tim. He also avoided showing any interest in the plot. *Evita*, he said, had attracted him because there had been a tremendous improvement in the acting ability of rock singers.

'Julie Covington proves that point,' he said. 'There are more rock singers now who can handle complex music. So the melodic line can be far more adventurous. People are aware that the music doesn't need to be strictly diatonic . . .'

But Miss Covington did not wish to prove that point at all. As a serious actress whose career was burgeoning, she had no desire, in spite of her talent as a singer, to make a detour via the musical theatre. To this end, she had already told Tim and Andrew that she had no desire to play the role of Eva in a stage production. Andrew had humoured her: actresses were like that; no one, surely, was going to turn down the lead role in a new show by Tim Rice and Andrew Lloyd Webber.

Tim, meanwhile, simply continued in the same insouciant vein.

'We became more and more interested,' he would say. 'It's the true Cinderella story, about a girl who came from the bottom of the heap to a position of incredible power. Evita could have been a Jackie Kennedy, content to sit at the top and enjoy the view. But instead she pushed on and got things done in an outsize showbusiness way. She was beautiful . . .

'Our show takes no political stance, although there's little doubt that old man Perón was a bit of a beast. I think that Eva herself saw Argentinian politics as a pretty murky game . . .'

The first *Evita* listening preview took place at the New London Theatre in Drury Lane on 9 November 1976. Guests were sent invitations with the legend printed in small letters at the bottom: 'This Is A Personal Invitation.' Reactions were instantly favourable. Ten days later, MCA released *Evita: an opera based on the life story of Eva Perón 1919–1952*. The elegantly packaged double album contained over a hundred minutes of music. MCA also released a single, the melody which had evolved from *Down Thru' Summer* and the lyric over which Tim had laboured long and hard: Julie Covington's rendition of *Don't Cry For Me Argentina*.

Both releases sold heavily the moment they entered the record shops. One in every four people who bought the single also bought the album, a tribute to the melodic, lyrical and

Andrew and Julian during the composition of *Variations* at Eaton Place, 1978. (Solo Syndication)

(BELOW) William 'Billy' Lloyd Webber in 1980, two years before his death. (Solo Syndication)

Andrew and Tim at the
recording of *Joseph and the
Amazing Technicolor Dreamco*
1968. (Gered Mankowitz)

Alan Doggett and the Colet Court choirboys at the recording of *Joseph and the Amazing Technicolor Dreamcoat*, 1968. (Gered Mankowitz)

An early Rice/Lloyd Webber collaboration, written for the *Evening Standard*
'Girl of the Year', 1967. (Gered Mankowitz)

(LEFT) 'Rock may never be quite the same
again . . .' Andrew and Tim in New York for th
album release of *Jesus Christ Superstar*, 1970.
(David Gahr/*Time*)

(OPPOSITE ABOVE) David Land, Andrew and Tim
during rehearsals for Evita, 1978. (Zoe
Dominic/Camera Press)

(RIGHT) Andrew the day he bought the Palace –
his toy theatre at last come to life. 1983.
(Syndication International)

(LEFT) 'If you marry very young, you either grow up together or grow far apart.' Andrew and Sarah One, 1981. In the background is Sydmonton Court. (The *Telegraph* Colour Library)

(RIGHT) Andrew and Sarah Two in Red Square, Moscow, 1989.

(BELOW LEFT) 'I'm too young to be pestered,' 16 year-old Sarah Brightman tells the press in 1977. (Jane Bown/*Observer*)

(RIGHT) Happy Birthday from Ronnie and me. 1988. (Associated Press)

Aspects of Love — Andrew, Sarah One, Sarah Two and the children at the opening of the show of the same name, London, 1989. (Alan Davidson)

Andrew and Sarah Two at home at Eaton Square. (Terry Smith/Camera Press)

vocal talents of the Lloyd Webber–Rice–Covington combination.

That winter, meanwhile, another, earlier Lloyd Webber–Rice work was revived in America. *Joseph*, directed by Frank Dunlop, opened for a limited season at the Brooklyn Academy of Music.

But Andrew was not particularly interested in either *Evita* or *Joseph* from the creative point of view. He was still working on an expanded version of the fugue for rock group and cello he had written for Julian for *The Odessa File*, and he still hoped to work with Tim on the train stories. But the records of the musical based on Tim's obsession with Eva Perón sold and sold and sold. By February 1977, three months after its release, MCA had sold 500,000 copies of *Evita* and two million copies of *Don't Cry For Me Argentina*. Even in Argentina, where the record was officially banned, no self-respecting bourgeois household was without a copy.

Sarah was seven months pregnant with their first child. Tim was impatient to see *Evita* on stage. David Land had to remind Andrew that it had been written for that purpose. Stigwood, though he had turned down the recording for his own RSO label, was willing to produce it. Eventually Andrew capitulated. He agreed to meet Swash and Tim for lunch at *L'Escargot* to discuss the idea.

L'Escargot in those days was a reasonably priced London restaurant where writers and agents used to lunch each other on their royalties. It was both shabby and grand and Swash, who took care in these matters, thought it would be the perfect place for a quiet working lunch. If he sensed any tension between his two fellow diners, he did not give it a second thought. There was tension in any decent creative partnership.

'Now,' he said amicably, 'we have a successful album and we have a Top Ten single, and time is going by. Let's get this show on the road. How are we going to do it?'

'Well,' said Andrew, 'of course, we'll need a sixty-piece orchestra.'

121

Swash and Tim looked at each other in disbelief.

'Andrew,' Swash told him, 'don't be ridiculous. If you have a sixty-piece orchestra, you know perfectly well you have to go into the Royal Opera House. The cost would be impossible.'

Andrew said nothing and stared across the table at his partner.

'Besides,' Swash continued, 'you know perfectly well *Evita* wasn't written for an opera house. Be reasonable.'

As composer and lyricist glowered at each other over the remains of their producer's 'civilised' lunch, Swash went on. 'What's more,' he said, 'Tim conceived of *Evita* as a stage work. Andrew, you're being very unkind to him.'

'Yes, Andrew,' said Tim, '*you're being very unkind to me.*'

Swash then leaned back out of the way while the two men had a heated exchange which continued on the pavement outside the restaurant. He last saw them storming off in the direction of David Land's Wardour Street offices.

He returned with relief to the relative calm of the Stigwood organisation in Brook Street. From here, he telephoned David Land.

'David,' he said, 'it's Bob. Is it all clear?'

In the background, two familiar voices were screaming at each other. The third voice was Land's. He sounded as though he was speaking from under his desk.

'I can't talk now,' he yelled, 'it's still all going on!'

Eventually they calmed down and Andrew conceded that, in spite of the fact that it was described as 'an opera' on the record cover and in spite of its adventurous melodic vocal lines, *Evita* did not need to be staged with a sixty-piece orchestra at the Royal Opera House.

Swash set about raising the £300,000 needed to stage the West End production. After the fiasco of *Jeeves* he was relieved to be able to tell would-be backers that this was the return of the successful Lloyd Webber–Rice combination. But privately he remained unsettled by the emotions he had seen stirred up that day. Swash thought he knew Andrew well by now; but he had never seen him like that before.

That April, their first child Imogen Lloyd Webber was born. Sarah's health was still stabilised by insulin and mother and child were brought home safely.

The Lloyd Webbers had now been married for nearly six years: Sarah was nearly twenty-four and Andrew was twenty-nine. The early age at which they had married and the clear delineation of their roles, meant they behaved as people who had known each other for a very long time. Biddy managed many of the day-to-day domestic details of Andrew's life in London. Sarah was mother and nanny in the emotional sense: 'Andrew,' she would say, 'you can't do *that*. It's *cheap*.' She had no desire for him to reinvent himself; and he was increasingly surrounded by people who encouraged him to do so.

While Sarah spent much of her time at Sydmonton with Imogen, Andrew threw himself into the preparations for *Evita*. He was still gloomy about the chances of a successful stage show. Stigwood, who had overcome his doubts about the production, if not his dislike of the album, eventually made up Andrew's mind for him.

'If we do the show,' he said, 'who do you want to direct?'

'Hal Prince,' Andrew told him.

'Have you asked him?'

'Well, I mean, er, er . . .' Andrew's eyes darted here and there; he rarely looked 'Stiggy' straight in the eye.

Stigwood picked up the telephone.

'Hal?' he said, 'this is Robert. We're going ahead with *Evita*. Would you like to direct it?'

'Yes,' said Prince.

Stigwood replaced the receiver. Prince would be over in May to start planning.

*

Andrew was also preoccupied with a new work which had evolved out of the fugue for rock group and cello. He was planning to première the expanded version at this year's festival. The tentative title was *Variations*.

Elsewhere, others were looking beyond the immediate present to a future full of opportunity and free of interference. In the *Observer* newspaper that May, the sixteen-year-old Hertfordshire schoolgirl who at thirteen had played Queen Victoria's daughter in *I and Albert*, posed provocatively in full lip gloss and gazed with big, worldly eyes straight into the camera lens:

Sarah was 'the right shape'

... At 16 she has realised the fantasy dreams of thousands of teenage girls by joining 'Pan's People', the select group of nubile dancers who until last year regularly appeared on *Top of the Pops* on BBC television. She is also modelling for *Vogue* and was chosen by Biba to advertise their cosmetics — all unheard-of achievements for a girl who took her O levels (passing five) only last year.

But life as a Pan's Person has its ups and downs. Sarah and her five colleagues recently turned down an opportunity to fly to Greece to pose on a yacht for the sex magazine *Penthouse*. 'They would probably have been asked to take their tops off,' explains *Penthouse* associate editor Neville Player. 'It wouldn't have been much use to us if they didn't.'

Sarah auditioned for Pan's People after going to stage school in London. 'My mother always wanted her daughter to dance, and she decided I was the right shape and everything and put me into it,' she says. She answers questions about her hobbies with all the aplomb of a Miss World entrant. 'Gosh ... I've always wanted to fly, and I would like to learn to glide. I also want to be a singer and make records.' She lives at home in Berkhamsted with her parents and two brothers and two sisters. Does she find drooling men a problem? 'I'm too young to be pestered. I make it very clear that I'm only 16, and they soon leave me alone.'

Apart from her mother and sisters, no one still quite knew what a girl from such a relatively comfortable background was doing at the rough and tumble end of showbusiness. But on one thing they were all agreed: she was not lacking in ambition. The world was going to hear more of Sarah Brightman.

5

Aspects of Love

To Andrew's disbelief, in spite of her huge success with the single *Don't Cry For Me Argentina*, Julie Covington had not changed her mind: she wanted to pursue her career as a serious actress. She was not interested in playing the stage role of Evita.

Strenuous efforts were made to persuade her. Huge financial inducements were offered, coupled with sympathetic words about her career. All were to no avail and Andrew would remain mystified by the fact that such a relatively little-known actress could have such a mature conception of her own career — in which, as it turned out, she was fully justified.

The search now began for another Evita. Auditions were held at the Palace Theatre, the magnificent late Victorian building on Cambridge Circus to which crowds still flooded nightly to see *Jesus Christ Superstar*. The press decided that the story warranted coverage and fanned the flames of publicity. Swash amused himself by bandying about unsuitable big names for the part. Raquel Welch, best known to British theatre-goers as the non-singing and non-talking sexy star of the prehistoric epic *One Million Years B.C.*, was one name he enjoyed dropping. Ann-Margaret, Shirley MacLaine and Faye Dunaway were others. Hal Prince took to confiding in a stage whisper outside the stage door that they were contemplating having two Evitas. Andrew, straight-faced, told people they might be hiring an opera singer.

This last joke had some basis in fact. Billy Lloyd Webber had heard that the job was vacant and proposed a candidate of his own. This was his young Spanish protégée, whose ambition unfortunately exceeded her talents as a would-be diva. Billy's suggestion was politely allowed to evaporate; and the search for a suitable candidate continued.

That year's Sydmonton Festival saw another fraught attempt to try out *Variations* by Julian and Yitkin Seow.

Andrew had reputedly written the piece after losing a bet with his brother over the fortunes of Leyton Orient Football Club: if Orient managed to avoid relegation that season, a feat which the congenitally pessimistic composer regarded as impossible, he would compose a piece for his brother. Orient beat Hull City and just managed to avoid relegation, and Andrew kept his side of the bargain. The idea, which had originally grown from the fugue for rock group and cello, now became Andrew Lloyd Webber's *Variations on the A minor Caprice by Niccolo Paganini*.

The *A minor Caprice* was Number 24 of Paganini's *Opus 1, 24 Caprici* for unaccompanied violin. The theme had inspired a host of 'Paganini Variations' by other composers and performers, many of which were familiar to Andrew. These included Rachmaninov's celebrated *Variation 18 in D flat major* which had formed the basis of the music for the 1953 film *Story of Three Loves*; the pianist Winifred Atwell, whose *Variation* had reached Number 9 in the UK pop Top Twenty in 1954; and the organist George Thalben Ball's *Variations on a Theme of Paganini*, published in 1962.

Andrew's *Variations* combined the inspired idea of a score for cello and rock band, worthy of the joint inventor of the rock opera, with an astute marketing sense. If there was a certain glibness about the packaging of Paganini as pop, the indications on past performance were that a high-calibre jazz-rock rendition of such an infectious motif would sell heavily in the popular music markets. The attempt to try out the piece at the festival was intended to precede the recording and publication of the music, for which another railway-orientated Lloyd Webber private company, Steampower Music Ltd., had been incorporated.

Thus it was that the Lloyd Webber nerves were already on edge at that year's festival, when they were pushed to breaking point. Once again, the unwitting perpetrator and victim was Yitkin Seow. He was returning from a concert in Belfast when bad weather forced his aircraft to divert from Heathrow to Gatwick. At Gatwick, Seow, who did not drive, received a garbled message from Julian's wife, Celia, apparently to the effect that he should wait for her to arrive and drive him to Sydmonton.

Seow waited and waited; eventually he telephoned Biddy Hayward and told her he was going to London, whence he would take a taxi. He eventually arrived at Sydmonton to be met by a furious Biddy. Andrew did not want to see him, she said; he was too busy and Seow was too late; he should go away. To add to the confusion, Julian appeared and apologised for his brother's behaviour. Seow departed in some distress, not least at the expense of his journey to and from Sydmonton. Eventually Andrew himself apologised, thus easing the wrath of his explosive younger brother. Seow and Julian continued to work together, but Seow never again attempted to work with Andrew Lloyd Webber.

The *Evita* auditions went on and on at the Palace. Hordes of hopefuls attended but only a few possessed the wide vocal range required for the title role. As was the case with the part of Judas in *JC*, the role of Evita taxed the *tessitura*: the range into which a voice comfortably falls. Elaine Paige, who had been in the *JC* chorus, was a strong candidate. She had the voice and the dramatic ability to appear convinced of her own, fatal destiny. She was also virtually unknown, which presented the producers with a publicity angle. *Evita* was a British show by British writers; why not a new British star? But Prince was nervous. He decided that he, Swash, Andrew and Tim should go to Washington to see *Side By Side By Sondheim*. The purpose of the visit was to inspect the young star of the show, the American singer Bonnie Schoen.

Prince was convinced that she was their Evita. Vocally she was outstanding, as Andrew agreed. Bonnie Schoen was duly flown over to London for a final audition at which they had to vote. Swash and Tim wanted Elaine Paige. Andrew did not dislike her, but still liked Bonnie Schoen. Prince had the casting vote.

'OK,' he said, 'it's Elaine.'

Thus the team was complete. Robert Stigwood was to present *Evita*, written by Tim Rice and Andrew Lloyd Webber, directed by Hal Prince and starring Elaine Paige, Joss Ackland and David Essex. Stigwood was by now convinced that Swash could raise the money and let him go about his task. Andrew turned his attention back to the recording of *Variations*. Tim returned to the affairs of the Heartaches Cricket Club and his growing record collection.

He was developing publishing interests, which apart from the book of *Evita* concentrated on cricket and music. He and Andrew let Prince perform the task of giving the show proper theatrical form. Tim, however, would take an interest in the progress of its unknown young female lead, Elaine Paige. Slowly, the lyricist who had written so many bittersweet love songs for young women, including this one, would become attracted in real life. This was a liaison of which neither Andrew nor Sarah, for different reasons, would approve.

Variations was recorded by MCA and performed by Julian and an elite team of jazz-rock musicians led by the drummer Jon Hiseman. The twenty-four pieces brilliantly exploited Paganini's motif and also contained a number of references back and forward to other works by Lloyd Webber. The introduction contained the mysterious notes of the synthesizer that were to open the world-famous dancing show which was at that moment only a thought in the composer's teeming mind. There were hints of *Rainbow High*, a song from *Evita*; and Julian played on his cello a rock and roll parody of Bill Haley, whose records had been played regularly in the toy theatre days at Harrington Court. The penchant for parody Andrew and Tim had pioneered could also be heard in the tremulous electric guitar reminiscent of Hank B. Marvin and the Shadows. Last, there was an intact melody drawn up from the bottom of the well and the earliest days of the Rice—Lloyd Webber partnership: played on the cello and in a slower tempo, this was the melody of the title song poignantly sung by the homeless orphans twelve years earlier in that first, unperformed musical, *The Likes of Us*.

Biddy co-ordinated the production and Andrew inserted a line into the credits which read 'Dedicated to the Small Vole', a reference to his daughter Imogen. He also featured on the recording playing synthesizers. These new machines attracted him; they claimed to be able to reproduce electronically any known orchestral sound. He ordered one from Yamaha and installed it at the rear of the drawing room of the flat in Eaton Place.

That autumn, Biddy became a director of the Really Useful Company. The company was now gearing up for the expiry of the Stigwood contract, which Andrew had not the slightest intention of renewing. Tim seemed happy to stay with Stigwood and Land; as far as he was concerned, life was too short to engage in complicated corporate calculations simply in order to prove that you and you alone could run your own affairs.

Tim was working on an idea of his own about two chess players, a Russian and an American, who fall for the same woman: the ultimate expression of his obsession with the idea of the game of love.

Elsewhere, forbidden love took other, sadder forms. Alan Doggett had run the London Boy Singers; he had left his post with the choir of Colet Court, but he had been unable to leave them alone. Faced with an allegation of indecency from the school, he had typed a farewell letter, photocopied and posted it to his few close friends, and boarded a train for the Home Counties. A few miles outside London, he threw himself in the path of an oncoming express.

Thus passed the man who, as self-appointed mentor, had persuaded Andrew to compose *Joseph* and helped with the score of *Jesus Christ Superstar*. Doggett's later contributions to Andrew's work had, like the man, been troubled. Lately, the spectacular progress of his protégé had made him look more and more like a man who had been left behind. Like the late Sefton Myers, after his death he would remain a little-known figure whose contribution to the career of Andrew Lloyd Webber would all too often go unsung.

In the early weeks of 1978, Julian was appointed to a Professorship at the Guildhall School of Music, where his elder brother had once pursued a part-time course in orchestration. He was one of the youngest to hold such a distinction; he was certainly the first Professor to have a record in the British Top Twenty.

Variations had been released and reached Number Two in the charts: only the fabulously successful Swedish group Abba, of whom Tim was an ardent admirer, prevented the Lloyd Webber brothers' first joint recording from reaching the Number One spot. Melvyn Bragg, presenter of the LWT *South Bank Show*, invited his old employer on to the programme to talk about his music. LWT also started to use part of *Variations* as the programme's theme music; a weekly burst of publicity which kept the record in the charts and added to its handsome royalties.

While Abba were at Number One and Julian and Andrew were at Number Two, Tim was in Australia. Andrew took the opportunity of the publicity surrounding *Variations* to broadcast to his absent partner, once more through the familiar channel of Angus McGill's newspaper, the *Evening Standard*.

This, too, was a variation on a familiar theme.

'I do sometimes wish he would write a bit more,' he told the reporter plaintively. 'Nothing would please me more than if he came back . . .

'Of course, he's got an awful lot of interests of his own, like broadcasting and the book he's put together. But I've only got music. I'm not good at anything else at all.

'I think the only other lyricist I would be over the moon to work with, is Stephen Sondheim. As for Tim, I'm not sure how to encourage him. I know he always wants to have a top hit single. Perhaps I should put him on *Top of the Pops* playing *Variations* . . . providing he produces some lyrics by the end of the year.'

Andrew, who had made sure a company was incorporated to handle the publishing, who had hired the cream of British rock and jazz-rock musicians to play on the recordings and who had astutely anticipated the enduring popularity of the Paganini piece while keeping a proprietary eye on the production costs, now cast himself in the role of humble composer with nothing more than the best interests of music at heart.

'I must admit, I didn't think there was much commercial potential in it at all,' he told the same reporter, 'all I really wanted to do was a piece that would show off the talents of the performers as best I could. I knew Julian was a good cellist and I thought the idea of a cello in rock would work because it is quite a physical instrument.'

Having announced only a year earlier that rock music was 'going round in ever-decreasing circles', he now appeared to have changed his point of view.

'I still believe everything is going on in rock. It can sound a bit over the top to say that, but never forgetting that rock has got to have popular roots as well, I'm sure it's got a lot to add to the serious music world. Contemporary serious music,' he added in an irresistible sideswipe at less bankable composers such as Berio, Boulez and Birtwhistle, 'seems to have become such a blind alley. I'm sure the number of people who like or understand it must be very, very few.'

Abba stayed at Number One and Julian and Andrew just failed to top the pop charts. Tim came back from Australia; he and Andrew tried to work together on words and music for the recording of a piece called *Variation 5*: the attempt ended in another row.

Hal Prince, meanwhile, had assembled the cast of *Evita* for rehearsals. He did not take long to live up to his reputation as a man who thought the English could be 'over-nice' to each other. The rehearsals were at Cecil Sharp House, the genteel North London home of the English Folk Dance and Song Society. But the cast soon found the American way of directing somewhat different from the British. Instead of developing relationships with the company, Prince's approach reflected his greater experience as a producer than as a director.

He rarely mixed socially with the cast: four weeks into rehearsals he would still be saying 'you in the green sweater'. British actors expected the director at least to know their first names, or to make a joke if he could not remember. When Elaine Paige, the unknown whose title role in the show had propelled her to the verge of international stardom, asked if they could go out for dinner, he declined the invitation. Most weekends he went back to New York. Paige found this frightening, given the demanding nature of the role she was expected to play.

Even Swash, who enjoyed a good relationship with him, found this behaviour a little wearing at times. In the best Broadway tradition, which Stigwood had upheld in firing Frank Corsaro from *Jesus Christ Superstar*, Prince's anxiety mounted to the point where the gods of the West End demanded a ritual sacrifice. Unable to fire himself, Prince cast around for a suitable candidate.

Swash could see nothing wrong with the actor in question and indulged in a little elementary psychology. At a series of lunchtime sessions, he presented the director with a procession of wildly unsuitable alternatives. Eventually Prince's anxiety subsided and the actor stayed on.

That spring saw the final exit of the earliest and most important theatrical influence on the life of Andrew Lloyd Webber. Aunt Vi and her husband George, who was fifteen years older than her, had no faith in Italian medicine and had returned to England so that George could receive proper medical treatment. Ironically, Vi died first. Twenty years earlier, as a retired actress, she had taken her clever little nephew to the London theatres where he had fallen in love with the musicals of Rodgers and Hammerstein. She had encouraged him to build his own toy theatre and he had not disappointed her. But even Vi had been dazed by aspects of her nephew's success. On their retirement to Brighton, the unworldly schoolboy who had so often stayed in their villa at Ventimiglia had insisted on buying them a house.

The *Evita* rehearsals proceeded apace. The show went into the Prince Edward Theatre, where the cast now came to grips with the set. This was designed with a moat-like gap at either side of the stage. Moving bridges transported the cast, or most of them, to and from the stage. The remainder fell off into the darkness; others missed their transport and were embarrassingly marooned on stage. Alterations were made and the lower casualty rate was accompanied by a corresponding surge in morale. Prince and his team, especially his choreographer Larry Fuller, were beginning to achieve results.

The musical director was again Anthony Bowles, who still conducted *Jesus Christ Superstar* once a week and enjoyed it as much as ever. He had recently been musical director of *Fire Angel*, one of the many rock musicals which *JC* had spawned and a disaster which briefly occupied the boards of Her Majesty's

Theatre. He was relieved to be back on board a Rice–Lloyd Webber reunion.

Bowles was informed by the Stigwood management that they had engaged the services of a well-known American orchestrator, Hershy Kay. (Swash had earlier told him that he intended to go to America to 'audition' the great orchestrator, Jonathan Tunick. Doubtful as to whether a man of Tunick's eminence would respond to such an approach, Bowles was not surprised when Swash returned empty-handed.) He was looking forward to meeting Kay whose orchestrations, he felt confident, would benefit *Evita* as much as *Jeeves*, so flawed in other ways, had benefited from those of Don Walker.

Kay's task was an apparently simple one for a man of his experience: to reduce Andrew's original orchestral score for the album to a smaller score for the orchestra pit of the Prince Edward Theatre. Bowles asked to see the scores as Kay finished them. Kay agreed and said he would supply lead sheets from which Bowles could conduct the rehearsals. These gave only the top line and the chorus – it was impossible to tell what the instruments in the orchestra were supposed to be playing. When Bowles demurred, Kay professed to be amazed: surely Bowles could conduct from a piano score; this was what they did on Broadway.

'Hershy,' Bowles replied in his inimitable fashion, 'I know nought of what they do on Broadway. And if this is the case on Broadway, which I find staggering, it is not the case in England. In England, Hershy, which is where this show is going on, we have conductors who can read scores and who, when asked at rehearsals by the first oboe what note he is supposed to play in four bars' time, are expected to be able to give an answer.'

Kay listened and went away. A short time later the first score arrived. Bowles was appalled by what he saw. The common procedure in orchestration for the musical theatre dictated that the orchestrator did not ask the orchestra to duplicate the

135

melody being sung by the singer. This was only done when a climactic effect was required. In Kay's score, not only had he done this for one melody, he had written it to be played throughout by the first trumpet.

Both Bowles and his assistant, David Firman, were mystified. They decided not to bother the composer. But, as the other scores arrived, their confusion intensified. Bowles had made one or two minor corrections on his copy of the album score, but Kay was working from a photocopy of Andrew's original. Even Andrew Lloyd Webber made mistakes — a C major chord with a flat accidentally written over the E — and Kay had faithfully duplicated them all.

Shortly afterwards, the telephone rang at 51 Eaton Place.

'Andrew? I'm sorry to bother you. It's Anthony. Andrew, the scores which are arriving are totally and utterly unplayable.'

Bowles did not wish to create too great a fuss; he himself had been offered the chance to orchestrate the pit score and turned it down. Andrew's good name was never far away from the orchestrations and Bowles did not wish to suggest that they had been carried out by an incompetent, let alone an incompetent hired at considerable expense.

Andrew went to the Prince Edward Theatre and was alarmed by what he saw. He and Bowles removed the doublings and patched up the pit score. At the band calls, where it was customary for the conductor to solicit comments from the orchestrator regarding how his work sounded, Kay did not breathe a single word.

Andrew and Tim were rarely seen at rehearsals: the arguments over *Variations 5* had reopened the divisions which had revealed themselves that day in *L'Escargot* and which had begun at the Waldorf Astoria in New York. Now their partnership was on the verge of total breakdown.

When Tim strolled in to rehearsals and Andrew asked where he had been, he replied truthfully: 'The Test Match.' When

Tim questioned the effectiveness of an orchestration, whether or not he knew the extent of the dramas which had bedevilled it behind the scenes, Andrew was immediately at boiling point.

'Where are you going?' Andrew screamed as, in full view of the orchestra, his partner headed for the exit. But Tim had had enough. He had had enough of anti-Perón demonstrators trying to break up a harmless *Evita* book signing. Andrew did not do book signings. Nor did he write, research or publish them. That was the problem, as far as Tim was concerned. Andrew was too bloody single-minded. All he did was write musicals.

There was more to life than musicals: there was cricket.

Tim's reply became a refrain: 'The Test Match.'

Evita opened at the Prince Edward Theatre on 21 June 1978. A giant back projection announced the presence of the doomed heroine on a Buenos Aires cinema screen. The action took place in cinematic flashback with razor precision: Eva dispatched a succession of increasingly influential lovers via a revolving door, each time returning more heavily jewelled, more expensively dressed, while Perón dispatched his rivals in a game of military musical chairs.

Prince's direction worked brilliantly, particularly in such numbers as *Dangerous Jade*, choreographed by Fuller to show the depth of opposition to Evita from the aristocracy and the army. *Another Suitcase in Another Hall* epitomised both Tim's talent for torch songs for rejected lovers and the depth of Andrew's well of melodies; it had begun life in *Jeeves* as the melody to a song called *Summer Day*.

Don't Cry For Me Argentina, which had begun life as an obscure single for the *Evening Standard* 'Girl of the Year' and then returned to climb the Top Twenty, found full theatrical expression at last as Eva's perfidious lullaby to her *descamisados*. The show was an immediate, monster hit.

Once again, the critics could only add their reviews as after-thoughts to a foregone conclusion:

Evita is a superb musical, but its heart is rotten. It is a glittering homage to a monster. Having been born and brought up under a totalitarian regime, I never cease to marvel at the fascination English people feel for political cannibals . . .

As a piece of stage-craft, no, stage-art, this is one of the very best musicals London has seen in years. The music is immensely more sophisticated than that of *Jesus Christ Superstar* . . .

I may as well say now that *Evita* (which opened, by a happy irony, while I was in Austria listening to Schubert) provided me when I saw it on my return with one of the most disagreeable evenings I have ever spent in my life, in or out of a theatre . . .

. . . a masterpiece . . . *Evita* is a quite marvellous modern opera, exceeding in stature even *Jesus Christ Superstar*. Lloyd Webber's score, so full of glorious melodies apart from the well-known *Don't Cry For Me Argentina*, is an unparalleled fusion of 20th century musical experience . . .

. . . its best tune, the already famous *Don't Cry For Me Argentina*, is inferior as a melody to the ones I used when a boy to hear improvised on a saxophone outside the Albert Hall by a busker with only three fingers to his left hand . . .

Lloyd Webber is perhaps the most remarkable musical child of his generation . . .

But there is a still greater corruption at the heart of this odious artefact, symbolised by the fact that it calls itself an opera . . .

. . . Masterpiece . . .

. . . Breathtaking . . .

Evita was taking £60,000 a week, but even the best reviews were the kind which Andrew had once envisaged for *Jeeves*. Now he had been given them for a show which he had not wanted to write and the result was a shift in the balance of power between himself and his partner. No matter that he and Tim now had two smash hit musicals running and the West End was running out of theatres. Andrew wanted more than ever to show that he could succeed in his own right.

To this end, he had been playing around with some settings of *Old Possum's Book of Practical Cats* by the late T. S. Eliot. Although Jean and Billy had been pushed out of Harrington Court by rising rents and expiring leases, the shade of Perseus lingered and cats of all shapes and sizes, animate and inanimate, still dominated their Sussex Mansions flat. Andrew regarded the Eliot poems as promising material.

That year's Sydmonton Festival took place from 8–10 September. Tickets were £33 for the weekend, which included a pilot performance of Eliot poems sung in St Mary's Church on the Saturday evening. Tim and Andrew captained opposing cricket teams drawn from the Festival audience and the cast of *Evita*. The Moving Picture Mime Show was on the bill, as were a preview of the animated film *Watership Down* and *Beethoven's Sketchbooks: A Composer at Work*, a lecture recital by Denis Matthews.

On 4 October *Jesus Christ Superstar* at the Palace Theatre became the longest-running show in British theatrical history. It had passed 2620 performances and taken £7 million at the box office, beating the previous record held by Lionel Bart's *Oliver!* Over two million people had seen these performances. Nine million albums sold worldwide had grossed over $100 million. The film had taken a further $30 million and the BBC had paid $2 million to show it over the coming Christmas. The stage show had been produced in over twenty countries; royalties flooded in; Stigwood had bought himself a £750,000 yacht.

Anthony Bowles, as original musical director, still conducted the show once a month. He was also still employed as musical director of *Evita*. Prince, who had established *Evita*, now went about other business, returning to check up on it from time to time.

Bowles had a professional respect for Hal Prince, even if he found him a monolithic and inaccessible character. He now discovered that the director was not a man who felt the urge to explain his actions.

Bowles had worked through the summer on the show and needed a holiday. Gary Bond was due to take over the part of Che from David Essex and Bowles agreed with Prince that he would deliver Bond note-perfect before he went away. He would return just before Bond was due to take over the part. He duly returned to conduct the show on the Thursday. On Friday morning, he was at home in North London when there was a knock at the door. It was his near neighbour, Bob Swash.

Swash looked ashen. 'Anthony,' he said, 'can I come in?'

Bowles's first thought was that something terrible had happened to Swash. He sat the producer down in the kitchen and asked him what the matter was. Swash told him that he had had a directive from Prince: Bowles was not to go into rehearsals that day. Not only that, he was forbidden to enter the theatre. Someone would deliver his belongings to him. He was fired. Swash commiserated and said he had no idea why. He left Bowles in a state of shock.

Bowles eventually pulled himself together sufficiently to telephone Prince at the Savoy. He had no desire to bother Andrew at this stage. Andrew would see that it had all been a terrible mistake.

He left a message for Prince to telephone him. He spent the next three days in a nightmare state, in which depression turned into anger and disbelief.

The following Tuesday, the telephone rang.

'This is Hal Prince. Good morning, chum.'

'Oh,' said Bowles, 'you've rung.'

'Yes. I'm just going back to the States.'

'Fine. Hal, just one thing before you go. Will you tell me what it is that I have done?'

'Anthony . . . there's no ill-feeling between us, is there?'

'No ill-feeling?' Bowles was incredulous, 'Hal, there are *oceans* of ill-feeling. What have I done wrong?'

'Absolutely nothing. I'm just ringing to tell you it was all a terrible mistake.'

With that Prince made his apologies and rang off. This was the last time they spoke.

There was consternation among the cast and orchestra of *Evita*. The Musicians' Union were up in arms; there was talk of compensation for breach of contract, of a walk-out. In the middle of all this Gary Bond had to take over the role of Che. Bowles did not want Bond to miss his first night. He refused to countenance the Musicians' Union suggestion that the show come to a halt unless he was reinstated. Besides, he was sure that Andrew would sort everything out.

It was with some relief, then, that he picked up the telephone and heard the voice of Andrew Lloyd Webber.

'Anthony, this is Andrew. I'm sorry about what's happened.'

'So am I, Andrew, so am I. But it's not your fault. I'm sure we can sort this out.'

'Anthony, I can't overrule Hal. You know that.'

Bowles did not believe his ears. 'Andrew,' he said, 'it's your show. You wrote it. You and I have worked together for six years. This is me, Anthony. *Of course you can overrule him.*'

Bowles listened in disgust as the young man who had entertained him to dinner at Eaton Place and for whom he had worked on *Jesus Christ Superstar* and *Evita*, now hid behind a succession of feeble excuses. Bowles had respected Andrew: amidst a growing number of sycophants and hangers-on, he had always talked straight to him. Andrew, who suspected that Bowles might have exceeded his brief in Prince's absence, was unable to reciprocate in kind. The English were no longer over-nice to each other when they staged musicals.

Bowles departed into the theatrical wilderness, in the form of a pantomime at the Royal Exchange Theatre, Manchester. Others were moving closer to the orbit of Andrew Lloyd Webber. Brian Brolly, the soft-spoken Ulsterman and former head of MCA (UK) who had commissioned the recording of *Superstar*, had since left the record company to manage the private financial affairs of ex-Beatle Paul McCartney. Brolly had made McCartney immensely rich. Now that the Stigwood contract was about to expire, Andrew needed someone he could trust. Working from the office in the house at 11 West Eaton Place, Brolly would become a shareholder and the first Managing Director of the Really Useful Company.

The big-eyed girl from Berkhamsted, who was too young to find drooling men a problem, had also moved on from the comparatively staid atmosphere of Pan's People. As an eighteen-year-old singer and dancer in the sexy dance group Hot Gossip she had aroused the displeasure of moral rearmament campaigners and the attentions of male TV viewers. Her hit record *I Lost My Heart To A Starship Trooper*, written by her twenty-seven-year-old boyfriend and manager Andrew Graham-Stewart, had climbed to Number 6 in the charts. Now she was going solo with her new record *Adventures of A Love Crusader*. Sarah Brightman had lost none of her flair for self-promotion.

'Our house is seven hundred years old and listed Grade A for preservation,' she told reporters. 'People come from all over to see it. So far,' she added blithely, 'we haven't had any problems with fans pretending they want to see the house just so they can get to see me. Anybody who tries that is likely to be disappointed – I'm so busy that I'm rarely at home.'

Andrew, whose knowledge of architecture was rather more extensive, was also so busy that he was rarely at home. He was preparing for the annual Society of West End Theatre Awards, to be held at the Café Royal. The organiser was the rising young producer Cameron Mackintosh.

The Café Royal was not a theatre and Mackintosh was experiencing technical difficulties in staging extracts from the six productions. Anthony Bowles, as conductor of the evening's cabaret performed by the cast of *Jesus Christ Superstar*, was also there. He had recently been telephoned by Bob Swash, his ex-colleague on *Evita*, who reminded him that before his departure he had agreed to conduct the excerpt from *Evita* at the SWET Awards. Swash wanted to confirm that the latter arrangement still held.

'Bob,' said Bowles, 'you have just paid me for breach of contract after wrongful dismissal from your show. You are now asking me to conduct that same company at the SWET Awards. You must be out of your mind. Of course I bloody well won't do it.'

Later that same day the telephone rang again. This time it was David Land.

'Anthony,' Land was at his most avuncular, 'come on ... we know who the best conductor is of *Evita*. We want you to conduct it. We want to win.'

'I'm sorry,' said Bowles, 'I don't know any more.' He put down the receiver. He was waiting for Andrew to call. By the Sunday before the awards, Andrew had still not telephoned. Bowles went to the Café Royal and conducted the *JC* cast in rehearsal. The *Evita* cast were rehearsing the same day. During their rehearsal Bowles was approached by Cameron Mackintosh.

'Anthony,' he said, 'I'm expecting you to conduct the *Evita* excerpt on the night.'

'Cameron,' said Bowles, 'in that case you are describing an event which is not going to happen. Anyway, they have a perfectly good conductor.'

'Anthony,' Mackintosh went on, 'I want you to go over there and politely take that stick out of his hand. Everyone will applaud you and put their arms around you.'

'Cameron, they may very well do that. But there is no way that I will go over there and take the stick out of another musician's hand.'

Mackintosh gave up and they said no more on the subject. Mackintosh, too, was having problems. Having decided that simplicity of presentation was paramount with such a crowded programme, he had been trying to persuade Andrew that *Evita* should be represented by *Don't Cry For Me Argentina*, with a simple set and a single radio microphone. To his dismay, Andrew wanted a medley of numbers with seven microphones, in a room which was already a sound engineer's nightmare. Eventually they went ahead with the composer's suggestion; the evening was a nightmare for Mackintosh.

Evita swept the awards. In his acceptance speech, Andrew paid tribute to the people behind the show.

'*Evita* would not have been possible,' he said, 'without the help of a lot of people who were not seen before your eyes this evening. They include everyone who worked on the original album.' He then read out a long list of names of those who had been present at the recordings at Olympic studios: the singers, the rock musicians, the orchestra, the cleaners, the milkman; all were given the Lloyd Webber stamp of approval. But the man who had conducted the recordings and whose name had figured prominently in the favourable reviews of the show, was missing from the list. Andrew made no mention of Anthony Bowles.

Bowles, who was sitting at the dinner table, would have to wait another ten years for a telephone call from Andrew Lloyd Webber.

Andrew did not stop there, however. As a parting shot, he praised the work of the man who thought the British were over-nice to each other.

'*Evita*,' he went on, 'was also a great show because it had a great director. That is exactly what this show needed tonight. Thank you very much.'

Mackintosh, who had consumed a large quantity of claret as defence against the stresses of the evening, now felt the anaesthetic wearing off. He was shortly to be seen rising unsteadily to his feet and weaving towards the composer. At his side, half urging him on and half concerned to protect his investment, was David Land. Fortunately for the diminutive composer, Mackintosh soon sank to the floor, only to regain full consciousness in the back of a taxi on his way home.

Unlike Bowles, a few days later Mackintosh had a letter. Andrew wanted to apologise: he had not meant to upset Mackintosh with his remarks. Mackintosh realised he had been dealing with a man who was routinely prepared to work himself up into a manic frenzy to achieve his ends, but who was also prepared to apologise when he overstepped the mark. He liked that. He now turned his attention to other matters. He had already proved that it was possible in a time of recession to bring big musicals successfully back into the West End. He had even persuaded the Arts Council of Great Britain to invest in his revival of *My Fair Lady*. Mackintosh was that rare breed, a young and hungry musical theatre animal. He had not seen the last of Andrew Lloyd Webber.

Escaway, the Lloyd Webber family company, had seen profits triple since the previous year to a pre-tax figure of £162,219. The tax laws of England had terrified Andrew throughout the years of Labour governments; while Bob Swash had tried unsuccessfully to convert him to socialism, Andrew had equally unsuccessfully tried to convert Anthony Bowles to free market capitalism during the recording of *Evita*. The coming to power of the Conservative Government of Margaret Thatcher gave hope to higher tax payers everywhere.

Jean's future daughter-in-law, meanwhile, was modelling for the *Evening News*:

What a Trouper . . .

Performing her new solo single *Adventures of a Love Crusader* she wears a sequinned and jewelled body stocking. The idea behind this current image is of a much stronger, older, predatory woman – or, as she puts it 'a sort of superwoman looking down on men!'

In fact, in spite of her mere 18 years, Sarah seems tongue-in-cheek and sensible about being a male turn-on.

'I didn't start out trying to be sexy,' she giggled, 'It just happened that way. I don't mind at all – it's quite a fun thing. It certainly doesn't stop me from writing and singing songs.

'Anyway, you'd be surprised how difficult it is to dance with lots of clothes on . . .'

The Stigwood contract ended and so began Brian Brolly's steward-ship of the Really Useful Company. Andrew and Sarah, the original shareholders, now had thirty-five shares each and Brolly had thirty. A tightly knit team of three – Brolly, Andrew and Biddy Hayward – now had executive responsibility for the commercial exploitation of every aspect of the work of Andrew Lloyd Webber.

The Really Useful Company had no rights over *Joseph, Jesus Christ Superstar* or *Evita* – these remained with Stigwood, al-though Andrew would continue to enjoy substantial royalties from them as the composer. As for whatever he wrote or produced in the future, the decision now belonged to him. This was the fulfilment of the dream he had had eight years earlier and which had gone unfulfilled in the dormant Qwertyuiop. The need now became an obsession for him to prove that anything Stigwood could do, he could do better.

On 22 June 1979, *Evita* celebrated its first birthday party. David Essex, Cliff Richard, for whom Tim had once been humble assistant producer, and Tim himself all joined in the festivities. Tim's party piece was his Elvis Presley impersonation: complete with rhinestone suit, receding hairline and bulging waist, it was a convincing rendition of the decline of the man who sang *That's When Your Heartaches Begin*. His friendship with Elaine Paige was as close as ever and, as ever, Andrew did not approve. When

146

Tim suggested they write a television special for her, he declined. But the idea of a one-woman show remained in Andrew's mind.

Andrew was in New York that summer, where Stigwood was preparing the Broadway production of *Evita*; having only arrived at a late preview of the show in London, Stigwood had been prompted by its success there to back the entire Broadway production. In New York, Andrew met the British lyricist Don Black, who had written scores of award-winning lyrics such as *Diamonds Are Forever*, *Thunderball* and *Born Free*, the last of which had won him an Oscar.

Black, like Tim Rice, was a few years older than Andrew and a man of considerable personal charm. Unlike Tim, he worked well for all the right reasons, which had made him a successful if intermittently memorable lyricist. He was a shrewd, amiable professional in the old Tin Pan Alley tradition.

He was also the manager of the British singer Marti Webb, who was about to alternate with Elaine Paige in the London production of *Evita*. Black liked Andrew's idea for a one-woman show: why not write something for Marti? Andrew told him about an idea he had, the story in song of the life and loves of an English girl abroad in America.

Black had been an expatriate in Beverly Hills and liked the idea. Tentatively they began work, exchanging music and lyrics, developing an acquaintance. After *Evita* had successfully opened on Broadway, making Stigwood even more money, the composer and his new lyricist friend returned to England. With Marti Webb singing the part, they premiered a rough workshop version of their efforts at that year's Sydmonton Festival; they called it *Tell Me On A Sunday*.

Also previewed that year was the Really Useful Company's first theatre venture, a co-production of Edward Duke's one-man show *Jeeves Takes Charge*. Andrew had still not exorcised his obsession with Wodehouse as a profitable West End theatre proposition.

With Sarah and Imogen at Sydmonton, Andrew invited Bob Swash back to Eaton Place after dinner one night and played him the *Tell Me On A Sunday* score. Swash liked it – it reminded him in places of *Jeeves* – but told him it was not for the theatre.

'Take it from me, Andrew,' he said, 'it's nice. It's very nice – but it's for TV.'

Andrew still envisaged a musical. He and Black conceived of a back-to-back idea: the second half being the story of an American girl abroad in England. The record might make it on to TV; but *en route* to the stage.

Black liked that idea too. That autumn, while the album of *Tell Me On A Sunday* was recorded, they worked on other ideas. One of these was a blockbuster musical of *Sunset Boulevard*, the classic *grand guignol* movie directed by Billy Wilder and starring Gloria Swanson. *Sunset Boulevard* was the definitive movie about Hollywood; it was also the story of a star who should have lived a short, fast life and died at the age of thirty-three and who suffered the ghastly consequences of failing to do so.

Tim was unimpressed; he could not see how anyone could improve on the movie. But Andrew persevered; he even came up with his best tune to date, an elegiac, emotional ballad for the doomed star to sing as she descended the staircase to relive what she thought were her past glories. He had originally written this for an unfinished *pastiche* of Puccini. As had been the case with *Kansas Morning*, it would be cast back into the well only to resurface in another show as the melody for another monster hit. Meanwhile, he missed Tim, but he was impressed by Black's ability to deliver. That winter, as the seventy-seven-year-old Richard Rodgers died in New York, Andrew began to wonder if at last he too might have found his Hammerstein.

Cameron Macintosh had not heard from Andrew since the latter apologised for his behaviour a year earlier. Mackintosh was now surprised and intrigued to receive a telephone call from Biddy Hayward. Andrew Lloyd Webber, she said, wished to invite him to lunch.

Mackintosh's career had gone from strength to strength since that drunken evening of the SWET Awards. He had mounted a successful production of *Side By Side By Sondheim* and a successful revival of *Oklahoma!* These were the kinds of achievement which did not go unnoticed at the offices of the Really Useful Company.

Andrew also concluded that anyone who could persuade the Arts Council to invest in a regional tour of Anna Neagle in *My Fair Lady* could no longer be ignored. He may have seen himself as an entrepreneur who no longer needed the likes of Stigwood, but he still needed someone with Mackintosh's organisational expertise. Over lunch at the Savile Club, the two men discovered to their delight a mutual passion for the important things in life: fine wine, good food and the musical theatre.

Mackintosh, too, had had a toy theatre as a child which he operated with his brother in his capacity as chief puppeteer. It was a role he was playing to increasing effect in real life. He had also seen *JC* and *Joseph* and *Jeeves* and *Evita.* He and Andrew talked at length, about bad British directors and good American ones, how a show should look and sound and what they were going to do together.

After lunch, Andrew invited Mackintosh back to Eaton Place and played him his settings of *Old Possum's Book of Practical Cats.* He told Mackintosh he had talked to everyone – to Stigwood, to Swash and to Michael White – and none of them was interested.

Mackintosh was interested. He extolled the virtues of the one British director on whose talent they were both agreed: Trevor Nunn, the artistic director of the Royal Shakespeare Company. They talked about the rise of dance as a popular art form, as exemplified that year in the success of the movie *Fame.* Andrew

149

and Mackintosh talked about staging *Old Possum* back to back with *Variations* in a dancing show. The first half would have Elaine Stritch and Liza Minelli standing at either side of the stage reading the poems; and in the second half *Variations* would form the music of the dance. The whole show would be just like a modern version of Edith Sitwell's *Façade*.

It was the beginning of a close personal friendship and a collaboration which would take them further and further away from the antiquarian image of Edith Sitwell, change the face of the musical theatre and make them both richer than the dreams of Stigwood.

Tell Me On A Sunday was premiered in a gala performance at the Royalty Theatre at the end of January 1980. Marti Webb's rendition of the song-cycle of an English girl abroad in America was the first fruit of the new Lloyd Webber–Black collaboration.

Sheldon Bloom contained musical echoes of *Jesus Christ Superstar*; although Tim might have pulled it off, when Don Black rhymed *viola* with *Emile Zola* it just did not work. *Come Back With That Same Look in Your Eyes* showed Black's talent for a title and ear for potential cover version; *I'm Very You, You're Very Me* plumbed new depths of ghastliness as melodic and lyrical doggerel. *Tell Me On A Sunday* instantly sounded like the hit single it became. Its message seemed to be that English girls went to America on a voyage of self-delusion. Marti Webb, in an accent which veered uncertainly between Santa Monica and Milton Keynes, came across as a suburban shrew in the making. The audience loved it.

Evita opened at the Shubert Theater in Los Angeles. Julian was preparing for a performance of sonatas by Debussy, Rachmaninov and Britten at the Queen Elizabeth Hall; he was also booked to perform the same works in New York at the Lincoln Center. *Tell Me On A Sunday* was released as an album on Polydor and shown on BBC TV. The show was well reviewed and repeated a few days later at prime time. But Andrew and Don Black abandoned their attempts to turn it into a show for the stage. Instead, Universal, who had made *JC* the movie, were attempting to turn it into a film for Norman Jewison.

The money kept rolling in. That year's Escaway return to 31 May would declare a turnover of £678,779, or over £10,000 a week – a fourfold increase on the previous year. Andrew, Sarah and the other directors shared remunerations of £613,460 and a pre-tax profit for the period of £21,889 was declared to the Inland Revenue by accountants Temple, Gothard.

Meanwhile, Andrew and Cameron Mackintosh were still trying to find a solution to the cat problem. Andrew told Mackintosh he was going ahead with a more advanced workshop performance of the settings at this year's Sydmonton Festival. Together they recruited the performers Gary Bond, Paul Nicholas and Gemma Craven. Trevor Nunn, on whom Andrew and Mackintosh had called at his new offices in the Barbican, was invited, as was the widow of the author of *Old Possum's Book of Practical Cats* and devoted steward of her husband's estate, Valerie Eliot.

Nunn had already grappled with the cat project and concluded it still lacked the necessary narrative link. One moment it was too much an aggregate of charming if not fey fragments; the next it was sinking under the weight of their latest narrative idea. But he was taken with the idea of a dancing show. Like Andrew and Mackintosh, he believed in the resurgence of modern dance and had recently directed a successful production of *A Comedy of Errors* with Britain's leading choreographer Gillian Lynne.

Lynne was a highly experienced workaholic with a high pain threshold and a reputation for persuading dancers to give performances of which they had never believed themselves capable. She was also capable of replacing them if they did not repeat the performances night after night. After the disaster of *Jeeves* and the success of *Evita*, Andrew was in favour of an American choreographer, but Mackintosh had worked with Lynne on *My Fair Lady* and knew that, even if they solved the narrative problem, they would never tempt Nunn into a sabbatical from his prestigious job with the RSC unless he was able to bring Lynne, as well as his stage and lighting designers, John Napier and David Hersey.

While he slowly acclimatised Andrew to the idea of hiring Nunn and Lynne, a package began to evolve in Mackintosh's agile entrepreneurial mind.

That Sydmonton Festival saw the successful workshop perform-ance of Andrew's settings of *Macavity the Mystery Cat, Skimble-shanks the Railway Cat* and *Old Deuteronomy.*

Jamie Muir filmed the proceedings. He felt he had come to know Andrew quite well. Andrew had talked about his lonely childhood and his unhappy father, and had often asked him if he knew any lyricists. Muir felt Andrew needed someone who represented an intellectual challenge; someone who could criticise him and reject inferior work. Andrew was not blind to this either; but time and time again, Muir felt, his wealth simply silenced people and isolated him from them.

'Jamie,' Andrew had asked him, 'what do *you* think of Trevor Nunn?'

Muir told him Nunn was the only person whose directorial abilities rivalled if not exceeded those of Hal Prince. 'Clever Trevor' was not a man to let sentiment cloud his vision of how he thought things should be: the standing joke about him was that 'his bite was worse than his bark'.

Andrew was pleased to hear this; he had already tentatively asked Muir's *South Bank Show* colleague Alan Benson if he was interested in directing a musical about cats. Benson, like Nunn but unlike Andrew, Mackintosh and Lynne, had no particular interest in cats; but he would have directed the London telephone directory if it was set to music by Andrew Lloyd Webber. He would be somewhat crestfallen when Andrew telephoned again and blithely informed him: 'Alan? It's OK. We've got Trevor Nunn.'

Valerie Eliot, too, pronounced herself pleased with the settings and their fidelity to her late husband's poems. Almost as an afterthought, she produced some of his unpublished lyrics on the same theme. As Andrew gazed at them with increasing excitement, she wondered aloud if they might be of any use to him and Mr Nunn.

The lyrics included one fragment which particularly caught the eye. This was *Grizabella the Glamour Cat*, an eight-line cameo showing how far a woman could fall. Eliot had not included it because he regarded his book as being primarily for children. That summer Valerie Eliot produced other fragments and unpublished writings, including a letter in which Eliot described his proposal that the cats should eventually go *Up up up past the Russell Hotel, up up up to the Heaviside Layer.* At last, they had their narrative link.

Thus it was that, outside Joe Allen's, the Covent Garden restaurant popular with actors and musicians, Cameron Mackintosh secured the services of the artistic director of the Royal Shakespeare Company. Trevor Nunn was to direct the next musical by Andrew Lloyd Webber.

'Cameron,' Nunn had told him, 'I have no more excuses not to say yes.'

Nunn, Lynne, Napier and Hersey were all on board. *Cats* was to be a Cameron Mackintosh–Really Useful Company co-production: each party undertaking to raise half of the £400,000 required to stage the show. Joining them was the West End theatrical advertising agency of Dewynters, run by 'Colonel' Robert De Wynter. The hunt began for angels, singers, dancers and a theatre; and a package. It was a short time, and a long way, from the day they had talked of *Cats* as a modern version of *Façade*.

There were other arrivals and departures: Nicholas Lloyd Webber arrived, the image of his father as his sister Imogen was of Sarah; *Jesus Christ Superstar* finally closed after eight years at the Palace Theatre; Julian had been to Spain and back, where a new work was being specially composed for him by the great Rodrigo. He was about to make his debut at the Promenade Concerts playing Delius's cello concerto. He had recently spent a considerable amount of time publicising his purchase of a 1790 Guadagnini cello.

In the midst of all this, Andrew went to the South of France with Tim to discuss musicals. The honeymoon period was over with the dependable Don Black. Tim had recently produced an album for Elaine Paige; he was still obsessed with the game of love. While Mackintosh and Brolly scrabbled to raise the money for *Cats* in London, the two young millionaires tried to recreate the energy and atmosphere of that week when they had created the bones of *Jesus Christ Superstar*. They drank wine and argued about the merits of a show about two chess players, one Russian and one American, competing for the love of the same woman. There were other ideas; most notably a novella by the Bloomsbury author and lothario David Garnett, *Aspects of Love*.

Aspects had been sent to Tim by a film director called Jason Pollock. Pollock had hoped Andrew and Tim might contribute a couple of songs and so turn just another piece of source material into a bankable movie proposition.

Both Andrew and Tim sensed there was something about *Aspects of Love* which made it a potential subject for a musical. Although the story of love and jealousy across three generations of characters was a slight one, it contained nuances and cyclical ironies of the sort suited to opera.

After overseeing a production of *Evita* in Australia, Andrew gave the book to Hal Prince to read on a flight back from Adelaide to Sydney.

'Andrew,' Prince told him after twenty minutes, 'I've read this book. You can't turn this into a musical.'

That November, as *Evita* celebrated its thousandth performance at the Prince Edward, the search went on for a suitable venue for *Cats*. It was with this problem in mind that Andrew was lured one night to one of the least attractive theatres in London: the New London Theatre in Drury Lane.

The New London had been the venue for the *Evita* listening previews four years earlier. Built on the site of the famous Winter Gardens it resembled an office block rather than a theatre; its lack of theatrical magic was accompanied by an utter absence of architectural merit. The sole redeeming feature was a revolving floor which accommodated the stage, the orchestra pit and part of the seating. Lately it had been used as a television studio and conference centre.

Andrew was lured there under a pretext only to discover he had been selected as victim for the long-running television show *This Is Your Life*. The evening involved the 'spontaneous' assembly of family and friends and purported to be a biographical voyage around the victim; who stood there twitching, eyes darting hither and thither, in the sort of situation he dreaded most: one where he was not in control.

After the show was over, he telephoned Cameron Mackintosh.

'I've got it,' he babbled. 'I'm standing in the perfect theatre for *Cats*. It's got a revolving stage. Cameron, you must come and see it. I'm standing here . . .'

Mackintosh was not a fan of *This Is Your Life* but he knew all about the New London Theatre. He decided to humour his friend, for whom he knew the evening must have been an acutely uncomfortable experience.

'Andrew,' he told him, 'you have to be kidding. That theatre is the white elephant of all time. The only reason we would *ever* go there is if all the other theatres were ridiculous.'

'I'll meet you there tomorrow.'

The following day Mackintosh, Andrew, Nunn and John Napier assembled at the drab venue in Drury Lane. After a lengthy inspection of the theatre, they conceded that he had a point. The revolving stage was perfect for what they planned to be an audience in the round at a revolutionary dancing show.

Nunn and Napier went away to start work on a scale model of the set. Mackintosh opened negotiations with the New London management. The management had built up a lucrative conference trade at the theatre, which they were loath to let slip in favour of an uncertain venture involving dancing cats. Mackintosh persevered; slowly, a deal came closer.

That winter the Really Useful Company won its first SWET Award with Edward Duke's performance in *Jeeves Takes Charge*. The show was co-produced with Mackintosh and choreographed by Gillian Lynne, but was not a commercial success: the RUC lost £8000 in the venture. Andrew gave up his attempts to make Wodehouse profitable for the stage.

By December, negotiations with the New London management had been finalised and Napier and Nunn had delivered their set. Finding financial backers was, however, proving difficult: in spite of the success of *Evita*, the spectre of *Jeeves*, the last Lloyd Webber solo offering, put most experienced angels off the show. Mackintosh's backers were traditionally loyal to him – such as the Honourable George Borwick of Borwick's Baking Powder, who had invested £1000 in *Side By Side By Sondheim* – but they too were nervous. He targeted the SWET list of would-be angels and bombarded them with publicity stressing the positive points of the production. Of the hundred or so people he persuaded to invest £2000 each, around eighty-five per cent were first-time angels. Some of them only succumbed after Mackintosh invited them to his Museum Street offices and played them the tunes. Others came, listened, and went away. Slowly, the figure crawled towards the £400,000 needed to stage the production.

Dewynters worked on the publicity. The aim with *Cats* was to create a homogeneous package which did not depend on names or numbers, but which would become an image of the widest possible appeal. This image had to be marketable in the form of merchandise: T-shirts, posters, records and books. The image had to be free of narrow cultural reference and linguistic restraint: it would be universal. *Cats* may have been Andrew's idea built on T. S. Eliot's invention, but it was also an adman's dream; and Dewynters were going to make it come true.

The casting of the show also presented peculiar opportunities and demands. There were half a dozen characters who behaved conventionally in that they came on stage, appeared against the background of the rest of the company, performed and withdrew. Brian Blessed, who played Old Deuteronomy and Bustopher Jones, was a familiar figure from television and theatre who possessed a willing tenor voice. Judi Dench, as Grizabella, had worked extensively with Trevor Nunn and was one of the Royal Shakespeare Company's most distinguished actresses. Paul Nicholas, the Rum Tum Tugger, was a successful pop singer and actor who had taken part in the workshop version at Sydmonton. Wayne Sleep, who played Quaxo, was the principal dancer with the Royal Ballet.

The *Cats* auditions attracted hundreds of dancers. They were divided into groups of fifty for the purpose of learning a routine, such as *The Jellicle Ball*. The dancers then had their names taken and were further divided into groups of ten. Four groups would wait, while one went on stage and danced. *You, you and you . . . the rest of you can go.* Then it was the turn of the next group. Some had five auditions. The survivors danced for final selection under the hypercritical gaze of Gillian Lynne.

Only the most determined and talented made it into the company. It was no surprise that they included some of the best-known young musical theatre stars in Britain. Bonnie Langford had been a child star of stage and screen who had made a career of her youthfulness. Finola Hughes had been chosen from six hundred applicants to represent Britain in an American television spectacular. Sharon Lee Hill had been acting since the age of

157

fifteen and played the lead in the London production of *A Chorus Line*. In the part of Jemima was the twenty-year-old singer and dancer who had sung *I Lost My Heart To A Starship Trooper*, Sarah Brightman.

Sarah Brightman was now married to Andrew Graham-Stewart. She could dance and she had an unusual voice, with which she sang the ethereal notes in the latter part of the show. The other girls sensed she was different from them: while they were working for a living, Sarah clearly had access to money. She floated in and out of the theatre in different dresses; she carried credit cards. She did not appear calculating; she just seemed to blow along on the wind. But just occasionally, in the dressing room, through the youthful, almost childlike façade, there was a glimpse of the person beneath.

Cats also created a host of technical problems and ingenious solutions. Technology had taken the art of illusion – the essence of theatre – to new extremes. Because of the strenuous nature of a show in which the majority of the cast were singing and dancing at the same time, there were moments which called for a little theatrical sleight of hand. The chorus was run from a tiny, blacked-out booth near the band pit, inside which four people clutching scores and wearing headphones huddled round a microphone and a flickering closed-circuit TV screen, on which they could see the conductor.

The booth singers were there to augment the voices of the dancers on stage. The latter sang all the numbers with the help of radio microphones, and the voice reinforcement never impinged on their performances. It was hot, soulless work; but at £24 for two and a half hours' work, five nights a week with a matinee on Saturdays, there was no shortage of applicants wanting to break into showbusiness or help pay their way through music school.

By January 1981 Nunn and Lynne had welded the company into a hungry, homogeneous whole. Hersey and Napier had supervised the building of a life-size set. David Cullen had come to grips with the orchestrations and David Firman, Anthony Bowles's former assistant, had established himself as musical director of the company. Cameron Mackintosh and Andrew were on the way to raising the backing. *Cats* was scheduled to open on 30 April 1981. Then, early that January, came disaster. The management of the New London Theatre changed its mind.

The more the management had heard about the new Lloyd Webber musical, the more they were unnerved by the idea. Now they decided that the fate of a musical about cats was of far less significance than the next conference of Berger Paints. George Biggs, general manager of the theatre, called a meeting with Cameron Mackintosh and Andrew Lloyd Webber. He gave them advance warning that he was calling off the deal.

Andrew arrived at the meeting with Lord Delfont, whom he had persuaded to accompany him and who with his brother, Lord Grade, represented the great traditions of British show-business. Delfont had presented over two hundred West End productions and believed in the tradition that said the show must go on. He was not without influence in Drury Lane and was a powerful advocate of the Lloyd Webber–Mackintosh case. Then, while Biggs and the theatre management listened doubtfully, Mackintosh proposed a new deal.

What worried Biggs and his colleagues was not the prospect of failure but of limited success. If the show folded three months after it opened, they would still be able to recapture the lucrative conference market. If the show ran for a year or two, however, before folding, they would have to rebuild their share of the conference market from scratch. What they wanted was some form of guarantee.

Mackintosh knew that he and Andrew had no real hope of finding *Cats* an alternative venue. Sure enough, in the weeks that elapsed before their final meeting with Biggs attempts to find such a venue came to nothing. He offered the theatre management a twofold incentive: a higher rent and a fixed-sum guarantee to be paid if the show closed within twenty-four months of opening.

The New London management agreed to this in principle, but wanted £75,000 for the latter. Mackintosh balked at this; privately he did not believe he would be able to raise this sum on top of the amount they needed to stage the show. Andrew stepped in and offered to supply his personal guarantee.

In years to come, he would enjoy telling people that he had taken a considerable risk in doing so; he would even hint that he had been compelled to raise a mortgage on his house. The reality was somewhat more prosaic. He had the money and he made it available. What he did not tell people was that in return for risking the loss of his £75,000, he also demanded that an extra five per cent of the profits of *Cats* be paid to one of his private companies. Eight years later, with *Cats* the longest-running musical since *Jesus Christ Superstar*, the indemnity period had long expired and he was still receiving an extra five per cent. Mackintosh, out of whose share of the profits came part of that extra percentage, was ruefully impressed: it was a deal of which Stigwood himself would have been proud. But then Andrew had always been careful with money.

As the last-minute casting for *Cats* proceeded at the South London premises of the Royal Ballet School, the director made an announcement. *Old Deuteronomy* was all very well, he said, but it was not a show-stopping piece. There was a hole in the show, where a great big ballad should be sung by Grizabella. What *Cats* needed, Nunn declared, was another song.

He turned and looked at the composer. Mackintosh and Lynne did the same. Andrew suddenly looked rather shifty. After a few moments he went over to the piano, sat down and played a tune.

Then he stopped and looked up. It was the tune he had originally written for the demented former film star Norma

Desmond to descend the staircase at the end of his and Don Black's abortive attempt at *Sunset Boulevard*.

He had always liked the tune; it had that Puccini-esque quality. Too much so, perhaps. He had once played it to Billy, to see if it would scrape past his educated ear.

'Does this sound like anything to you?' he had asked anxiously.

There had been a pause. William Lloyd Webber CBE FRCM FRCO FLCM had looked at him and said: 'Yes, Andrew. It sounds like a million pounds.'

At the Royal Ballet School, Nunn looked around for a clock.

'What is the time?' he said, in mock-theatrical tones, 'the day, the hour? Remember this day. For you have just heard a gigantic, enormous, smash hit by Andrew Lloyd Webber.'

Then they went back to work.

Andrew now did what he still always did when he needed a new lyric for an old song. He telephoned Tim and asked him to help.

But Tim was not interested in *Cats*; he felt the show should be a small-scale production staged somewhere like the Young Vic. Andrew then telephoned his budding Hammerstein, Don Black.

Black was eager to help.

'It's a great big ballad,' Andrew told him, 'but it mustn't come across merely as that. It's got to be bittersweet ... it's got to communicate intense pathos with just that hint of the possibility of redemption. Anyway,' he told him, 'that's what Trevor thinks.'

Black nodded to himself and went away. Not long afterwards, he came back again with his solution:

Good times ... won't you give me the good times ...

Mackintosh kept a tape of this in his drawer. Sometimes in the future, when he was feeling in need of a little light relief, he would take it out and play it and chuckle gently to himself.

Trevor Nunn then offered to try. Although he had little experience as a lyricist, he understood Eliot and what was needed in this context. *Memory*, he told them, *that's got to be the theme.*

There were only a few weeks to the opening night of the show. Nunn spent what little spare time he had struggling through the *Collected Poems of T. S. Eliot* in his search for inspiration. Andrew was becoming increasingly anxious. He was convinced the show was going to fail. One day, he finally snapped.

'Cameron,' he told him frantically, 'it's going to be a disaster! *It's going to be a disaster!'*

Mackintosh had not seen him quite so agitated before. They were standing in the theatre, which Napier appeared to be dismantling bit by bit. Another of Andrew's commitments under the indemnity he had made was to reinstate the original theatre after the alterations. They were still short of backers. In the midst of all this Nunn was trying to direct his first musical.

'Andrew,' Mackintosh said, 'I think we'd better get out of Trevor's hair.'

They drove to Belgravia and visited a church at which T. S. Eliot had been a regular worshipper. After offering up a prayer of their own they adjourned to Eaton Place. Fortified with drink, they then returned to the fray.

Three weeks before the show was to open, Nunn came up with a half-finished lyric. True to his word, he called it *Memory*. Judi Dench meanwhile, having mastered the role of Grizabella, had strained her Achilles tendon and been removed to hospital. Nunn sent her a copy of the lyrics to learn in bed. A few days later, word-perfect, she hobbled gingerly into the theatre. Alone on the moonlit stage, like the true professional she was, she sang *Memory* to a deserted house. Then she hobbled off the stage, tripped on the ramp, and pitched headfirst into the front stalls.

There followed yet another emergency last-minute meeting between producer and composer.

'Andrew,' said Mackintosh, 'what about Elaine?'

Thus it was that Mackintosh was dispatched to the BBC, where Elaine Paige was working. In a hotel next door he offered her the role of Grizabella the Glamour Cat in Andrew Lloyd Webber's new musical. She did not take much persuading. After a couple of days' intensive coaching she was word-perfect. The only problem was that Trevor Nunn had still not managed to complete the fruits of his debut as lyricist and they were still uncertain as to the exact words she was supposed to sing.

'Get hold of Tim,' Andrew told Mackintosh. 'Now Elaine is back in the picture, he's bound to do it.'

Having worked so hard on the song, Nunn was somewhat disappointed to hear that Tim Rice had changed his mind. While Nunn gritted his teeth and Paige rehearsed on stage, Tim barricaded himself in a side room of the theatre and worked on his own lyric to *Memory*. There would be much nonsense in the gossip columns of the press about who wrote *Memory* and what effect it had on the Lloyd Webber–Rice–Paige relationship. The truth was refreshingly prosaic.

Tim produced a lyric which was at least finished, if not entirely to Nunn's liking. Nunn, having subjected it to close textual exegesis worthy of the artistic director of the Royal Shakespeare Company, pronounced quite impartially that he felt his own lyric was still more in keeping with the general tenor of the show.

On the other hand, he still had not finished it. Unlike Tim, and in spite of his admiration for the tune, he probably had no idea how much money he stood to make by writing words to the centrepiece in a musical by Andrew Lloyd Webber. This was on a Monday, two days before the first preview of the show.

On the Tuesday, Nunn was still slaving away at his lyric: 'I've nearly finished,' he told them.

'Well, f——— the lot of you,' was Elaine Paige's considered reaction, 'I'm the one who's got to go on and make a c——— of herself tomorrow night. These f———ing high heels . . . f———ing dry ice . . . fall over and break me neck . . . and all you lot can worry about is the f———ing number. I can't learn another number. I'm going to sing the finished one.'

With that, she went on stage on the Wednesday night and sang the completed Rice lyric. The preview audience loved it. The following night she sang Nunn's version. Mackintosh was in the back of the stalls. He turned to one of the usherettes: 'What,' he asked her, 'did you think of *Memory* tonight?'

'Oh,' she said, 'oh, it was wonderful.'

'Oh good,' said Mackintosh.

'But then,' she said, 'I loved it last night.'

The usherette had not noticed the change. Tim, on the other hand, was rather upset. Afterwards, he would let it be known that his lyric for *Memory* had been rejected by Trevor Nunn with unseemly lack of opposition from Andrew Lloyd Webber. He and Andrew avoided each other and Tim was not at the first night of the show. But this time Tim was in the losing corner. After the dual humiliations of the failure of *Jeeves* and the success of *Evita*, Andrew had finally proved he could work with or without Tim Rice. Andrew, Mackintosh and Nunn had hit on a formula that dispensed with the liability of an independent-minded lyricist. Now they were to pursue it with a vengeance that was to bring them riches beyond the dreams of avarice.

Cats opened at the New London Theatre on 11 May 1981. The stage revolved and with it the first half-dozen rows of the audience. The giant moonlit rubbish heap became the backdrop to a dancing stage for cats. In *Jellicle Songs for Jellicle Cats* the company hypnotised the audience into a trance from which they would not awake until the interval. Bustopher Jones rolled and capered with the gait of the fat cat from clubland. Macavity impressed with the scale of his depravity and *Memory* brought the house down. Even the man with the Irish accent who telephoned halfway through the standing ovation to inform the management that there were three bombs planted under the stage, failed to spoil the show. Afterwards, the cast and audience adjourned in their hundreds to Whitbreads Brewery in the City, where the party went on into the early hours of the morning.

Once again, the critics departed powerlessly into the night:

. . . an exhilarating piece of total theatre that demolishes several myths at one go: that the British can't get a musical together, that our dancers are below American standard and that musicals with a literary source always dilute their origins . . .

As a dance musical *Cats* knocks spots off Mr Fosse's *Dancin'*, but it can't match *West Side Story* or *Chorus Line*, because though it tries to be more than a series of charming vignettes, it doesn't really go anywhere . . .

Many hands have made *Cats* work. But in the end one comes back to Lloyd Webber's remarkable ability to find tunes that fit each specific feline . . .

Cats isn't perfect . . .

Cats is among the most exhilarating and innovative musicals ever staged . . .

'Strange how potent cheap music is,' said Noël Coward. And cheap, I'm afraid, is the right word for Mr Lloyd Webber's music . . .

Lloyd Webber's most remarkable gift burns as constant as ever. He has drunk in the popular sounds and styles of this and other centuries to produce evocative melodies and fine orchestrations . . .

Don't miss it . . .

Go and see it . . .

Cats had already taken £400,000 in advance bookings. Andrew and Mackintosh had a success on their hands which exceeded their wildest dreams. They decided to go to America to sell it. As a reward for all their hard work, they booked first class berths on the transatlantic liner, the *QE2*.

At first this was rather like checking into an expensive nursing home. Within a day or so it was like being back at boarding school. They began to like it; in fact even Andrew forgot about the outside world for a while, and about musicals. To the two self-confessed epicures the important matters in life now consisted of what to eat and drink. The huge *à la carte* menu contained surprises which were not always of a pleasant nature. The meats and the seafood were excellent; but what brought the conversation down to earth, was an impenetrable avocado mousse.

The tope was covered with gelatine. Andrew and Mackintosh, both heavily intoxicated, began to attack it with spoons.

'What are we going to do,' BANG, 'about *Tell Me on a Sunday*?'

'Why don't we do something,' WOBBLE, 'with *Variations*?'

'Why ever not?'

Eventually Andrew said: 'What shall we call it?'

Mackintosh hardly paused: 'Why don't we call it *Song and Dance*?' he said, 'because that's exactly what it is.'

The liner cruised on to New York, where Andrew and Mackintosh spent several days reconnoitring theatres, ballrooms and disused opera houses. Broadway managements and producers had already begun viewing the show in London, with the Shubert Organisation, which had staged *Evita*, heading the pack.

Back in London, Andrew had the future of his relationship with Tim to consider. Tim had sent him a 4000-word, scene-by-scene synopsis of *Chess*, his idea for a musical about the game of love. After the success of *Cats*, Andrew had less need to prove that he could do without his partner. The previous winter they had spent a pleasant if fruitless week trying to work on ideas in the South of France; the prospect of another was not entirely unpleasant.

At the Really Useful Company offices, Biddy was busy organising the production of *Song and Dance.* Don Black was commissioned to write the extra material. Under Brolly's expert stewardship, the Really Useful Company had turned over £337,000 in the past twelve months. Brolly was looking for an accountant to join the company: the right candidate had the prospect of becoming finance director.

He interviewed a number of candidates before taking them to meet Andrew. To those he liked, he said: 'You can work with a creative genius, can't you?'

One candidate, Andrew Duncan, was not sure what he meant.

'Well,' said Brolly, 'someone who will ring you up from the airport as he is about to step on board Concorde to go to New York, and say: "I've got this great idea for a musical." You can work with that sort of person, can't you?'

'Why ever not?'

Brolly took the interviewee to Eaton Place. Biddy did most of the talking; until the candidate asked: 'How do I know there will be another *Cats*?'

Duncan was contemplating a considerable career move. He was interested in the arts; but he also wanted to know how successful Andrew thought he would be in four or five years' time.

Andrew had been largely silent; now he appeared to take an interest.

Biddy said: 'Have you seen Andrew's shows?'

Duncan said he had not.

'Have you listened to the music?'

'I've heard *Variations.*'

'That was a long time ago,' said Biddy. 'You say you take an active interest in the arts. But you haven't seen Andrew's shows?'

'Yes, I do take an active interest. I go to the theatre . . . the opera. But I'm not really into musicals.'

Andrew seemed to experience an electric shock: 'I know it

167

sounds pompous,' he said, 'but you do realise I am the most successful opera composer writing today?'

Duncan did not know what to say to this; but he had a strong impression that the temperature had suddenly lowered in the room.

'I mean,' Andrew went on, 'I suppose there *was* Benjamin Britten. But it's rather a long time since he wrote *Peter Grimes* . . . isn't it?'

They parted on that chilly note. Brolly eventually found the right man for the job.

The Escaway annual turnover had doubled since last year to a staggering £1,190,981, with the directors' remuneration reaching nearly £1 million. The success of *Cats* extended all the way from the stage show to sales of the record and the other merchandise. *Cats* was a bonanza; the financial caution of the composer now reached new levels. He adroitly short-circuited conversations concerning its profitability by quoting a mass of figures to remind people of its high overheads. By the time they saw past this smokescreen, he was usually gone.

It was at this point that Andrew received an invitation to speak at an end of term dinner at his old school, Westminster. He accepted, without quite knowing why, and found himself sharing the bill with comedian John Cleese. As a public appearance this was somewhat less disconcerting than *This Is Your Life*. He arrived alone, having arranged a rendezvous for later at Joe Allen's with his friend the hard-living David Crewe-Read.

When Andrew eventually arrived at the restaurant, his friend was surprised to see him accompanied by an attractive blonde in her early twenties. She had introduced herself to him at the Westminster dinner and they had struck up a conversation. She was bright and bouncy and in carefree mood, having just resigned from her job. She also knew a lot about architecture. She came from a similar background. There were aspects of her which belied her giddy appearance. Andrew, who had been married now for nearly ten years and who, unlike Tim, had little experience of independent women, had extended an invitation to the restaurant. To his surprise, she accepted.

Afterwards, the three of them adjourned to Eaton Place and drank further quantities of wine. Andrew talked excitedly about his favourite subject: his next musical. Before she left, he asked for her telephone number. To her, he was a multi-millionaire whose life plainly consisted of nothing but his work. Besides, his world was full of pretty showgirls of whom he could presumably have taken his pick, although he did not seem the type to do so. She knew he was married; although he did not seem to be the marrying kind, either. She gave him her number and thought little more of it.

That year's Sydmonton Festival included the performance in St Mary's Church of a brief religious work by Andrew Lloyd Webber. Elsewhere that same month, on 24 July, the young woman who would one day sing the soprano part in Westminster Abbey continued her publicity campaign in the *Daily Express*:

Sarah Brightman has always been an early starter. She was the youngest Pan's People dancer at 16, the youngest in the controversial and sexy Hot Gossip at 17 and had a Top Ten record *Starship Trooper* at 18.

But her career has left little time for love. Now at 19 and in the hit musical *Cats* she has fallen for a man older than her father.

He is 46-year-old property developer Max Franklyn, who commutes between home in Minorca and London to see her. 'It is my first true love,' says Sarah, 'and I feel happy all the time . . .

'I had already noticed him because of his red hair. I have had two red-headed boyfriends before and love the fire they always seem to have . . .

'It was like one of those perfect romantic evenings in fiction. Candlelit tables and wine. Suddenly, it clicked.

'That night we went back to his home in London and made love – it was perfect and natural.

'He is a gentleman . . . What does he love about me? I think he likes my freshness and youth.

'My own parents are very good to me. My father feels that my private life is my own business . . . My mother is quite strict, but the only time she asks any questions is when she sees me looking low . . .'

That summer, Tim tried to persuade Andrew to come to grips with *Chess* and Andrew tried to persuade Tim of the attractions of *Aspects of Love*. Andrew even gave a copy of the book to the young woman he had met that night at Westminster School. He asked her to report on it. She sensed both its slightness and its appeal: the characters appeared able to enjoy sensual pleasures without hurting themselves and each other. This had been a piece of conspicuously wishful thinking on the part of the author. Ultimately, the principal character collapsed and died in a paroxysm of jealous rage. She knew Andrew saw it as the vehicle for a dramatic show. She told him she did not think it would work.

She began to see more of him under this arrangement. She was loyal and discreet. Thus it was that, one day, she found herself at the house in West Eaton Place with Barbra Streisand.

Streisand had come over to London to record *Memory*. That day at the house, Andrew accompanied her at the piano. Streisand's vocal body and soul made Elaine Paige's version seem two-dimensional. She and Andrew played around at the piano; she could just pick up a piece of music and sing. As his new friend looked on, Andrew and Streisand, a most unlikely couple, seemed to be transported into a magical world of their own. A couple of days later, the three of them went to the recording studios. Andrew was unable to contain his admiration for Streisand. He kept saying how wonderful it was to be with a woman who *really* understood music.

That summer, while Sarah and the children remained at Sydmonton and Brolly managed the finances and Biddy worked on *Song and Dance*, Andrew intensified his work on *Aspects of Love*. He had already persuaded Tim to write some lyrics (which would later be put to different use). He still had high hopes of working with Tim on the film of *Evita*. But the stars who clamoured to play her were either vocally incapable or too old, or both.

Nor would Streisand touch it: 'I'm not interested,' she said, 'she was a fascist.'

Tim meanwhile intensified his work on *Chess*. But, although it was a departure from Tim's long-standing obsession with fast-living heroes, Andrew could not summon up enthusiasm for the idea.

He began to confide in his new friend. She listened while he described his need to work on his own terms with Tim. He told her about his childhood; about his Aunt Vi and his mother's interest in John Lill. He told her about how he wanted to outdo Stigwood. He took her out to dinner with Billy at *L'Etoile*. Afterwards, Andrew took her back to the Sussex Mansions flat and Billy gave them some whisky. Later, Billy wrote her an affectionate letter. Andrew told her about Sarah; he was worried that her diabetes would be aggravated by the stress any prolonged absence of his might impose on her; he told her they were a couple who had grown up together.

Andrew decided to give her a job. She was to produce a history of the musical. He gave her an office at West Eaton Place. Brolly was affable; Biddy was not amused.

Don Black, meanwhile, was working away at the extra material for *Song and Dance*. The first half of this was an expanded version of *Tell Me On A Sunday*. One of the new songs was called *Married Man*:

> *I'll be discreet*
> *I won't hiss at your wife when I see her*

And though I'd love to be her
She'll never know it . . .

That summer Andrew flew to Paris. His intention was to meet Tim in the South of France to work on *Aspects*. He took his friend with him and in Paris they hired a car. In the middle of Burgundy the car broke down.

Andrew, who was congenitally unable to change a wheel or even identify a spark plug, flew into a rage and telephoned the office in London. He spoke heatedly and at length to Biddy. Then they went off for lunch.

Eventually a replacement car arrived, almost as decrepit as the first. *En route*, he talked more about himself. At school he had been less than at ease. He told her he would like to have been physically admired. When he was not talking, he was humming. When he was not humming, he was worried. He told her about the bottom drawer — the well of tunes from which he ceaselessly had to draw. He lived in fear that one day the bottom drawer would be empty — that 'it', the indefinable, the ineffable, would have gone. Then he started humming again. They clattered on towards the Swiss border and another fruitless Rice–Lloyd Webber reunion.

In November he flew to New York to discuss with the Shubert Organisation their forthcoming production of *Cats* at the Winter Garden. Crewe-Read and Andrew's companion flew out on Concorde to meet him: they were in search of yet another Pre-Raphaelite painting.

Sarah and Biddy made no secret of their distrust of Andrew's new friend. Andrew went to luncheon at Buckingham Palace; a few years later, he would employ one of its residents. Meanwhile, having reassured Sarah and Biddy that there was nothing salacious about the new relationship, he flew to Paris. He needed to write, he told them. He took his friend with him.

They rented the penthouse suite of a Paris hotel. There was a problem transporting a piano up there from the ground floor. She bore this with good humour. One of the things he liked about her, he said, was that he felt relaxed enough to do nothing in her presence. From him, this was a rare compliment.

She tried to teach him about mathematics. *Sweet Sixteen* for example, was *Two to the power of two to the power of two*. Andrew liked that. He wrote a song of the same name. After her giddy looks, he called her 'the golden gollywog'. There was a golden gollywog song for her and, that Christmas, a golden gollywog brooch, with diamond eyes.

He told her about his toy theatre; and how he wanted a real-life theatre of his own.

Cats won five SWET Awards, including the award for best musical. Andrew and Tim were seen together again; this time in the company of the celebrated Spanish tenor Placido Domingo. Domingo had just recorded an album with the American folk singer John Denver, whose career would plumb new depths with his hymn to the victims of the explosion of the Columbia space shuttle. After seeing Domingo in *Tosca*, Andrew and Tim took him to see *Cats*. Domingo would shortly be featured in a BBC TV special singing a song which Andrew and Tim had originally written for *Aspects of Love*.

Andrew was trying to buy his own theatre. He had offered £1,250,000 for the Aldwych in the face of a rival bid from the American producer James Nederlander. The Aldwych had been home for twenty-one years to the Royal Shakespeare Company, which was moving to the Barbican.

£1,250,000 was not enough. Andrew increased his offer to £1,350,000; he had only to stand in the deserted auditorium to be transported back to the toy theatre of his childhood. But Nederlander and his associate Michael Codron had sewn up a

173

deal. Andrew withdrew his offer and continued his search elsewhere.

He stood in the Lyceum, a few yards from the Aldwych, and rhapsodised about acoustics and sightlines. He made enquiries about the Old Vic, the future of which was in doubt since the theatre had gone into liquidation.

At the Young Vic, a musical was in preparation of *Masquerade*, the bestselling treasure hunt book by Kit Williams. The central character was a girl called Tara Treetops, who fell from the clouds to bewitch the hero on his way to the sun. Not long before the show opened, the star was to be seen disporting herself outside the theatre for photocalls. In a white leotard and dancing shoes, she constituted something of a distraction for the rush-hour traffic.

Andrew already knew about Sarah Brightman. He and Crewe-Read had frequently remarked to each other on the attractive and energetic manner of the girl whom one newspaper had described as 'one of those hyper-active pussies from *Cats*'. The *Cats* girls had something of an offstage reputation: Trevor Nunn, then married to the actress Janet Suzman, and designer John Napier had both formed attachments to dancers from the show. In the case of Sarah Brightman, Crewe-Read possibly attached more significance to her exotic manner than to her musical abilities; but the latter was to bring her closer to the attention of Andrew Lloyd Webber.

Meanwhile, his friendship with the golden golliwog continued to divert Crewe-Read and Mackintosh and cause Biddy and Sarah concern. He invited her to Sydmonton, where Jamie Muir filmed them in a parlour version of Chekhov's *The Three Sisters*. They had drinks at Crewe-Read's little house near Sydmonton and she had dinner with Andrew, his mother-in-law and Sarah. He asked her to read *A Diamond As Big As The Ritz* to see if it would make a good musical — she told him it would not. She assiduously carried on researching a history of the musical. She was closer in age to Sarah, but Sarah's relationship with him was in some ways closer to that he had had with his mother. Mothering them all, meanwhile, with increasing exasperation, was Biddy Hayward.

Biddy was happy to project a sophisticated image but, in spite of her jetsetting on Andrew's behalf, she was essentially down to earth. She had a quietly solid marriage to a tunnel engineer called Colin. She and Andrew had a stormy relationship, based on neither quite being able to do without the other. His installation of an outsider in her preserve at West Eaton Place was the last straw. Relations between the two women deteriorated.

Sarah, the woman on whom he depended to a degree way beyond his comprehension, now ventured to make her feelings publicly known.

'I married the first boyfriend I ever had,' she told a reporter. 'I have spent my entire adult life looking after Andrew.'

He *was* neurotic, she added wistfully, and he had a terrible temper when things did not go according to plan.

'If you marry very young,' she said, 'you either grow up together or grow far apart.' She did not say which she thought they had done. 'Our outlook is different today, because we were immature when we married. I have learned patience . . .'

That spring, they held Andrew's thirty-fourth birthday party at the New London Theatre. Andrew and the patient Sarah cut a giant cake while Cameron Mackintosh beamed proprietorially and two hundred showbusiness guests looked on. But Sarah's patience was running out; in less than a year's time, she would not find the attention of the press quite so sympathetic or so welcome.

Song and Dance opened at the Palace Theatre, where *Jesus Christ Superstar* had run for eight years, on 7 April 1982. Andrew and Cameron Mackintosh's back-to-back creation, conceived on the *QE2* over an avocado mousse and billed as 'A Concert For The

175

Theatre' (Mackintosh did not know what that meant, but he knew what sounded good on a poster) was an instant box-office success. The *Cats* investors had rushed to back the show; those who had refused to invest in *Cats* now clamoured to be included in this one, but the names of those of little faith had been faithfully remembered, by Sarah, and they were all refused.

Tell Me On A Sunday, *Song and Dance*'s first half, had grown in its charting of the journey of a dim English girl abroad in America. Apart from *Married Man*, Andrew and Don Black had come up with a good new song in the shape of *The Last Man In My Life*, another out-take from their abandoned version of *Sunset Boulevard*. The second half consisted of Wayne Sleep and company dancing memorably to *Variations*, the introduction to which had spawned the opening to *Cats* in which Sleep had opened as principal dancer.

But this time the critics scented weaknesses. While the audience went away satisfied and *Evita* and *Cats* still ran in the West End, they sharpened their pencils:

> It is a long time since I have sat through a more ostentatious, less theatrically coherent evening . . .

> I am delighted that Miss Webb, who took over in the role of Evita, has been given her big stage chance. The voice is full, expressive and with a fine range. But shut your eyes and it could be anyone. No distinguishing features . . .

> The mundane lyrics for the first half are by Don Black . . .

> . . . all the memorability of a year-old women's magazine story read in a dentist's waiting room . . .

> Mr Lloyd Webber's score catches its monotonously glum or fractious tone with dispiriting accuracy. Miss Webb's is a clear, exact and expressive, if unduly nasal voice; but amplification in this vast theatre has the same unflattering effect as magnification has on one's face in one's shaving mirror . . .

. . . the second half of the programme thrills in a way that the first half dismally fails to do . . .

The flaw is that nothing happens to her in New York (and what's she doing there? For a living, I mean?) . . .

What the talented Lloyd Webber and his team . . . have done is mount a musical without the bother of finding a story or working out a plot . . .

Song and Dance would remain at the Palace Theatre for the next two years. Andrew had always liked the Palace: built by Richard D'Oyly Carte, its magnificent Victorian façade dominates Cambridge Circus and makes it the most imposing theatre in London. The Palace was made for musicals: apart from *Jesus Christ Superstar* and *Song and Dance*, other productions had included Rodgers and Hammerstein's *Flower Drum Song* and *Oklahoma!*

The owners of the Palace were a little-known company called Stock Conversions Ltd. The manager and co-owner with Lord Delfont of its rapidly expiring lease was Sir Emile Littler. Littler was the man who had once told Stigwood's associate Bob Swash: 'Oh, my boy, we *never* call up the overcall.' He now found himself having to refute rumours that his theatre was about to be bought lock, stock and barrel, by Andrew Lloyd Webber.

Andrew also persisted in his enquiries concerning the possible sale of the Old Vic. The Charity Commissioners in charge of the sale had let it be known that they were obliged to sell the theatre to the highest bidder rather than the most artistically suitable contender. Here again, he was outbid by another party, the Canadian entrepreneur Ed Mirvish, and by his own innate caution with money.

As he became still richer, his concern to refute rumours of the same understandably grew more insistent. That year the Escaway accounts alone revealed a turnover of £1.75 million, while the Really Useful Company increased its turnover to £443,000. He did not object to it being wrongly reported that he had mortgaged everything he owned to put up £500,000 in guarantees for *Cats.*

He told others: 'I'm not good at investing. The last few years, I haven't really thought about money. But five years ago, I was very worried . . . God, I thought we might go under. I was going to take precautionary action. I mean, I would have left England, but then the Tories got in and made it easier. Now I've paid off all my mortgages. I feel more confident . . .'

Andrew could never quite understand why the likes of Bowles and Swash tried to encourage him to consider the virtues of socialism. Surely, building the perfect world was simply a matter of finding the money. The same sort of assumption enabled him to tell people that being happily married for so long had given him a solid base which enabled him to get on with his work.

Sarah's was the view from the 'solid base': 'We don't have holidays,' she told an interviewer. 'Andrew can't bear to be away from the telephone. He never relaxes. He has a hundred ideas at a time. He is exhausting to be with . . .'

The rumours about the golden golliwog had pushed her patience beyond its limits. But the latter had realised that she could not spend for ever researching a history of the musical. One evening she went round to Eaton Place and told Andrew so. There were tears on both sides. She suddenly realised the truth: he genuinely had difficulty seeing the situation from her – and Sarah's – point of view. Thereafter they saw less of each other but others, Jean included, now looked on apparently helpless as Andrew and Sarah laboured under the tensions which had surfaced in their marriage.

That year's Sydmonton Festival included a musical tribute to Duke Ellington by Derek Jewell and a rough workshop version of a new musical by the Chairman of Escaway Ltd.

This one was about trains. Andrew still harboured the desire to write a musical based on the railway stories of the Reverend

E. W. Awdry. Thomas the Tank Engine, Henry the Green Engine and James the Really Useful Engine had been embedded in his imagination ever since the days of the toy trains at Harrington Court. Together with the remains of his treasured toy theatre, the remnants of his train set were still safely stowed in the attic at Sydmonton Court, where a man was hired from time to time to dust off the track and sidings.

Tim was as uninterested in the idea now as he had been five years ago. Andrew had found a willing lyricist in the shape of the musician, performer and wit, Richard Stilgoe. Stilgoe and Andrew had set to work on the rough outline of a *Cinderella* idea in which a steam engine won a steam rally, beat a 'beastly' diesel engine and a 'horrible' electric engine and sparked off a steam revival. In keeping with this idea, Andrew would shortly engage in unsuccessful negotiations to buy the Roundhouse Theatre, a converted North London engine shed. So far, going by the monosyllabic if rather more evocative precedent of *Cats*, the work in progress enjoyed the title of *Trains*.

That summer, the Lloyd Webber family gathered *en masse* in New York in preparation for the Broadway opening of *Cats*. Andrew, Sarah, Imogen, Nicholas, Billy, Jean, Julian and Celia were all on hand. After a while the children were sent home to Sydmonton. Andrew, Sarah and Mackintosh remained, in the suite at the Mayflower Hotel, on Central Park West near Columbus Circle.

A Broadway production now cost as much to stage as an averagely expensive Hollywood movie. $3 million or $4 million were not unusual figures. The costs of failure were high. *A Doll's Life*, directed by Hal Prince, had just closed after a few nights and lost millions. *Ghosts* starring Richard Burton and Elizabeth Taylor had done the same. *Lolita*, directed by Frank Dunlop and starring Donald Sutherland, was another casualty. On Broadway, 'the fabulous invalid', failure was never far away.

A successful transfer from elsewhere at least cost less than an original production. Fourteen British productions were currently showing. They included *Amadeus, Pirates of Penzance, Evita* and *Joseph*; black market tickets for *Nicholas Nickleby* were fetching $500 a pair. The *Cats* advance publicity had been spectacular even by Broadway standards. Mackintosh and De Wynters' integrated packaging had paid off. The show was sold out for the next six months with advance bookings of over $10 million.

Andrew seemed to be giving an interview every fifteen minutes. One of these was with the BBC television director Robin Lough.

Lough's father Ernest had achieved lasting fame as the first superstar choirboy, with his rendition of *Oh, For The Wings Of A Dove!* Lough and Andrew had met a few years earlier, after *Variations*. In those days talking to Andrew was simply a matter of obtaining his telephone number and arranging a place to meet. They had chatted on about church music and Billy and about Sir George Thalben Ball, the great organist who had also recorded a Paganini variation.

Lough had had rather more trouble this time in arranging a meeting. After numerous telephone conversations via the Really Useful Company, Andrew eventually agreed to meet him on top of the RCA building, with its memorable gargoyles in the shapes of record styli and its panoramic views of Manhattan. Andrew needed the publicity and this was a fitting place to film an interview with the latest King of New York.

Andrew, Lough, Lough's production assistant and the interviewer Barry Norman arrived on the roof of the skyscraper. It was a beautiful morning; the Manhattan skyline shimmered in the haze.

Andrew said: 'I must have a cup of coffee.'

'Andrew,' Norman said, 'the nearest coffee bar is at the bottom of the building.'

'I must have a cup of coffee.'

Lough's assistant offered to go and fetch one, but the offer was turned down. Lough told the film crew to take a break while they trooped downstairs to the coffee bar; then they came back up and did the interview, Manhattan skyline and all.

Afterwards, through gritted teeth, Lough and Norman thanked him for being so co-operative: 'Good luck with *Cats*,' they said. 'We hope it goes well.'

'Would you like some tickets?' he asked.

As these were currently fetching hundreds of dollars on the black market, the response was rapid and unequivocal.

'Call Sarah at the hotel. I'll make sure there are two tickets for you.'

Thus it was that Lough found himself knocking on the door at the Mayflower Hotel. Sarah was alone. When he admired the gracious apartment she told him Andrew wanted to buy it. She gave him the tickets and he departed. On the way back down, he realised the name of the tune being played in the lift. It was *Memory*.

Cats opened to that fabulous first night audience at the Winter Garden on Broadway on 7 October 1982. Andrew escorted Valerie Eliot. Matthew Evans, the Managing Director of Faber & Faber, her late husband's publishers and to whose Chairman he had originally written the poems as letters to a child, hovered close behind. Once through the crush, they and a thousand others took their seats around the moonlit rubbish dump. The overture began.

Afterwards, the whole glittering company adjourned to the Waldorf Astoria. The band played *Chariots of Fire* and *Memory* and an army of waiters served up roast beef and Yorkshire pudding. Andrew sat with Billy and Jean and kissed an uneasy Sarah who shooed him away with the instruction to circulate. Mikhail Baryshnikov, Mary Tyler Moore, Placido Domingo, Andy Warhol, Bianca Jagger and Steven Spielberg played themselves and Trevor Nunn talked on and on to the men from the

181

BBC. The London *Times* man did his best and the *New York Times* man his worst. Andrew bought the cat cartoon from the latter for his mother to hang on her wall. *Cats* was a guaranteed hit but, while the dream gathered steam at the Winter Garden, the pressure mounted daily at Sydmonton Court.

On 29 October, three weeks after he had attended the spectacular party at the Waldorf Astoria, Billy Lloyd Webber died at the age of sixty-eight. The man whose amiable melancholy had permeated the bohemian life at Harrington Court, who had written down the piano score for *Joseph* and nursed unfulfilled desires to become a successful composer, had lived to see his eldest son become his most famous creation. Billy had always wanted a daughter and was hard hit by the deterioration of Andrew and Sarah's marriage. Biddy, too, had reached the end of her patience and resigned as director of both Escaway and the Really Useful Company.

That December, a new Charles Strouse operetta came from the Buxton Festival to the Lyric Theatre, Hammersmith. The operetta was *Nightingale*, the musical director was the long-time Lloyd Webber associate David Firman and the bird in question was the ex-cat, Sarah Brightman.

Andrew had heard flattering descriptions of her from Arlene Phillips, who had choreographed *Hot Gossip* and was now at work on the choreography of *Trains*. *Trains* had begun life like *Joseph*, as a cantata for children, but now Andrew, Phillips and Nunn were reworking it for roller-skaters. The Broadway producers liked that. Andrew had also given it a new name: the title of an obscure piece by Elgar for children. He called it *Starlight Express*.

The star of *Nightingale* received good reviews. To play the lead successfully in a new show from the author of *Applause* and *Annie* was a great achievement in the eyes of Andrew Lloyd Webber.

Strouse, too, had a dry respect for Andrew: 'Whatever you say about that show,' he liked to say, 'it sure gives you a lot of cats.'

Sarah Brightman could not only sing and dance; now, it seemed, she could combine 'exciting trills with a leggy, elfin grace'. Others, too, remarked on the 'pure, sweet voice that can trill up and down scales like a songbird'. Sarah had been working hard on her voice with her coach, the former Scottish Opera singer Ian Adam. Andrew, in his capacity as impresario and talent-spotter, engineered a meeting and was staggered by what he heard.

Her voice lacked colour, but she was possessed of a truly tremendous *tessitura*. This extended from a strong, virtually tenor-like G below middle C all the way up to a top D – two and a half octaves in all. This was the girl he and Crewe-Read had so often joked about. He invited her to Eaton Place. He played the piano and she sang. She was not Streisand, but she could sing. Not only that, she could sing Rachmaninov in Russian. *How wonderful it was, to be with a woman who really understood music . . .*

That Christmas, one performance of *Joseph and the Amazing Technicolor Dreamcoat*, still playing on Broadway, occurred in London. But this one was unique: it took place at Colet Court School, for which it had first been commissioned by the late Alan Doggett. Doggett's choirboys were now in their twenties, but his successor at Colet Court, Ian Hunter, was still wielding the baton.

It was exactly fifteen years since Hunter had met the multi-millionaire composer whom he now read about in the papers. The prickly, eccentric young man in the music room of the old school buildings near Hammersmith Broadway had long since found the Broadway for which he was really searching. *Joseph* had a knowing innocence, a childlike worldliness, which Andrew would never recapture. Ideas which began as cantatas for children these days soon disappeared in a welter of dry ice and roller-skates. Andrew did not attend this performance of the show which had launched his career.

Andrew and Sarah Brightman soon found the need to give their relationship some sort of professional foundation. As one newspaper put it:

> As a musician, he is become increasingly interested in writing for women singers with a wider vocal range than 12 notes but who yet, unlike most operatic sopranos, care about language and do not distort vowel sounds. He had written (with his *Memory* lyricist, Mr Nunn) a unique solo for Sarah Brightman, star of the Lyric Hammersmith's *Nightingale*, who looks lovely and fulfils these demands.

Sarah Brightman took care not to distort her vowel sounds and prepared to take over from Bonnie Langford in *Pirates of Penzance*. Andrew, the composer of the unique solo, absorbed himself in the Really Useful Theatre Company's first wholly independent production in the West End, *Daisy Pulls It Off*. The Really Useful Company offices were set to move to 20 Greek Street, within striking distance of the West End theatres and in the heart of Soho, a stone's throw from David Land's offices in Wardour Street.

Apart from the corporate requirements of the Really Useful Company and the Really Useful Theatre Company, however, there was another reason for the move: this was so that Sarah, Imogen and Nicholas could move out of Sydmonton and into the house at 11 West Eaton Place. Sarah had set a date for a separation.

This was Monday, 18 April 1983. This was also the night of the opening of *Daisy Pulls It Off*. Denise Deegan's nostalgic essay on the days of Angela Brazil charted the tale of Daisy, an elementary schoolgirl who triumphs at the snooty Grangewood

School for Girls. Next to Andrew, Sarah and Jean sat gamely in the front row while the cast wielded their hockey sticks and went through a triumphant first-night performance. Afterwards he was going on to the first-night party to meet Sarah Brightman. In the circumstances, Sarah and Jean had decided to go elsewhere for dinner.

She and Andrew said goodbye to each other and Jean took her outside the theatre to a taxi. Once inside, she broke down in tears. Jean took her back to her flat at Sussex Mansions. That night, while Andrew Lloyd Webber partied with Sarah Brightman at the Dolphin Square Restaurant, Pimlico, Jean and Sarah Lloyd Webber dined off frozen fish fingers from an all-night foodstore on the Brompton Road.

6

The Second Mrs Lloyd Webber

In April 1983, Andrew issued a statement which he hoped would pre-empt any unwelcome enquiries into his private affairs. In the event, it had precisely the opposite effect:

> In the past two weeks there appears to have been speculation about my marriage to Sarah Lloyd Webber. I want to record that my affection for Sarah is still very great, but unhappily we will be seeking a divorce in the near future.
>
> I also want to confirm my great friendship for Sarah Brightman. Sarah Brightman and I have known each other professionally for several years but it is only recently that our relationship has developed.
>
> Both of us are entirely aware that our personal circumstances do not allow us to take our friendship further for the moment. However, it is our present intention to marry when we are honourably able to.

There had been little or no such speculation. Sarah Lloyd Webber had simply called his bluff. Andrew realised that this time her intentions to divorce him were serious. Unlike Tim and Elaine Paige, he and Sarah Brightman were not going to get away with it for long.

He tried to promote an image of himself as a man torn between his devotion to family and his love for another woman. For a few days this strategy seemed to work. Jean, Julian and Sarah Lloyd Webber all steadfastly refused to comment. So did Biddy and Crewe-Read. So did Sarah Brightman.

The only person who was unable to keep his mouth shut, in the event, was Andrew.

He threw a party in New York's Studio 54 to celebrate the fact that with *Evita*, *Cats* and *Joseph* he was the first composer to have three shows running on Broadway since Richard Rodgers had achieved it with *Carousel*, *The King and I* and *South Pacific*. As the evening wore on, however, it seemed to many present that the real reason they were there was to celebrate the fact that, unlike Rodgers, Andrew seemed to think he could also have two women running at the same time.

'I adore my wife and children,' he told them – then went on: 'but Sarah and I desperately want to get married. This is one of the most painful periods of my life.' He and Sarah locked in another passionate embrace. 'You see!' he cried. 'You could hardly pretend that this isn't happening!'

Nobody was pretending, except Andrew. As the British press began to take an interest, he seemed unable to acknowledge the truth.

'My marriage isn't over!' he maintained to one newspaper. 'I'm still living at home. I've been married for twelve years. I adore my wife . . .'

He was living at the Pierre Hotel, New York with Sarah Brightman at the time. When they returned to London, what might have been a brief item for the gossip columns had become a full-blown tabloid story. This was better than speculating about Tim and Elaine, or who was going to play *Evita*. Andrew continued to cast himself in the role of agonised victim of love and of his own emotional honesty. Sarah Brightman walked straight into the newspapers' trap.

'I've met Sarah, Andrew's wife,' [she told a reporter] 'and I like her very much . . . There is no problem with Andrew's children – I adore them.

'When Andrew and I are married I want us to have children of our own . . .

'My mother absolutely adores him. And I was *so* worried about my parents' reaction . . .

'That was a big hurdle for me, the day I took Andrew home to meet them. Of course I knew that I wasn't just taking on a man – I was taking on a whole new lifestyle . . .

'Andrew's world is one of travel, entertaining and large houses to run. He is also a famous face, so I've had to get used to a certain lack of privacy.

'I don't mind that too much . . .'

Straightfaced, the reporter asked her if she did not worry just a little, in case she was tempted by such a prospect of domestic bliss to give up her career:

The question removes her smile and for the first time you notice ambition on the cute face of the girl who had a hit with *Starship Trooper*.

'I might be Mrs Lloyd Webber, but I'll always be Sarah Brightman,' she says firmly.

She said: 'I've always wanted to make it. Ever since I was a child I knew I would have to push to get anywhere.

'So I'm not about to stop now.'

No, but the large diamonds on the third finger of her left hand will ensure that she will not have to push quite so hard.

The press could not believe their luck. Nor could they see any reason why Sarah Lloyd Webber should not have her say. This was in spite of the fact that Sarah, unlike Andrew and Sarah Two, as the latter had necessarily become known, had maintained a dignified silence to date.

The letters from the *Daily Brute*, trying to persuade her to sell her side of the story, now arrived in piles on the doormat of the house in West Eaton Place: 'It may help you through this difficult time . . .'

But Sarah One had no intention of breaking her silence.

Andrew had already formed one private company, Oiseau Productions, to produce records by the songbird with whom he had fallen in love while she was in *Nightingale*. On 19 May, four weeks after he and Sarah One had separated, Andrew formed another private company. This one was called Chackton Ltd. Its purpose was to own and manage a theatre.

Cats won seven Broadway Tony awards, including the award for best musical. Valerie Eliot went to New York to collect them on behalf of Andrew and her late husband. Julian spent £192,000 on a Stradivarius cello and made sure that the newspapers were aware of the fact. His thoughts on marriage were reflected in his relief that, in spite of his absolute dedication to his art, his marriage to Celia had lasted nine years to date. Like Andrew, he had married young to the first girl he met. Like Andrew's, too, his own marriage had only a short time to live.

Sarah One looked after the children and tried to complete the move to West Eaton Place. Andrew and Sarah Two went on holiday to the South of France. From here Andrew issued a stream of denials that Sarah would automatically be given the starring role in *Starlight Express*. Sarah, he said, would have to audition like everyone else.

In England, Andrew's wife's lawyers waded through his assets in search of a divorce settlement. Escaway alone had turned over £2.5 million that year and the Really Useful Company, of which Sarah was also a major shareholder with Andrew and Brolly, turned over in excess of £2 million. Andrew was hoping that Sarah would accept £500,000; but her solicitors, Clintons of Upper St Martins Lane, had decided that she should receive rather more than that.

Andrew had his eye on premises just round the corner from their offices. While Sarah Lloyd Webber was awarded a 'quickie' decree nisi by Judge Slot in the Divorce Court, Andrew was buying the Palace Theatre on Cambridge Circus, where audiences still flocked nightly to see *Song and Dance*. The Really Useful Company and Chackton Ltd., the latter wholly owned by Andrew, each acquired a fifty per cent interest at a cost of around £1.6 million. At last, in this magnificent building, he had acquired his own, grown-up, life-size version of the toy theatre he had possessed as a boy.

The ninth Sydmonton Festival was the first without Sarah and the children. The cricket match between the guests and the villagers was rained off, but there were other attractions. With the proximity of Greenham Common in mind, the mind, the theme of the festival debate was Nuclear Disarmament. Videos on the big screen in the billiard room showed work in progress on *Starlight Express*. There was a cabaret rendition of songs for *Aspects of Love*, with lyrics by Trevor Nunn. The young violinist Nigel Kennedy gave a much-admired recital; as did Sarah Brightman.

As well as being besotted by thePre-Raphaelite looks which had encouraged him to shower her with gifts including a Porsche sports car, Andrew believed that Sarah had the makings of a great *coloratura* soprano. He was going to make her the biggest thing since Callas. He had in mind a number of vehicles to show off her extraordinary *tessitura*. He arranged for her to have private lessons with Placido Domingo. Sarah trained and trained for the opera stage with the same remorseless application she had shown with Hot Gossip. Andrew's impresario instincts now knew no bounds.

That month they also travelled to the opening of *Cats* in Vienna. The show was already a smash hit in London, New York, Boston and Budapest. This was the first time *Cats* had been presented in a proscenium production; Gillian Lynne directed and the opening was a success.

In London, Biddy Hayward returned after her eleven-month absence to take charge of the Palace Theatre; she and Andrew would never be able to do without each other for long. Sarah Brightman was divorced from Andrew Graham-Stewart and she and Andrew Two now lived mainly at the flat in Eaton Place, but Andrew's decree absolute still depended on his agreeing a divorce settlement with his wife.

At the Old Vic, the theatre he had tried to buy and which was now owned by Ed Mirvish, preparations were under way for *Blondel*, the new musical by Stephen Oliver and Tim Rice, produced by Cameron Mackintosh. The character of Richard the Lionheart's favourite troubadour had edged the hero of *Come Back Richard* from the centre of the stage in Tim's new version, which none the less still strongly supported the ethos of short, fast lives and violent coves who hung around the Middle East. *Saladin Days* made a comeback in *Blondel*, the plot of which had Richard missing in action and Blondel dreaming of finding him and of showbusiness stardom for his backing group, the Blondettes.

Motivation, Tim freely admitted, was harder to come by these days. *Blondel* would not set the West End alight. Tim's publishing interests, his cricket team and his ideas for other musicals would continue to jostle for positions in his mind. One of the latter was now under way: he had recently spent several weeks working on *Chess* with Abba in a hotel on the Baltic.

He had been unimpressed with Andrew's flirtation with Don Black and had not forgotten the bickering over *Memory*, but his attitude to Andrew was the same as ever: he was loyal, and he enjoyed the occasional joke at Andrew's expense. Writing a musical with him, he liked to tell people, was like negotiating with a multinational corporation. He quickly dispelled the image Andrew liked to promote of himself as a man who did not particularly care about money.

'He was definitely always good with money,' he told people, 'it was me who found it all boring. I didn't want to spend half my life at accountants' meetings. When we had those meetings, I'd take along one or two people, but Andrew always seemed to turn up with about nine advisers. He loves all that. You know – half a Liberian tanker. Forests in Wales.'

On 15 November 1983, a competition for organists began at the church of St John's, Smith Square, in memory of Billy Lloyd

Webber. Andrew was absorbed in preparations for *Starlight Express*. This was to be the biggest, the most spectacular, the most ambitious production yet. The entire interior of the Apollo Theatre in Victoria was being gutted and criss-crossed with railway tracks. A huge sound system hung silently like an unprimed bomb. The last show at the Apollo had been a revival of *Fiddler on the Roof* with Topol. Now, the effect was a cross between Grand Central Station and a disco from Dante's *Inferno*. At Eaton Place, Andrew polished the image of himself as an artistic risk-taker.

'I could come completely unstuck over this,' he told his old friend Derek Jewell. 'Perhaps people won't understand what I'm trying to do. I'm taking more chances than I've ever taken before.'

The element of risk would be almost entirely restricted to the cast, who would be expected to hurtle around the auditorium at speeds of up to thirty-five miles per hour. Long gone was the *Cinderella* concept of a story based on the railway stories of E. W. Awdry. Andrew and Stilgoe had been informed by Trevor Nunn that this idea had 'a depressing and cosy Englishness'. What *Starlight* needed, Nunn told them, was roller skates.

Stilgoe had been working on the lyrics for some time and found this a little difficult to swallow. But he bit his tongue and kept his job. *Cats* had made Nunn, Gillian Lynne and Valerie Eliot millionaires and millionairesses. Stilgoe was a hired hand; and hired hands, like dead men, delivered the goods and did not answer back. Only in this way did they prosper under the new, winning formula which dispensed with the liability of independent-minded lyricists.

Jewell listened as Andrew expanded on his theme of himself as financially disinterested artistic risk-taker but, away from the hype of his coming show, Andrew had in reality embarked on a different artistically risky venture. The salient ingredients were the death of his father and the voice of the woman he wanted to marry. The setting would be a sacred one. But the promotion would bring out every aspect of the battle between God and Mammon for the soul of the composer.

On 9 January 1984, a forty-eight-ton steam locomotive from the Kent and East Sussex Railway appeared on the road outside the Apollo Theatre, Victoria. Inside the theatre, forty workmen hammered away under the direction of John Napier and the cast of *Starlight Express* met for the first time.

After *Cats*, which Andrew had taken to calling 'the pension fund', angels had rushed to invest in the show. Investors who had put up £1000 for *Cats* were now £3500 richer. Andrew's Really Useful Theatre Company, this time without Cameron Mackintosh as co-producer, had swiftly raised the £2.3 million woth of £2000 shares needed to stage the show. £1.4 million had been spent on redesigning the interior of the theatre. Phonogram had paid over £1 million for the record. The show needed to sell out for forty-three weeks before the investors began to see a return. It was already sold out for fourteen.

The Royal Gala performance of *Starlight Express* was set for 22 March. This was Andrew's thirty-sixth birthday. As the day grew nearer, activity at the Apollo grew frenzied; and the need became pressing for a solution to another problem: Andrew and Sarah's divorce.

Sarah's solicitors had waited for Andrew to come up with a better offer than £500,000. Andrew had been impatient to marry Sarah Two before 22 March, not least so that he could present her to the Queen and Prince Philip as his wife. The game of brinkmanship which ensued was always bound to go in favour of Sarah Lloyd Webber.

Andrew had continued to stress the high level of his overheads and the inaccuracy of estimates of his wealth, which varied from £65,000 a day to £300 million in all – a figure which led to the unwelcome sobriquet 'Andrew Lloyd's Bank'. He had even claimed on one occasion that he could not afford to invest in *Starlight Express*. He would later maintain that his divorce was held up because he could not lay his hands on the last £25,000. In the event, he and Sarah settled for a seven-figure sum and were granted their decree absolute.

On 22 March, the day of the opening night, Andrew Lloyd Webber and Sarah Brightman were married by special licence at Kingsclere, near Sydmonton. Sarah's parents were the only guests. Afterwards her mother took photographs. Then they sped off to London.

Starlight Express opened as planned in the presence of the Queen and the Duke of Edinburgh. Andrew introduced them to the new Mrs Lloyd Webber. Then they all sat back to watch, while thirty-three men and women on roller skates pretended to be railway engines and railway carriages in order to determine which was the fastest engine in America.

A twelve piece band occupied the orchestra pit, but the main source of sound was the powerful synthesised disco-rock music which roared out of the loudspeakers. The cast hurtled around the banked track at high speed and went through an exhausting repertoire of current street-dancing styles from backflips to break-dancing. *AC/DC* flirted with the sexual ambivalence of pomp-rock and *Uncoupled* was a Country and Western parody. *Only He Has the Power to Move Me* was a big ballad which imposed big demands on the singer in the Lloyd Webber tradition and *He Whistled At Me* had its origins in *Variations*. The anthropomorphised descendants of the Revd. E. W. Awdry whistled and hooted at each other all night long.

The entire show took place at top speed and maximum volume. The first night audience, including the Queen and the Duke of Edinburgh, came away deafened and dazzled and at first unable to remember a word. Then the lyrics came trickling back . . . *Rolling Stock, Rolling Stock . . . Freight is Great . . . Nobody Can*

Do It Like A Steam Train . . . and with them, the awareness of a paradox in the story. Rusty the Stream Train, having chuffed up a prayer to his ineffable deity the starlight express, had just triumphed over electricity, without which the show would not have been possible in the first place:

> The most recklessly extravagant entertainment to hit London since the retirement from public life of Inigo Jones . . .
>
> A mindless spectacle of stunning stage management but no actual theatrical intensity at all . . .
>
> Artistically dead as a landing strip . . .
>
> A millionaire's folly which happens to be open to the public . . .
>
> A triumph of technology over banality . . .
>
> This banal storyline is told in lyrics of thumping predictability . . .
>
> A triumph of engineering over content that dazzles the eye but numbs the brain . . .
>
> Whatever happened to heart and soul?

Starlight Express was an instant smash hit.

Richard Stilgoe, who had done his best with the lyrics in the circumstances, told people: 'It's my forty-first birthday and the notices are the best present I could have hoped for – either way they would have been my birthday present from the critics.'

Five years later, Stilgoe's one and half per cent share of the royalties meant he would still be giving away over £150,000 a year to charity.

In May *Song and Dance* closed after two years at Andrew's new theatre, the Palace. Late that month, Andrew staged a one-off performance of the show filmed for American television and starring Sarah in the role made well known by Marti Webb.

195

The reviewers were unkind about her performance, hard as it was to imagine her as a vulnerable English girl abroad in America. They also mocked Andrew's naïve insistence that Sarah had had to audition for the part. The bad publicity which had followed that first public statement about the break-up of his marriage would never quite go away. Henceforth, she would be portrayed in the British popular press as the ex-dancer and marriage-wrecker, while he would be painted as the multi-millionaire showman who had uncharacteristically allowed passion to cloud his judgement.

That May he was, with Charlie Chaplin and Paul McCartney, one of the few Britons ever to make the cover of *Time* magazine. 'Andrew Lloyd's Bank' became *Andrew Lloyd Webber: Master of the Musical*. The American press would be kinder to him; Andrew frequently threatened to go and live there. The British tax system continued to irritate him, but he could not imagine life without Sydmonton.

Instead, he accumulated bolt-holes in Europe and across the Atlantic. He sold the flat in Eaton Place and bought a grander, two-storey affair for himself and Sarah, a little further away from Sarah One and the children, off Park Lane among the ambassadors, oil billionaires and exiled rulers. He investigated property in his beloved South of France, settling on a villa in the village of St Jean-Cap Ferrat. He still shuttled between them at the same punishing pace but, unlike Sarah One, this lifestyle seemed to suit the second Mrs Lloyd Webber.

That summer, members of the Lloyd Webber family continued to find their way into the newspapers. Julian announced that he had been writing a book entitled *Travels with My Cello*. According to one article, he hated 'to go even a day without practising and he and Celia have decided not to have children as they would inevitably disrupt Julian's absolute dedication to his music.'

Sarah Two found herself being told off at the sweltering Royal Ascot race meeting for being insufficiently dressed to enter the Royal Enclosure. Eventually she and Andrew were admitted.

The Lloyd Webber companies continue to prosper – *Cats* and *Starlight Express* sold out night after night seemingly without end; Escaway's turnover rose by £1 million to £3.5 million; the Really Useful Company turnover trebled to an astonishing £6.5 million in only its fifth year of proper trading. Now, at the age of thirty-six, Andrew was poised not only to become the first ever company director to have a sacred work performed in Westminster Abbey; he was also about to be the first composer in history to see shares in his company appear in the London Stock Exchange.

Sydmonton lay only twenty-five miles or so north of Winchester, the cathedral town of Hampshire. Apårt from the eponymous public school, which rivalled even the great school of Westminster, the old city was dominated by the Cathedral. The Organist and Master of Music of Winchester Cathedral was Martin Neary.

Neary was in his own quiet way no mean entrepreneur, whose career had seen the Martin Neary Singers perform madrigals at 10 Downing Street and the subsequent Directorship of the choir of this great English cathedral. But in spite of his diverse achievements, ultimately he represented establishment *gravitas*; he was suitably surprised, therefore, to receive a telephone call from the popular musical composer Andrew Lloyd Webber.

Neary knew who Andrew was, of course; he had hugely enjoyed *Cats*. He was intrigued when Andrew told him of his plans for his very own *Requiem Mass*. He had this annual festival . . . one did not wish to sound pompous . . . but, in the circumstances, he wondered if Neary was interested.

Neary was flattered but adopted a suitably downbeat demeanour. Could his choir *really* supply the sort of sound it sounded as if Andrew wanted . . . loved *Cats*, of course . . . but was he sure, absolutely *sure*, that the sound of a cathedral choir was *really* right?

Andrew agreed that this was something they should discuss. If

Neary could spare the time from his busy schedule, he added politely, perhaps they could have a meeting.

They met shortly afterwards. Neary's initial misgivings were allayed by the fact that Billy, the inspiration for the piece, had been a noted church organist. Furthermore, whatever doubts he had concerning Andrew's artistic inclinations were positively annihilated when they started talking about English cathedral architecture.

Pevsner, whom even the most blatant salesman could have quoted knowledgeably in the circumstances, was only the starting point. Dom David Knowles's *Monastic Sites From the Air* and the eight volumes of *Dugdale's Monasticum Anglicanum* were also among the *arcana* the one-time Oxford history undergraduate liked to lob at unsuspecting guests.

Neary went home in something of a daze. To his further amazement, the fragments of the Lloyd Webber *Requiem* soon started arriving. Not only that, they were brought in the Bentley by Andrew's chauffeur.

Andrew was keen that his latest work should have a respected and established conductor. To this end he sent a copy of the score to André Previn.

Previn was the brilliant all-rounder who had salvaged the soundtrack of the *Jesus Christ Superstar* film from the mess left by the late Alan Doggett. He was now in two minds: on the one hand, he, too, was intrigued by the latest offering from Andrew Lloyd Webber; on the other hand, he had reservations about the score.

Besides, he was busy at the time. He wrote back, agreeing that the interesting project needed a little more time to mature, and encouraging Andrew to send it to him again when that time was nigh.

The first performance of *Requiem* took place at the 1984 Syd-monton Festival, in the small church at Burghclere. Andrew had written it for soprano, boy treble, tenor and baritone. He was fascinated by the range of Sarah's voice and the aural and theatrical combination of his wife and a choirboy. Neary had chosen one of his choristers, Paul Miles-Kingston, for the latter part.

It was an intimate and sparing performance: the Winchester Cathedral Choir sang with Sarah, Miles-Kingston, a tenor from the choir and a baritone soloist. A small group of jazz-rock musicians featured with a piano and an electric organ. Neary was impressed; they had put this version of the piece together over a relatively short time and had only finished it that afternoon.

That summer Andrew and Sarah went to New York, where they took in a night of Wagner at the Metropolitan Opera. Andrew then departed for the South of France and a cool, shuttered villa a few miles down the coast from where he used to stay with Aunt Vi at Ventimiglia. Here he toiled over the orchestrations for his new work; turning it into something more complex and extravagant, and more passionate, than the comparatively simple piece performed at Sydmonton.

The potent combination of Sarah and Miles-Kingston had focused his imagination on a duet in the *Pie Jesu*. His experience of writing for boys' voices, which had begun with *The Likes of Us* and *Joseph*, now led him via his own childhood memories of sacred songs and a schoolboy visit to Britten's *War Requiem*, to give theatrical echoes of those pieces to the *Hosanna* and the *Lux Aeterna*. Slowly, while keeping more or less to the accepted order of service in a form tackled by hundreds of composers before him including Palestrina, Dvořák, Brahms and Mozart, his own version took shape.

He told people this was a personal work which would probably sell less than a dozen copies. Privately, as ever, a package was in the making. *Requiem*, the first such piece to be produced by the Really Useful Company, was due to be recorded at Number 1 Studio, Abbey Road, from 20–22 December. After Previn had

declined to conduct, Andrew had issued an invitation to Lorin
Maazel, who had eagerly accepted. The English Chamber Or-
chestra were to be on hand with James Lancelot at the organ.
Neary had agreed to lend the services of Paul Miles-Kingston
and the Winchester Cathedral Choir. The baritone part had been
dropped and the sole adult male soloist, a tenor, was to be
Placido Domingo. Finally, the soprano was, of course, to be
Sarah.

By the beginning of November, while Sarah continued with
her singing lessons, Andrew was back in London, this time in his
capacity as impresario and producer of the Melvyn Bragg–
Howard Goodall musical play *The Hired Man*. That same week,
on another first night, the first Mrs Lloyd Webber went out to
the theatre.

Sarah One had continued to live quietly with Imogen and
Nicholas, while her successor had distracted the attention of the
newspapers. This was a discreet public appearance with her new
husband-to-be, Jeremy Norris, a businessman five years younger
than her whom she had met at a health farm. She had continued
to bring up the children away from the razzmatazz of show
business.

Requiem was recorded at Abbey Road as planned immediately
before Christmas. Andrew and his associate David Cullen had
rescored the piece extensively and, as Fauré had done, had
dispensed with the violins which competed with the boys'
voices. Under the baton of Maazel the orchestra, choir and
soloists, accompanied in places by a battery of percussion instruments, produced a work in which an emotional, theatrical effect
was counterpointed by an austere ecclesiastical setting. The
release of the record was set for 1 March.

That Christmas, the composer could be seen leafing through
another lengthy document with extreme concentration. This was
not, however, an orchestral score or the synopsis of his next

musical; it was a report supplied by merchant bankers J. Henry Schroder Wagg.

Ever since buying the Palace Theatre, Andrew had toyed with the idea of raising the £3.5 million he needed for the renovations by floating the Really Useful Company on the London Stock Exchange. This was not as outlandish an idea as it sounded; angels queued up to invest in the shows and thus to invest in Andrew Lloyd Webber; and Andrew Lloyd Webber, to all intents and purposes, *was* the Really Useful Company.

At least Andrew saw it that way. Since Sarah One and Biddy's departure from the board, he and Brolly had been in sole executive charge. Brolly was keen for the business to diversify and acquire a safer financial footing. But while Andrew whole-heartedly endorsed this principle in his private finances, he had no desire to see his work competing with rival RUC properties. However, neither did he have any desire to give up composing and become a full-time executive. While the prospect of 'Puccini goes Public' was an attractive one, the riddle had yet to be solved of who else was going to sit as an executive on the board. The answer was a person who had been there all along.

Requiem went from the master tapes on to magnetic tape and plastic, and the thousands of covers came off the presses. The composer was already turning his mind to the second half of his master plan for Sarah. Just as there had never been any doubt that she would be the female soloist in *Requiem*, so his attempt was now under way to create a spectacular vehicle for her as a full-blown *coloratura* opera soprano. To this end, he and Richard Stilgoe had been working on the idea of the *Phantom of the Opera*.

The original novel by Gaston Leroux was published in 1911 and the story had been filmed and staged dozens of times, in incarnations as diverse as the 1925 Lon Chaney horror movie, the Claude Rains remake of 1943, a 1962 Hammer Films version with Herbert Lom and Brian Da Palma's rock music version *Phantom of Paradise*. The most recent version had been staged by Ken Hill in London's East End. Sarah had been offered a part in this production, which she declined. But the idea had appealed to Andrew, who had visited the Theatre Royal in Stratford East and chatted to the director.

He and Stilgoe had then read the original novel which, like Mary Shelley's *Frankenstein*, proved far worthier of attention than any of the subsequent renditions. What attracted them was the central plot of the horribly disfigured genius who haunts the Paris Opera House and the young Swedish soprano who becomes both the beneficiary of his love and instrument of his revenge.

As a tale of beauty and the beast it had the universal attraction – and commercial possibilities – of the best of fairy tales. As a piece of extravagant nineteenth-century melodrama set in Paris, it appealed to Andrew the Francophile Pre-Raphaelite art collector. As a drama set in an opera house, it presented the perfect opportunity for him to stage a West End opera in all but name. As the Grand Guignol tale of the calamities of a *coloratura*, it was perfect for Sarah.

There were added opportunities: the imaginary Phantom's real-life contemporaries were Gounod, Délibes and Meyerbeer. Andrew sensed fertile ground here for harvesting a factional blend of cross-reference and parody. The Really Useful Theatre Company and Cameron Mackintosh were reunited and De- wynters began the search for an integrated package for the worldwide marketing of *Phantom of the Opera*.

Mackintosh had become something of a mephistophelean figure to the established theatre, since he had shown how much money their finest directors such as Trevor Nunn could make by taking sabbaticals in the 'commercial' sector. His current production, also directed by Nunn, was the fabulously successful adaptation of *Les Misérables*, which was to take vast sums at the box-office of the Palace Theatre.

Stilgoe laboured manfully over the first draft of a libretto. Andrew continued to grapple with the problems of melody and stock market flotation. Then, on 12 February 1985, he arrived in New York.

Here, in two weeks' time, the date was fixed for the world première of *Requiem*. Last-minute rehearsals followed and two days before the performance the streets around the church of St Thomas on Fifth Avenue were jammed with mobile TV vans. Both the BBC and American TV were filming the première, the latter for the popular TV show *Entertainment Tonight*. As the composer himself observed, if a bet had to be taken on the most unlikely thing they had ever shown, the favourite would have to be an excerpt from a Latin requiem.

This was Andrew at his disingenuous best. The mass of New York *glitterati* had already been invited to this première as if it were the first night of *Cats*. In their hotel suite, Andrew and Sarah entertained a stream of journalists from Britain and America. While Domingo was preoccupied with last-minute rehearsals – he still found some of the rhythms tricky – Lorin Maazel felt free to offer his interpretation of why Sarah suited the soprano role.

'It's terribly unfair to say that someone has only got where they have because of who they're married to. Sarah's very disciplined, works very hard and has a very pure voice with a remarkable two-and-a-half octave range.

'She sings the part of a young girl in the requiem and, frankly, I wouldn't have been happy with some huge 400lb opera star, weighed down with fat and operatic prejudices, blasting the roof off!

'I think she's perfect for the role . . .'

The object of this tribute was at that moment curled up on the hotel sofa with a bowl of potato soup, which was apparently good for her throat.

'If I kept thinking, wow, here I am singing with Domingo,' she could be heard saying, 'and Maazel's conducting. . . I'd just freak out!'

Requiem was premiered in New York City on 24 February 1985. The Winchester Cathedral Choir first sang Purcell's *Jehovah, Quam Multi Sunt Hostes Mei!* and the St Thomas's Choir sang Bach's *Zinget Dem Herren*. The two choirs then combined for *Requiem*. Domingo, Sarah Brightman and Paul Miles-Kingston sang with calm and control as the orchestra of St Luke's, New York, minus its violins but augmented to the tune of twelve violas, two saxophones, harp, piano-celeste and organ, performed under Maazel's baton. The *Hosanna* and *Pie Jesu* proved particularly effective. The applause was prolonged. Jean and Celia Lloyd Webber were among the audience.

Martin Neary felt that although the work was uneven, it had thrilling moments; gone for ever were his misgivings as to whether he and his choir were prostituting themselves into the world of pop. Here, he realised, was a man who, having been extraordinarily successful in one field, had earned the right to cross over into another.

In New York, television viewers immediately besieged their local record stores. Apart from *Requiem*, the other big seller was the album of Tim Rice's *Chess*, which had yet to be seen on stage. Thus it was that, fourteen years after their joint creation *Jesus Christ Superstar* had opened on Broadway, Andrew and Tim found themselves in open competition in New York. Only this time *Pie Jesu* (*Merciful Jesus, who takest away the sins of the world, grant them rest*) was in competition with *Nobody's Side* (*Never stay too long in your bed, never lose your heart, use your head*).

In Britain the album was released to mixed reviews. In truth, the British classical musical establishment, having kept him at arm's length for so many years, could neither ignore nor decide exactly what they made of Andrew Lloyd Webber:

Imagine that Carl Orff had rewritten the Verdi Requiem with a little help from Leonard Bernstein, and you will get a fair idea

of the latest, much-publicised work of Andrew Lloyd
Webber . . .

Derivative he may be at every turn, but his power to
communicate is as clear as in his musicals. He may be short-
winded in argument, and some of the themes are too facile, but
his gift of memorability has not deserted him . . .

I shudder to think what an underpowered performance would
be like . . .

The recording is very fine . . .

I enjoyed most of it and found some of it very beautiful, while
never feeling that I was listening to a requiem . . .

A surprisingly demure affair; it was as though a worldly sixth-
former were reading the lesson in chapel . . .

Beyond question, it is an accomplished score . . .

It borrows, probably unconsciously, from sources as far apart as
Puccini, Messiaen and Fauré, but develops few of its ideas
beyond two or three bars. It cashes in on every possible
marketing angle, including the inevitable single of the pretty
choirboy and the composer's wife duetting in a mawkish *Pie
Jesu*; and all this is seen as perfectly normal and tolerable by an
artistic establishment which dare not let itself seem idealistic or
out of touch . . .

After three weeks, the album of *Requiem* had sold 100,000 copies
and the single of *Pie Jesu* had reached Number 3 in the UK Top
Twenty. In America it knocked the album of *Amadeus* off the top
of the charts. Andrew now felt secure enough to scale new
heights of disingenuousness.

'I honestly couldn't have conceived,' he said, 'that this record
would take off in the way that it has done. I'm still stunned by
the news . . .'

As the single climbed higher, his excitement reached childlike
proportions. He would telephone Martin Neary at the latter's

splendid new quarters in the cloisters of Westminster Abbey, where he had recently been appointed Director of Music.

'Martin?' he would say, 'it's Andrew. Have you heard? We're at Number 3!'

But when the single of *Pie Jesu* did not reach Number 1 he stopped telephoning. In the meantime, *I Know Him So Well*, the smash hit single from Tim's show *Chess*, had stormed the charts and spent four weeks in the top slot.

Elsewhere, reactions remained polarised. André Previn was in Vienna on a film reconnaissance, and wanted to buy a classical record. He went into Columbia Records: the ground floor of the huge shop seemed to have been converted into a sales room for Andrew Lloyd Webber. *Requiem* was everywhere.

The first floor of Columbia Records in Vienna was for classical records and the ground floor was for pop. As Previn went up the stairs to the first floor, he turned to his companion.

'At least,' he muttered, 'it's in the right section.'

Others differed widely in their reactions. Martin Neary found that in spite of the adverse press criticism, the piece had had an unparalleled popular impact. After performances in Winchester he received more complimentary letters than he had done for any other work. Whatever people said about the unevenness of the piece, it had struck a chord in a manner unheard of by the composers of the day.

Meanwhile, the day of the British première in Westminster Abbey approached. Andrew, Sarah and Miles-Kingston went to Lambeth Palace, where the Archbishop of Canterbury presented them with gold records for album sales.

'The profound sentiments of the Requiem,' he said, 'come through in any language.'

The proceeds from the sale of the single went, amidst much publicity, to the Save the Children Fund. The proceeds from the British première were to be donated to charities dealing with the aftermath of the IRA bomb attack on the Conservative Party in Brighton.

Requiem was performed publicly in Britain for the first time in Westminster Abbey on 21 April 1985. Mrs Thatcher, Andrew's friend and Conservative Party Chairman John Selwyn Gummer and members of the Cabinet were among the 2000-strong audience, which also included nurses and rescue workers who had helped the victims of the bombing.

Martin Neary and the Winchester Cathedral Choir commenced with Gibbons's *O Clap Your Hands*, Taverner's *Dum Transisset Sabbatum* and three motets by Stanford. Domingo, Sarah and Miles-Kingston then repeated the successful performance given in New York eight weeks earlier. In the final movement, James Lancelot unleashed the full might of the main organ with a power and bravado which carried far beyond the unsighted £5 tickets, as if to stir the shade of Billy Lloyd Webber. The organist to whose memory the work was dedicated, and who would have viewed it with the same ambivalence as he did all his son's works, would none the less finally have given his blessing.

Fresh from her triumph in *Requiem*, Sarah accepted the role of Valencienne in the New Sadlers Wells Opera autumn production of *The Merry Widow*. Her husband had already taken to comparing her with the young Joan Sutherland. Now he started telling people he was delighted with her success; but he wished they could have a baby.

Sarah, he said, would make a wonderful mother. She came from a large family. Like Andrew, she was in some ways like a child herself; at the Nearys she would play for hours with the children and the dog while the others were closeted and working. As the star of *Nightingale* in its trial run at the Buxton Festival, she had been at her happiest off-duty in the company of the children in the cast.

207

She told Jean she wanted to have wild animals at Sydmonton; just like a safari park. Jean had noted with approval Sarah's fondness for cats but as an ardent conservationist she found her predilection for mink coats unsettling.

'Oh, but it's all right,' Sarah would assure her, 'they're bred for it especially, so they don't know the freedom they're missing.'

Like the argument over the mink, the idea of a baby was to become something of a familiar refrain and, like the wild animals at Sydmonton, it was not to be.

7

All The Land You Can See

The first Mrs Lloyd Webber married Jeremy Norris and the new family continued to live quietly at West Eaton Place. Escaway, the private family company from which she had resigned a year earlier, maintained its turnover of nearly £4 million a year. The Really Useful Company, her other previous directorship, now doubled its turnover to over £12 million. That year's Sydmonton Festival saw her first husband present his second wife in a preview of *Phantom of the Opera*.

This was the most lavish festival to date. Apart from *Phantom*, there was Robin Ray's musical entertainment *Butterfly, Tosca, Mimi and Me*, an intimate and witty show which reflected Andrew's obsession with Puccini. Mackintosh had grandiose ambitions for it, but a year later it was to sink after only an eight-week West End run.

The debate, which was always a feature of the festival, was 'Sydmonton Fears for the Future of the Popular Press' — a prophetic motion for Andrew and Sarah — argued over loudly by Robert Maxwell, David Frost, Andrew Neil and Derek Jameson. The cricket match was between Andrew Lloyd Webber's Eleven and past and present cast members of *Daisy Pulls It Off*. The all-female visiting team won by two runs.

But the highlight of the weekend was the preview of *Phantom*. Colm Wilkinson, a long-time Lloyd Webber performer who had sung the part of Che on the recording of *Evita*, sang the title role. Sarah sang Christine. The audience were given a glimpse of the famous scene from the book in which the opera house chandelier crashed to the ground: this time, it came to a swinging halt a foot or so above their heads. The masked Phantom propelled himself and Christine down the underground waterways of Paris in a satanic punting parody. Mackintosh pronounced himself pleased with the response.

But behind the scenes there were problems: Andrew and Richard Stilgoe did not always see eye to eye and the need became apparent for a fresh approach. Andrew and Mackintosh had both been judges on the panel of the annual Vivien Ellis awards for promising newcomers in the musical theatre. A runner-up, who had already come to their attention, was now contacted and asked to audition as a lyricist. He accepted and was promptly put to work.

Charles Hart was the youthful grandson of Glen Byam Shaw and Angela Baddeley. He was a graduate of the Guildhall School of Music and had worked as an assistant musical director. Unknown as a lyricist, he proved to have a serviceable talent.

In the tradition of unknowns propelled to wealth and eminence, he would come to occupy a stable place in the reckoning of the composer. Andrew had already conducted exploratory talks with other lyricists, such as Herbert Kretzmer who had worked on *Les Misérables*. He would also seek out the legendary lyricist of *My Fair Lady*, Alan Jay Lerner.

Lerner was a sick man, but still well enough to give a lesson in one-liners to Andrew Lloyd Webber.

'I don't know why, Alan,' Andrew said, 'but some people dislike me as soon as they meet me.'

'Perhaps,' said Lerner, 'it saves time.'

The new recruit was far from the calibre of Kretzmer and Lerner. But in the absence of Tim Rice, and after the flirtation with Don Black, the lyricist who, ironically, came closest to playing the role of Hammerstein to Andrew Lloyd Webber, was the young man named Hart.

*

That July, Andrew announced he wanted to buy another London theatre.

This was the Lyceum, where Sir John Gielgud had played *Hamlet* and which had closed as a theatre in 1939. It was now a seedy venue for pop concerts. Andrew had been there during the hunt for his first theatre; now he offered to head a consortium to rescue the building from the Mecca gambling organisation, which wanted to turn it into a discotheque and restaurant.

But Mecca carried the day, and Andrew turned his attention to other matters. In August, three familiar Lloyd Webber ventures were incorporated as American companies in Delaware: the Really Useful Company Inc., the Really Useful Music Company Inc. and Steampower Music Inc. *On Your Toes* closed at the Palace Theatre and preparations began to house *Les Misérables*, the smash hit directed by Nunn and produced by Mackintosh. *Song and Dance* opened at the Royale Theater on Broadway, choreographed by the master-in-chief of the New York City Ballet.

In October, in between preparations for the arrival of *Les Misérables*, the musicians of the Lloyd Webber family began their first round of joint appearances in the lifesize version of the Lloyd Webber theatre. In the first half of a double bill performed for seven nights at the Palace, Julian presented a symphonic rendition of *Variations* performed with the English Chamber Orchestra. In the second half, Sarah and Paul Miles-Kingston were among the performers of *Requiem*.

Sarah had opened at the New Sadler's Wells Opera in *The Merry Widow*. The general consensus was that the ethereal high register she had demonstrated so spectacularly in *Requiem* was shown to be lacking in colour and expression; but she more than made up for this with her dancing. A month later, in the Royal Variety Performance at Drury Lane, she excelled in the less operatic role of impersonating Jessie Matthews in *Dancing on the Ceiling*.

The Really Useful Company produced Sarah in a preview video

of *Phantom of the Opera* with ex-Cockney Rebel singer Steve Harley. Andrew and Hart laboured over the melodies and libretto of *Phantom* and engaged in long discussions with Hal Prince at the latter's suite on the Avenue of the Americas in New York.

Prince had had a couple of flops since *Evita* and had directed *Turandot* at the Vienna State Opera; he was glad to be back on board. Mackintosh, whose backers now included not just Baking Powder magnates but big corporations like ABC and Fifth Avenue Productions, was raising forty per cent of the investment and the Really Useful Theatre Company was raising the balance. *Phantom* looked to Prince like a good career move.

That winter, a new list of names was added to the cast of characters on the Really Useful Company board. Tim Rice joined as a non-executive director. Madeleine Gore was an investor in Lloyd Webber shows and an assistant director of N. M. Rothschild Asset Management Ltd. who specialised in managing large private portfolios. Sir Richard Baker Wilbraham, Bart., another Lloyd Webber angel, was a director of J. Henry Schroder Wagg, the merchant bank handling the Really Useful Company flotation. The Right Honourable Patrick Greysteil Ruthven, Second Earl of Gowrie, had recently resigned from the Government as Minister for the Arts after complaining that he could not live in London on his salary of £33,000 a year.

Tim Rice, Madeleine Gore, Baker Wilbraham and Lord Gowrie were all non-executive directors. Lord Gowrie became Chairman of the new Really Useful Group. On the board as executive directors were Andrew and Brian Brolly. The third executive director was Biddy, who had rejoined the company to run the Palace Theatre. She was the person who knew him better than anyone else. Somehow she managed to serve his interests, her interests and those of the company in equal measure.

That December, *Les Misérables* opened at the Palace and the assembly of the above notables was formalised. Andrew Lloyd Webber had become the proprietor of the finest theatre in London and host to its most successful new musical. Now, at the age of only thirty-seven, with the imminent flotation of the Really Useful Group, he was poised to become the first ever publicly quoted composer in the long and hitherto disparate histories of the stock exchange and popular music.

The flotation of the Really Useful Group plc in January 1986 valued the £100 private company started by Andrew and Sarah Lloyd Webber less than ten years earlier at over £35 million. Andrew received £9 million by selling 2.8 million shares. The new Group also purchased from Sarastone Ltd. one of Andrew's private companies, the other half of the interest in the Palace Theatre. This still left him with a thirty-three per cent personal holding in the new public company worth over £13 million. Brolly made £4 million by reducing his holding to sixteen per cent.

But this was only a fraction of Andrew's total worth. While shares began trading at a starting price of around £3.20, and although he had assigned to the new Group the worldwide copyrights to all new works he wrote during the next seven years, he still retained a huge income in royalties from the Stigwood days and thereafter. Andrew's earnings as a composer still accrued directly to him and did not form part of the income of the new Group.

Apart from making Brolly rich and Andrew even richer, the flotation achieved its main purpose, which was to leave Andrew freer to compose and to realise funds for the renovation of the Palace Theatre. The reaction in the City was satisfactory, given that no one knew quite what to make of an issue the likes of which they had never seen before.

'We didn't expect a *lot* of stagging,' declared Schroders's man

Nigel Saxby-Soffe, 'and the market had been absolutely grotty recently . . . I think the issue has been a great success.'

Sarah One, as a founder director and former shareholder, saw no harm in making a rare public statement: 'I need my money more than he does,' she was heard to say. 'If Andrew wants to make even more money, then good luck to him. I certainly won't be buying any shares.'

Four weeks later, Really Useful Group shares traded briskly with the Top Ten success of the single *Phantom of the Opera* sung by Sarah Brightman and Steve Harley. *Evita* closed in London after a run of eight years. Andrew was unable to attend the farewell party, having flown with Sarah to Chicago where she was to appear in *Requiem*.

Evita, the show which had given Bernard Levin one of the most disagreeable evenings of his life inside or outside a theatre, had given three thousand audiences agreeable evenings and made money for backers, composers and stars alike. *Evita* had taken £23 million at the box-office in London alone. A Mrs Mave Briggs of Romford Essex was reputed to have seen the show three hundred and thirty times. Backers who invested £500 in the production had recouped their money within six months and made £900 a year ever since.

The film had not yet been made but Andrew, Tim, Land and Stigwood still shared £1 million from the movie rights. In Argentina, where the show was banned, an enraged right-wing arts establishment had been prompted to stage a counter-version so anodyne that thousands went to Brazil to see the real thing instead. In Austria, a film director had been sentenced to two years' imprisonment for having the Austrian Evita beaten up so that his girlfriend could take her place. The show had closed in London; but it was reopening at the Manchester Opera House in a few weeks' time.

The composer and the lyricist, now executive and non-executive director of a company which had rather exceeded the aims of their original joint venture Qwertyuiop, were to be seen taking their newly restored amicability beyond the boardroom. Andrew and Tim were working together again.

The object of their attentions was *Cricket*, a twenty-minute Victorian piece rehearsed in the church theatre at Sydmonton and commissioned by HRH Prince Edward as a sixtieth birthday present for Her Majesty the Queen. It was performed at Windsor Castle on her birthday. The subject matter alone had been enough to tempt Tim away from his multifarious activities. In spite of the slightness of the piece − although aspects of some of the tunes were cast back into the well for future use − this was enough to persuade Andrew to take the opportunity to reunite with his old partner.

The reunion, like the work in question, did not last long. Their busy schedules kept them apart. Andrew had just won a Grammy Award for Best Contemporary Classical Composer and was making a new West End appearance at the Globe Theatre as producer of *Lend Me A Tenor*. Tim's new musical *Chess*, the £4 million blockbuster vehicle for Elaine Paige, opened in the West End. Andrew was too busy to attend the first night and sent Sarah instead. That same month of May 1986, the cast was announced of *Phantom of the Opera*.

Sarah's casting in the role of Christine was a foregone conclusion; she was the reason for the whole project. The role of the Phantom did not, however, go to Steve Harley, who had sung it on the promotional video. In an unexpected move, Andrew had cast Michael Crawford in the leading male part.

This was astute. Crawford, like Andrew, was a workaholic prepared to go to any lengths to achieve his artistic ends. As a boy soprano he had studied with Benjamin Britten and his willingness to stage his own stunts was legendary. He was a familiar face to British television viewers. He had achieved musical theatre stardom in *Barnum*. He was the perfect choice to launch the show in London and New York.

215

That June, as preparations for *Phantom* and the Sydmonton Festival were under way, Andrew finally fulfilled a longstanding ambition. Charles Clifford Kingsmill, from whom he had bought Sydmonton Court, also owned 1200 acres of adjoining land, including most of the villages of Sydmonton and Ecchinswell and the farms of Wergs, Cowhouse and Malthouse. This was fine arable and dairy land, prime rabbit country, which the Kingsmill family had bought from Henry VIII after the dissolution of the monasteries in 1542. The asking price then had been £760. Andrew, the expert on monasteries, paid £2.3 million. Now, at last, he owned all the land he could see.

The Sydmonton Festival saw the return of Tim for a performance of *Cricket*. In St Mary's Church, Andrew accompanied Sarah at the piano in a new song for *Phantom of the Opera*.

Andrew's purchase of the land adjoining Sydmonton Court inevitably revived speculation about his wealth and stimulated behaviour implicit in the theme of last year's festival debate 'Sydmonton Fears for the Future of the Popular Press.' The ink on the contract was not yet dry when the new squire was falsely credited with the sacking of a forester, a gamekeeper and a village postmaster. The tabloid reporters descended on the sleepy villages of Sydmonton and Ecchinswell. Having stirred up the traditional British characteristics of envy, mean-mindedness and polite innuendo, they returned to their newspaper offices to accuse the new landlord of meddling in the affairs of people who could not answer back. Eventually they had to admit they were wrong and bided their time for their next attack.

Preparations for *Phantom* now began in earnest. In a warehouse by a canal behind King's Cross station, the opera designer Maria Bjornson oversaw mock-ups of her designs for set and costumes. She was trying to persuade Mackintosh that the Phantom should wear a mask covering only half his face. At Her Majesty's Theatre, Haymarket, painters on scaffolding worked on the life-size fibre-glass figures of the Paris Opera House proscenium which had begun life on Bjornson's drawing-board. Half a hundred-weight of hydraulic tackle held the polycarbonate chandelier. In August Andrew, Mackintsoh, Bjornson, Charles Hart, Sarah, Michael Crawford and others met Hal Prince for the first day of rehearsals in a community hall on the south side of the Thames in Vauxhall.

The director still felt the British could be too nice to each other when staging musicals. This production, however, would lead him to change his mind. The six-week rehearsal period proved too short and tensions mounted in the best Broadway tradition. Unkind rumours abounded: there was disagreement over how Stilgoe and Hart should be billed for the lyrics; Andrew and Sarah were revealing the volatile side of their relationship; she was having difficulty with her voice, but still had enough of one allegedly to call him 'a slug in flared trousers'.

Andrew stepped down as an executive director of the Really Useful Group to non-executive status, saying he needed more time to concentrate on music. None of these goings-on had anything but a beneficial effect: as had been the case with *Evita*, they simply fanned the advance publicity. The casting of Crawford had been an inspired move; advance bookings already exceeded £1.5 million. Crawford, too, was pleased: he was on seven and a half per cent of the box-office take. Shares in the Really Useful Group continued to rise; they were now at £3.70, forty pence over the issuing price.

Andrew and Sarah gave interviews in the tunnels under the real Paris Opera House. Upstairs in his new offices at the Palace Theatre Andrew told people how happy his ex-wife and children were. Downstairs he told them how surprised he was that *Pie Jesu* had been a Top Ten success. In the new penthouse flat in Eaton Square Sarah described herself as a shy person who hated publicity. Andrew told the story of how he had to take out a mortgage on Sydmonton to cover the cost of *Cats*. He told them

217

how he had known *Jeeves* would be a disaster; how he had urged the producers to close it before it reached the West End. He and Sarah were living in separate flats in order to concentrate on the new show without distraction. He and Tim were going to be associated in a lot of ventures from now on.

He seemed obsessed with remaking the past into a seamless garment for him to wear which shone brightly in every direction; like Joseph, he had trouble understanding why some people took exception to this. When a canny journalist refused to fall for the normally effective Lloyd Webber self-promotion strategy, he was to be seen glancing at Biddy in visible distress.

Mackintosh continued in his own low-profile way with the business of creating another integrated package. Dewynters again threw their considerable experience into the task. The *Phantom* half-mask had to become as familiar an image as the little girl from *Les Miserables* and the yellow eyes of *Cats. Phantom* paperweights were produced under a franchise. A *Phantom* pop-up book was under way, the final page of which, when opened, played the *Phantom* theme.

Brian Brolly was confident that *Phantom* would follow *Cats* as a major source of income to the shareholders of the Really Useful Group. Advance figures showed that the Group was on target for a £4.3 million profit in its first year as a public company. *Cats* was a success in London, New York, Los Angeles, San Francisco, Vienna, Budapest, Oslo, Hamburg and Helsinki. *Song and Dance* was about to close on Broadway after a run of fourteen months. *Starlight Express* had passed its thousandth London performance and was scheduled to open in March at the Gershwin Theater in New York.

Brolly now planned to diversify by acquisition in the classic manner. He still felt that to depend on the work of one man to such a heavy extent constituted an unacceptable business risk. *Cats* still supplied over seventy per cent of the RUG's income. The flotation had left Andrew free to compose, but there were

also the shareholders to consider. That autumn, as Brolly calculated the dividend payable and Andrew reasserted that he did
not often think about money, the seeds were sown of a polite
disagreement over the direction of the company.

Phantom of the Opera opened at Her Majesty's Theatre, Haymarket
on 9 October 1986. Prince proved he could do for this show
what he had done for *Evita*. Under his direction Crawford and
Sarah sang their way through a series of *coups de théâtre* which
dazzled the audience and made the evening a roaring success.
This was in spite of the fact that, unlike *Evita*, *Phantom* for all its
romantic orchestral sweep and vocal heroics, contained little
individual sung character and a melody which barely survived
being so frequently reprised.

The first-night audience, and the reviewers, loved it:

It's fantastic, fabulous and phantasmagorical . . . the special
effects are among the most spectacular ever seen in the West
End . . .

A hanged scene shifter is suddenly, hideously dropped onto the
stage . . . a vast crystal chandelier crashes onto the audience . . .
a dreadful climax is fast approaching . . .

The reception was understandable, indeed deserved, although
the substance of the work is unmitigated tosh . . .

A blessedly trad antidote to the current craze for shows
chockablock with laser beams, video screams and fake
holographs . . .

The music is occasionally glorious, includes two excellent
pastiches of real opera, but also languishes at times in swirling
fussiness . . .

A gorgeous trick, directed with great imagination and
sumptuously well-designed . . .

Andrew Lloyd Webber's melodious and flamboyant score . . .

Two themes stand for the Phantom as objects of fear and are repeated frequently. Both are absurd . . . The first is a sequence of descending minor chords of the kind against which Sylvester the Cat used to creep up on the unsuspecting Tweety Pie . . .

This is bogey-man music and these are tinsel terrors beside those of, say, Sondheim's *Sweeney Todd* . . .

If you only see one show this year, make it this one!

Andrew arranged for a *Phantom* coach party of villagers from Sydmonton and Ecchinswell. *Phantom of the Opera* and Michael Crawford won the categories for Musical of the Year and Outstanding Actor in a Musical in that December's Olivier Awards. The Lloyd Webber family were also featured on their symphonic recording of *Variations* and Billy's beautiful, romantic tone poem to the goddess of dawn, *Aurora*.

Julian's book *Travels with my Cello* had just been published by Pavilion Books, whose proprietors included Tim Rice. Julian had not lost his own gift for publicity: 'Celia,' he told people, 'knows exactly what it means coming second to a cello.' Their divorce inevitably received less attention than Andrew and Sarah Two now experienced for their own alleged marital problems.

The high profile of the Lloyd Webbers was not helped by the quality of the coverage, which swung from the salacious to the excessively anodyne. If the former was to be found in the popular press, the latter was embodied in a *South Bank Show Special* presented by Andrew's longstanding associate Melvyn Bragg.

Bragg, co-scriptwriter of *JC* the movie and author of *The Hired Man*, a production for which Andrew had put up the money, produced a profile so tame that it was left to Tim, in a brief but memorable sequence, to supply a glimmer of wit.

'I think Andrew's greatest musical indiosyncracy,' he said, 'is that he writes a jolly good melody.'

Andrew understandably grasped the opportunity for some further self-promotion. On the touchy subject of *Jeeves* he adroitly steered the conversation to the Beatles and the failure of *Sergeant Pepper* as a stage musical; even though the latter, unlike *Jeeves*, had never been intended for the stage. At the first sound of the word 'plagiarism' he again steered the conversation away, this time towards Stephen Sondheim, whom he asserted had been the victim of a similar 'campaign' in America. Andrew liked to link his name with that of Sondheim, although there was little evidence to suggest that Sondheim reciprocated in kind.

'It's very difficult,' Andrew declared to the press immediately before the programme was broadcast, 'to travel on the trains any more. I regret hugely that I can't go wandering off in the middle of the afternoon to look at a building or church without some, er, person coming and saying: "Ooh! ooh! it's Andrew Lloyd Webber!" That is very sad, because I used to like the anonymity . . .'

Andrew would never quite understand that, in Britain, the penalty for being caught red-handed in the act of such blatant self-promotion was to be labelled as rather smug.

Bragg, who genuinely liked Andrew, appeared not to understand either. Two years later, in recognition of his eminent contribution to the world of broadcasting and the arts, he would be appointed to the board of the Really Useful Group.

In February 1987 *Phantom of the Opera* became the top-selling album in Britain, displacing Paul Simon's *Graceland* and at one point selling a copy every fifty seconds. *Aurora*, released the same month, sold rather fewer copies but reached a wider audience than it might otherwise have done. Keith Turner, a showbusiness solicitor, joined the board of the Really Useful Group. In March, Broadway saw the New York opening of *Starlight Express*.

221

Broadway, 'the fabulous invalid', had mixed feelings about Andrew Lloyd Webber. *Starlight Express* had taken $6 million in advance and opened, of all places, at the Gershwin Theater. Jule Styne, who had known Gershwin, went to see it.

Styne had come to Broadway in 1919. His offices were backstage at the Mark Hellinger Theater, where Broadway had reeled under the impact of *Jesus Christ Superstar*. The walls were covered with pictures of celebrities. Styne knew everybody. In 1959 he had composed the score for *Gypsy*, with Stephen Sondheim as lyricist, rated by many as the finest musical ever. In 1964 he had come up with *Funny Girl* and made a star out of the woman who had sung at Andrew's piano, Barbra Streisand.

Styne was a legend in his own lunchtime — usually spent in Sardi's — founder of the 'brotherhood of those who do not speak shit' and unrivalled commentator on Broadway.

'What makes a Broadway musical?' people would ask him earnestly.

'Jews and fags,' came the reply, 'Jews and fags, my boy.'

The evening Styne went to see *Starlight Express* was one of the saddest of his life: 'What does he think he's doing?' came the cry. 'In fifty years' time, nobody will be whistling the special effects from *Starlight Express!*'

But Styne was the last representative of a vanished era. The spirit of Rodgers too was long departed. Alan Jay Lerner was dead. Of the younger composers, whatever Andrew said about wanting to work with him, Sondheim had taken a different, less commercially minded course. Andrew stood alone among the ghosts of those he had once striven to emulate. The big shows on Broadway these days were sure-fire transfers: *Cats* and *Starlight Express*.

The man who had composed them was conspicuous on the *Starlight Express* opening night by his Macavity-like absence. Sydmonton's worst fears had been realised: the popular press had returned to the attack. Stories concerning Sarah's alleged liaison

222

with a pop songwriter had driven her and Andrew to the villa at St Jean-Cap Ferrat, where the ever-obliging Crewe-Read was in charge of renovations. Here they were to be seen strolling along the beach hand in hand, in a reunion amid the frenzy of their separate schedules.

The Really Useful Group won a Queen's Award for Export Achievement. Sarah finished her six-month run in *Phantom* and they returned to the villa at St Jean-Cap Ferrat. As he had done after she had finished in *Requiem*, Andrew repeated his refrain that they wanted to have a baby. He and Sarah certainly intended to have a family, he said. But the problem was when: he did not want her to miss the opportunity to play Christine in the New York production of *Phantom of the Opera*.

This was not a view shared by American Equity: the union declared that Sarah Brightman was not a star of sufficient magnitude to warrant her depriving an American of the job. Michael Crawford, on the other hand, was deemed to be sufficiently eminent. Protracted wrangling ensued between American Equity and the Really Useful Group. Sarah missed most of this, commuting as she did between a private clinic in London where she was undergoing internal surgery and convalescence in the South of France.

At the villa at St Jean-Cap Ferrat, her husband was to be seen hopping up and down with rage and uttering Phantom-like threats of revenge for this snub to his protégée. Fortunately, however, he was not driven to apply the ultimate sanction: to pull out of Broadway altogether and have Sarah star in a film version of *Phantom* by Steven Spielberg. American Equity swiftly relented: she could open the role on Broadway, on condition that British Equity gave a similar opportunity to an equally unknown American.

Brolly was putting into practice his corporate aquisitions strategy. The Really Useful Group pre-tax profits were up again by thirty-three per cent to £5.7 million at the end of June. In August, the RUG bought Aurum Press, publishers of Tom Bower's biography of Robert Maxwell and, recalling one of Andrew's childhood obsessions, future publishers of Ordnance Survey maps of great British walks. In October the Group bought into Interactive Information Systems Ltd., an electronic publishing company; the Really Useful Record Company was formed; there was even talk of buying a radio station. *Phantom*, despite the fuss over casting, had already taken $10 million in advance bookings on Broadway. The box office sold nearly $1 million worth of tickets to nineteen thousand people on the first day.

Given the satisfactory state of the coprorate finances, the man who to all intents and purposes *was* the company made another discreet acquisition. To go with the Eaton Square penthouse, the manor at Sydmonton and the villa at St Jean-Cap Ferrat, Andrew spent $6 million on a luxurious duplex apartment in Manhattan's Trump Tower. Here he could discuss a wide range of subjects with the people he chanced to meet in the residents-only elevator: the art of self-promotion with Johnny Carson; acting and cookery with Sophia Loren; corporate finance with Lee Iacocca and film-making with his new friend Steven Spielberg.

But in truth he had little or no time to do any of these things. The Trump Tower apartment, like the others, was just another point between which he shuttled in his chauffeur-driven Bentley and his leased Hawker Siddeley 125 jet. Like a pinball in one of the machines he had installed at Sydmonton, he ricocheted off them, one after another, until the game was over. But of course, even when you had won all there was to win, there was always another game to play

8

Fanfare (Reprise)

Andrew now spent most of his time commuting between continents as if they were mid-morning appointments, but he still liked to think of himself as a British resident. His premières were graced by the presence of royalty. His chairman of the board was a Lord and his other directors included a baronet. His prized possession was a West End theatre. It was hard, therefore, to take seriously his repeated threat to leave England.

'It is possible I might shift over to America and just become American,' he announced. 'Sarah and I are seriously thinking about it.'

This was a familiar refrain. He loved Britain, but the British tax system made it hard for him to do so. The best brains in British showbusiness were being tempted to Broadway by higher pay and lower taxes; Andrew had never disguised his enthusiasm for either. He had incorporated companies in America and opened a production office in New York. Now, however, he appeared as a crusading figure holding out for the values of art over those of the box-office.

'Of course I would miss Britain,' he went on, 'but I would only make this move if I felt it was naturally right and that I was going to be working far more on Broadway.

'But I would never allow my life to be ruled by money. If you want to do that, you can be sure your theatre work will go to pieces because you are doing everything for the wrong reasons. And my pleasure comes from the music, not the money the shows make . . .'

In New York, the *Phantom* pre-launch publicity reached heights as spectacular as the show itself. Advance bookings had now topped $16 million. The *Phantom* half-mask logo was emblazoned across record shop windows and department stores. Black market tickets were changing hands for $800. The saga of Sarah and American Equity had become fodder for breakfast TV and the evening newspapers. New Yorkers bought *Phantom* albums, *Phantom* mugs, *Phantom* cigarette lighters, *Phantom* pens and *Phantom* hand towels. In a short while they would be able to buy *Phantom* earrings (in the shape of chandeliers) and *Phantom* perfume. Andrew still appeared to be surprised when, after all the packaging and the dozens of feature articles and interviews about his work and lifestyle, he was recognised by people in the street.

Phantom of the Opera opened at the Majestic Theater in New York on 26 January 1988. Crawford and Sarah went through their vocal heroics with considerable bravery and aplomb. The hundred and twenty tiny trapdoors opened on cue to reveal tiny flickering candles; the one-ton, thirty thousand crystal-bead chandelier descended precisely on time; the boat carrying the Phantom and Christine glided triumphantly across the subterranean waters of the Paris Opera House. The first-night audience rose and cheered.

Afterwards, Andrew, Jean, Sarah, her mother Paula, Crawford and a thousand others adjourned to another of Mackintosh's fabulous first-night parties; this time at the Beacon Theater on 74th Street. The old movie palace had been specially converted into a Victorian opera house for the occasion. Here, under back projections of the *Phantom* logo and amid hallways lit by gaslight and manned by men in black opera capes, they danced the night away and dined on caviar, cassoulet of shrimp, stuffed quail and magnums of the finest champagne.

The reviewers did their best, and worst:

It brings with it a new Broadway star of the greatest magnitude in Michael Crawford, gorgeously spectral and suavely romantic as that disfigured Phantom. He and it really are terrific . . .

Sarah Brightman is fine . . .

Sarah Brightman couldn't act scared on a New York subway at four in the morning . . .

The icily attractive Miss Brightman possesses a lush soprano by Broadway standards but reveals little competence as an actress. After months of playing *Phantom* in London, she still simulates fear and affection alike by screwing her face into bug-eyed, chipmunk-cheeked poses . . .

It would be ludicrous – and an invitation to severe disappointment – to let the hype kindle the hope that *Phantom* is a credible heir to the Rodgers and Hammerstein musical.

What one finds is a characteristic Lloyd Webber project – long on pop professionalism and melody, impoverished of artistic personality and passion – that director Hal Prince, designer Maria Bjornson and the mesmerising Michael Crawford have elevated, quite literally, to the roof.

Mr Lloyd Webber has again written a score so generic that most of the songs could be recorded and redistributed among the characters (indeed, among other Lloyd Webber musicals) without altering the show's story or meaning . . .

A spectacular entertainment, visually the most impressive of the British musicals . . .

Broadway's biggest ever, super-heated mega-hit . . .

The composer retreated to his sixtieth floor duplex to lick his wounds and count his blessings. In compensation for the attack mounted on him and his wife by the *New York Times*, he accepted a fortieth birthday present from Nancy Reagan. The First Lady gave him a box of jelly beans – after all, they had done so much for her husband.

Then, in his usual fashion, he returned to work on his next

musical. After *Phantom*, Mackintosh had urged him to retire. But this was his long-cherished scheme to stage David Garnett's delicate, anachronistic novella *Aspects of Love*.

Aspects was to be a sole production of the Really Useful Theatre Company, run by Biddy Hayward. Biddy had recently made an acquisition of her own: a starstruck young production assistant who had recently retired from what would have been a bracing but aesthetically unrewarding career as a Royal Marine Commando.

One of his first tasks was to ascertain the current whereabouts of the rights for *Aspects of Love*.

Thus it was that the telephone rang in the Sussex home of Professor Quentin Bell. Bell was the nephew of Virginia Woolf and a survivor of the Bloomsbury Group, of which the late David Garnett had also been an enthusiastic if minor member.

'Who's that?' Bell barked; he was used to being telephoned by young people in search of information about Bloomsbury.

'My name,' the voice announced, 'is Edward Windsor.'

Bell had never heard of him. He gave the necessary information and rang off.

The young man to whom he had spoken was only doing his job. The fact that he had a job at all was something of a surprise. His full name was His Royal Highness The Prince Edward Antony Richard Louis Windsor, third son of Her Majesty the Queen and third in the line of succession to the throne of England.

The acquisition of Prince Edward was not the only good news for investors in Andrew Lloyd Webber. Apart from the publicity and income generated by *Phantom*, *Starlight Express* continued to pump funds into the balance sheet. The show opened in Sydney, Australia in time for the bicentennial celebrations before moving on to Brisbane, Melbourne, Adelaide and Perth. In Japan, the show had played to capacity crowds of 8500 a performance and grossed $20 million. *Cats* opened in Moscow. Andrew found himself dining at the American Embassy there with Mr and Mrs Gorbachov and his old friends the Reagans. *Requiem* was performed in Leningrad. The Really Useful Group share price had risen by seventeen per cent in the three weeks before *Phantom* opened in New York. After the uncomplimentary *New York Times* review the share price fell, but was still buoyant. Pre-tax profits were up to £5.75 million, a thirty-three per cent increase on the previous year. When *Phantom* won seven Tony Awards, the price rose yet again.

Brian Brolly was exultant. His declared aim was nothing less than to create a 'fully fledged communication and creative company' in which arena tours of *Starlight Express* around America were financed by Japanese money to the gain of British shareholders. Brolly was pursuing his policy of corporate diversification: the Really Useful Picture Company had started to produce TV commercials and corporate videos.

The City of London approved: Andrew, after all, still accounted for eighty-five per cent of the Group's income. To them, the weak point in the Really Useful Group was its dependence upon the talent of Andrew Lloyd Webber. But they were making a big mistake in assuming that Brolly's policy of diversification would carry the day.

The squire of Sydmonton and the surrounding land had meanwhile revised his plans for the villagers of Ecchinswell. Having stocked the village shop with caviar, smoked salmon, champagne and pâté, he was surprised to hear that it was losing money. He decided to close it and wrote them a circular letter:

Dear Ecchinswell

I had really thought that we were all trying to create something which could have been a lot of joy and fun not only for myself but also for the many people who were excited by what I intended.

It was never my intention to do anything that would jeopardise the environment of this village . . .

He was even more surprised to hear the village was up in arms.

'That place used to make money,' car repairer Dave Lee was quoted as saying. 'To my mind, the only reason it doesn't now is because it's not a shop for the villagers. It's a shop for bloody yuppies.'

Eventually, the squire relented, although he would revive his upmarket strategy in future. He was too busy with *Aspects of Love* and the affairs of the Really Useful Group. The latest incarnation of the musical on which he had begun work with Tim and continued with Trevor Nunn, was now due to be previewed at the Sydmonton Festival, with lyrics by Don Black and Charles Hart.

Dinsdale Landen sang the older male role of George at the Festival, but the part was not to be his in the West End. Nor was the lead female part to be Sarah's; not least because of the reciprocal deal with American Equity. In case the message was not loudly and clearly received, her husband took the precaution of telling the press that she would be 'wildly unsuitable' for the part.

He also made his opinion known over the lead role in the film of *Evita*. Stigwood planned to produce this, but Andrew and Tim had right of veto over casting. Tim had long questioned all other suggestions in the hope that Elaine Paige would be given the role. Stigwood wanted Meryl Streep; but she would have to submit a satisfactory tape of her singing for the composer's approval.

'If she can't sing,' Andrew announced, 'she can't have the part.'

That October, unable to pursue his diversification strategy to the extent he desired, Brian Brolly resigned from the board of the Really Useful Group. The company he had helped build had become a unique institution in the worlds of popular music and the stock exchange. Brolly departed amicably after ten years, a multi-millionaire with a golden handshake of £200,000 and £600,000 in lieu of pension rights. Tim also departed, bored by board meetings and bemused at the direction the company was taking. He had been hard hit by the failure of *Chess* on Broadway and the breakdown of his own marriage. He had no plans to write another musical with or without Andrew Lloyd Webber.

Keith Turner took over. Turner was not an advocate of diversification; he favoured the interests of the company's prime asset.

'Music,' he said, 'is where our skills lie.'

He meant the music of Andrew Lloyd Webber. Andrew was back on the board.

The first night of *Aspects of Love* was announced for 12 April 1989. The box office took £130,000 on its first day. Andrew had continued working on his next piece as usual, amid the frenzy of his current production. On the sixtieth floor of the Trump Tower he tapped out the tunes on the Steinway grand and reworked them at the Blüthner in the drawing room of the penthouse in Eaton Square. In the front of the Bentley, sitting next to Bill the chauffeur, he talked on the telephone to Biddy, to Nunn and to his fellow orchestrator David Cullen.

The Bentley was so conspicuous that he had also acquired a black London taxicab. Bill often drove him in it, unnoticed, to and from the stage doors of the theatres which were showing his productions. This solved Andrew's problem, but meant that Bill was frequently hailed as a taxi-driver.

Sarah persisted in her own hyper-active schedule of recordings, recitals and singing lessons. She was currently recording an album for Andrew called *Songs That Got Away*: a compendium of good songs from musicals which had flopped. One was from *Rex* by Richard Rodgers; another was *Meadowlark* from *The Baker's Wife* by Stephen Schwartz, co-author of *Godspell*; a third was *Half a Moment* from *Jeeves*.

Andrew was also engaged in a campaign to purchase Novello and Company, the music publishers of the works of Billy Lloyd Webber and of *Joseph*.

Aspects of Love was being cast and by December advance bookings had reached £2 million. This pleasant news came as no surprise; except to the five children of the late David Garnett.

As beneficiaries of his will, they had inherited little or no money. As beneficiaries of the staging of the book, they stood to gain one per cent of gross box-office takings until the show recovered its production costs and one and a half per cent thereafter. Henrietta Garnett lived in France in somewhat bohemian circumstances: 'You mean I won't have to spend the rest of my life frozen?' she enquired disbelievingly. 'I will be able to afford central heating?'

Julian was incorrectly rumoured to be making an acquisiton of his own: Leyton Orient Football Club. In spite of his own success, he was not financially placed to make such a purchase, nor did his brother consider it a sufficiently sound investment to buy the club for him. Julian's place would remain on the concert platform rather than in the directors' box; although he did take a keen interest in the club's proposed purchase of a new striker.

In January 1989, three months before *Aspects* was due to open in London, *Starlight Express* closed on Broadway at the Gershwin Theater. The New York production of Jule Styne's *bête noire* had cost a cool £8 million to mount and recouped only eighty per cent of its investment. This was by no means a failure on the scale of *Chess*; but to some it signalled the twilight of the age of the technology-centred stage musical which Andrew had ushered in five years earlier.

Andrew returned from St Jean-Cap Ferrat to London and the preparations for *Aspects of Love*. In what seemed like another astute piece of casting, the former James Bond Roger Moore had been given the key older role. Andrew had met him at a party given by Leslie Bricusse; later Moore had visited him and Sarah at St Jean-Cap Ferrat.

Moore was to play George Dillingham, the aristocratic expatriate painter whose lifelong quest for free love without injury to himself or others eventually led to his death in a paroxysm of jealousy. Like George, Moore was suave and charismatic, an international star of the old-fashioned kind such as the late David Niven.

Moore, ever the professional, made light work of doubts about his singing: 'When you're sixty-one, like me, it's an effort to talk and walk at the same time,' he declared straightfacedly, 'let alone having to sing as well. But you don't turn down a Lloyd Webber with the music of *Phantom* still ringing in your ears, and I do find George a brilliantly wicked old fellow to play. So I'm just hoping to get through the first night in a Valium haze. After that I think I'll probably settle down and be all right, and my singing teacher even thinks I might have a light baritone . . .'

Andrew, too, dismissed doubts about the casting: 'It's not as though we were looking for a Pavarotti,' he declared, 'but there's no doubt that Roger can sing, and from what I've seen so far I think he's going to be a revelation.'

At the penthouse in Eaton Square, he fretted over the preparations: the stage at the Prince of Wales Theatre had to be rearranged; Maria Bjornson's designs demanded lightning-swift set changes – a single delay or fault would destroy the delicate narrative fabric of the piece. Black and Hart had delivered a serviceable libretto, but he still wanted to contact Tim. *Love Changes Everything*, the single from the show sung by Michael Ball, was already in the UK Top Twenty. But still he fretted; the

233

show was too long; there was a scene which was too short; there was a gap where a scene should be.

One night, he was going over the pictures of Maria Bjornson's sets with Biddy. Sarah was having singing lessons in New York. She had been touring the world in *The Andrew Lloyd Webber Music Show*. A visiting writer rang the bell and made his way upstairs. The first two floors of the building were marked on the button in the lift; he pressed the third, unmarked button and glided up into the world of Andrew Lloyd Webber.

Biddy, as was her wont, politely interrogated the visitor. He had been warned to expect her company throughout the evening, but she decided he was harmless enough to allow Andrew to take care of himself. While she and Andrew concluded their business the writer, armed with the large glass of Chablis customarily offered on these occasions, wandered about the flat.

In the lavatory, which was fitted out in black marble, two items of interest caught the eye. One was a small trophy, of the kind awarded for swimming or tennis, resting on the side. Engraved on the base was the legend: *The Desmond Elliott Memorial Trophy. Awarded every 25 years for outstanding achievement.*

Andrew and Biddy chatted next door. The writer read on:

> *1848–1873 W. G. Grace*
> *1874–1897 Jack the Ripper*
> *1898–1923 Mata Hari*
> *1924–1947 Stalin*
> *1948–1973 Andrew Lloyd Webber*

Above the cistern hung a Clive Arrowsmith photograph of the second Mrs Lloyd Webber. As the visitor stood relieving himself, he could hardly avoid the sensation that she was staring sexily back at him.

Andrew, Biddy and the writer descended in the lift to the elegant porch on Eaton Square. The Bentley appeared from nowhere and whisked them away. Eight hundred yards round the square, Andrew and his dinner guest were deposited outside a small Italian restaurant. They went inside, sat down, ordered dinner and Andrew talked about *Aspects of Love*.

Halfway through the evening a note arrived at their table addressed to 'Sir Andrew' from 'Sir George.' The note contained greetings from Roger Moore, seated with his wife at another table.

After Andrew and his guest had spoken to Moore, and in view of the fact that the two men clearly enjoyed each other's company, the writer felt sufficiently emboldened to ask Andrew the following question:

'What is it,' he enquired, 'about Roger Moore's singing that makes you think he is right for such a demanding part?'

Andrew then did something he did not often do. He looked his dinner guest straight in the eye: 'I don't know,' he said, '*can he sing?*'

The conversation turned to other aspects of the production. Andrew talked about how he had been to the Royal Opera House to see Prokofiev's *Romeo and Juliet* with his godson, Felix Gummer. He had been struck by the fact that no expense seemed to have been spared on the production.

'Why not put on my show there?' he enquired, raising his eyebrows. 'They put on *The Magic Flute* there. *Aspects* is not un-Mozartian.'

Suddenly he stopped promoting his new show and started to talk about the book his grandmother Molly kept all those years ago at Harrington Court. It was called *Why Do Men Suffer?* He talked about pain, and about what he wanted to write next.

'I'm not going to get it right,' he said, 'but I must try. It's a piece about a child, in a situation which is beyond that child's control . . .'

It was as if he was suddenly transported back in time, a child trapped in a grown-up's body, to the South Kensington of the 1950s. Then, he said, he was going to give up music and write a learned book on Victorian churches. Then, just as suddenly, he returned to the subject of *Aspects of Love*.

The Bentley materialised as swiftly as before and they went back to Eaton Square. After more Chablis and music played on the latest, state-of-the-art sound equipment, the writer departed into the night.

Three days later Andrew and Sarah were in Russia. In Moscow, the chief conductor of the Moscow Philharmonic and the Latvian State Choir, together with Sarah, a Muscovite treble and a tenor from Riga, gave three performances of *Requiem*. Then they flew back to London for the opening rehearsals of *Aspects of Love*.

Really Useful Group profits fell slightly in the aftermath of Brolly's departure, but investors were reassured by the record advance bookings for *Aspects*. Andrew voiced his familiar refrain that he longed for Sarah to have a baby, but there was always another production on the way; at this moment she was on a concert tour of Australia and she was due to open in *Phantom of the Opera* in Los Angeles. The notion of a real child for Andrew and Sarah remained more remote than his idea of a musical work about an imaginary child in circumstances beyond his or her control.

Then the familiar last-minute crisis struck. Roger Moore pulled out of *Aspects of Love*.

There was no ill-feeling towards him on the part of the company. Moore had fought valiantly to master what had proved an impossible vocal role for a man of his limited musical experience. Kevin Colson, who took over with only four weeks to go, had sung in *Chess* and *Follies*. The public opening was postponed for a few days; but this was as much due to problems over scene changes and the excessive length of the show.

On the other side of London from the Prince of Wales Theatre, in the Barbican Arts Centre, Tim was introducing a brief revival of *Jesus Christ Superstar*.

This special Easter production was performed by an all-black cast. The show he and Andrew had written that cold winter in a Herefordshire hotel was conducted by its original music director Anthony Bowles. The Stephen Hill Singers, who backed up the London Community Choir, had begun life when Hill had organised the cramped little booth at *Cats*. Bowles had recently heard from Andrew after ten years in the wilderness; but he would never know exactly why he had been fired from *Evita*. That night, in a time warp, he conducted the show in front of 2000 people as appreciative as their parents' generation had been on the first night nearly twenty years ago.

At last, on the night of 10 April 1989, the great and the good were able to attend the Royal Preview of the new Andrew Lloyd Webber musical *Aspects of Love*. Her Majesty the Queen, patron of the Family Welfare Association in whose aid the evening was held, arrived to the strains of the national anthem. First on his feet downstairs was her son, the young production assistant Edward Windsor. Michael Ball, the young tenor recently signed to the Really Useful Record Company, waited in a state of extreme nervousness to open the most eagerly awaited show of the year. Neither he nor the audience were to be disappointed.

A week later came the delayed performance for the press and the public. With this came the realisation, both puzzling and refreshing, that *Aspects of Love* was not just another musical by Andrew Lloyd Webber. Nor was it an opera masquerading as a musical. *Aspects of Love* was an attempt at a fully blown, bittersweet opera.

Echoes of *Jeeves*, *Cats* and *Cricket* were present. Black and Hart had written lyrics which were resolutely expository, at times to an excruciating degree. But ironically, even without his real Hart, it became clear that Andrew, and not Tim, had at last produced an essay on the theme of the endless game of love.

Backstage Andrew, his children, Sarah One and Sarah Two posed uneasily together for photographs. The captions could easily have been supplied by the opera's libretto. Jean hovered at a safe distance, ever wary of what she felt fame and fortune had done to her talented son.

The critics did as they might have been expected to do:

He is a natural and prolific melodist, and if melody were all in musical theatre he would be home and dry . . . For something quite ambitious is being attempted in *Aspects of Love* . . .

On the evidence of this score Lloyd Webber's power as a producer is not yet matched by his inventiveness as a composer . . .

Here, for the first time in nearly a decade, Lloyd Webber offers us people we can care about in emotionally gripping situations . . .

The craftsmanship is deft, but the musical material strikes me as timid and uninteresting . . .

No writer, composer or artist has ever fulfilled him or herself without testing new territory.

It takes courage and a sure nerve, not to mention the sort of bankable reputation of Andrew Lloyd Webber . . .

I don't think you have to be steeped in classical opera to respond to this; and if this is the new direction of Lloyd Webber's work then we have a lot to look forward to.

Down went the curtain and home went the audience all over the world. In London, the lights went out at the Prince of Wales Theatre, Her Majesty's Theatre in the Haymarket and the New London Theatre in Drury Lane. Five hours later, they would do the same at the Winter Garden and the Majestic Theater in New York.

In Hampshire, the floodlights went out on the façade of a

magnificent country house. Inside, on the ground floor, the letter hung on the wall where it had always done:

Dear Andrew

I have been told you are looking for a 'with-it' writer of lyrics for your songs and as I have been writing pop songs for a while now and particularly enjoy writing the lyrics I wondered if you considered it worth your while meeting me . . .

Upstairs, in the attic, dust gathered on the remains of a toy theatre. The voices of the brothers were long since silent. In their place were the words of a long-forgotten song:

A Man on His Own

He stands alone
And sees the crowd around him
And hears their voices call his name
He will always stay far away
Is he right or wrong?
Is he weak or strong?
He only knows he's a man on his own.

Who will hide him? Guide him?
Guide a man on his own?

I stand alone
And see the crowd all around me
And hear their voices call my name
In the dark alone I'm sure I'm known
And though I call to reach them all
They only see a man on his own

Andrew and Tim had written this song nearly twenty-five years earlier. Andrew had come a long way since then, in the pursuit of a dream which must have seemed so real to him that it could hardly fail. Not a moment passed, after all, when someone,

239

somewhere, was not playing one of his tunes. But one day, in some way, he still believed the two of them would be together again.

Acknowledgements

The author wishes to thank Andrew Lloyd Webber, Jean Lloyd Webber and Julian Lloyd Webber.

The author is also extremely grateful to the following for their help in his researches for this book:

Ivon Asquith, Virginia Bell, Alan Benson, Anthony Bowles, William Cran, Peter Dale, Andrew Duncan, Desmond Elliott, Tom Faber, Kenneth Fleet, Biddy Hayward, Father Kenneth Hewitt, Stephen Hill, Ian Hunter, David Irwin, Marjorie Kerr, John Lill, Mary Loring, Robin Lough, Cameron Mackintosh, Angus McGill, Gerald McKnight, Howard Milner, Jamie Muir, Maggie Pringle, Heidi Raj, Gaetano Rea, Meryl Richardson, Martin Neary, Yitkin Seow, Dasha Shenkman, Mark Steyn, Christopher Strangeways, Bob Swash, Edda Tasiemka, and all those who wish to remain off the record or in the chorus.

The author is grateful for permission to quote from the following published sources: *Daily Express*, *Evening Standard*, *New York Times*, *Observer*, *Time*, *The Times*.

The author is also grateful for permission to quote from the works of Tim Rice and Andrew Lloyd Webber: MCA Music Ltd, Peer-Southern Organisation Ltd, The Really Useful Group plc.

Index